BEAM ANTENNA

HANDBOOK

William I. Orr, W6SAI
Stuart D. Cowan, W2LX

RADIO AMATEUR CALLBOOK

P.O. BOX 2013 LAKEWOOD, NEW JERSEY 08701

Caution: Working on antennas or towers can be dangerous. All warnings on the equipment and all operating and use instructions should be adhered to. Make sure that the antenna is disconnected from the station equipment before you begin to work on it. Make sure that your antenna is not close to power lines, and that it cannot drop on a power line if wires or supports fail. Do not attempt to climb a tower without a safety belt. It is best to work on your antenna with someone who can assist you with tools and will be able to help in the event of a problem or an emergency.

Copyright © 1990 by Radio Publications, Inc.

Published in 1993 by Radio Amateur Callbook
(an imprint of Watson-Guptill Publications,
a division of BPI Communications, Inc.),
P.O. Box 2013, Lakewood, New Jersey 08701

Library of Congress Catalog Card Number: 83-061824
ISBN 0-8230-8704-2

Manufactured in the United States of America

1 2 3 4 5 6 7 8 9/01 00 99 98 97 96 95 94 93

TABLE OF CONTENTS

FOREWORD

Building a rotary beam antenna in 1935 was no easy job. The authors of this handbook found this out first-hand. Construction plans and tuning data were unavailable. Aluminum tubing did not exist. There were no coaxial cables, there were no readily available towers, or rotators, and the SWR meter was unknown. The task was formidable and it took over a year for W6SAI (then W2HCE) to assemble a simple, awkward, and heavy hand-turned two element 20 meter beam. The on-the-air results were incredible. Only a handful of 20 meter beams existed in the ham world, and using one placed the modest station of W2HCE near the top of the DX heap. W2LX (then W2DQT), who had helped to assemble W2HCE's antenna, immediately started to build one of his own and found his beam to be head and shoulders above his old single wire antenna.

Since those early experiments by the authors and others, the rotary Yagi beam has attained an important place in the world of commercial, military and amateur radio. In recent years mechanical design and feed systems have been improved and the electrical dimensions of the beam antenna have been refined and reaffirmed by computer programs. Today's Yagi antenna is a far cry from the cumbersome and mysterious designs used decades ago.

Both authors, having followed the development of the Yagi antenna over the years, are ardent enthusiasts of this compact and efficient array. The information gained in their experiments, plus the work done by other enthusiasts, have been distilled into the new BEAM ANTENNA HANDBOOK. This new, up-dated handbook covers all aspects of hf and vhf Yagi antenna design, construction, installation, testing and operation. New information is provided on the effects of element taper, mounting hardware and matching systems. Dimensions are provided in both English and Metric systems. Also included is information for the new 30, 17 and 12 meter amateur bands. In addition, specific computer-derived, high gain antenna designs are described for the hf and vhf amateur bands. Finally, scaling information is provided that permits many designs to be used on frequencies outside the amateur bands.

The BEAM ANTENNA HANDBOOK is compiled from data obtained in experiments conducted by the authors, and from information provided by scientists and engineers working on commercial and military antenna ranges. To these friends who encouraged and assisted in the publication of this handbook, the authors extend their warmest thanks.

Chapter 1

Radiation and Propagation

The radio spectrum is but a small portion of the electromagnetic spectrum of radiant energy which includes light, alternating current, X-rays, cosmic rays and other forms of natural radiation. The DX-minded radio amateur's immediate interest are those frequencies of the radio spectrum falling between 1.8 and 50 MHz since ionospheric-reflected radio communication over long distances takes place in this region using radio antennas to launch and intercept the waves.

The concept of the radio antenna is not new. Benjamin Franklin used a rudimentary antenna when he flew a kite and extracted a spark from nearby lightning about the time the United States was born. Marconi developed a practical antenna in 1892 to use with his revolutionary wireless equipment. And even before Marconi, Hertz experimented with simple beam antennas during his demonstrations of electromagnetic waves earlier in the nineteenth century.

From these humble beginnings, the modern beam antenna is a direct descendant, a summation of years of study, research and experimentation. Yet, if Hertz, Marconi or Franklin were alive today, they would understand the operating principles of the most modern and sophisticated antenna, as it follows the natural laws of electricity discovered by those pioneer experimenters so many years ago.

This handbook covers the theory, design, construction and evaluation of the highly efficient parasitic beam antenna, developed by H. Yagi and S. Uda of Tohoku University, Japan, about 1925. The work of these scientists, and other pioneers in the antenna field, is gratefully acknowledged by the authors of this handbook.

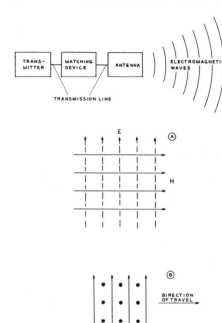

Fig. 1 The transmitter generates electric waves which are converted into electromagnetic waves by antenna (top). End-on view of plane wave (A) shows perpendicular electric (E) and magnetic (H) waves. In side view (B), arrows that come out of the page are shown as dots. This wave is vertically polarized because electric field is vertical.

THE ANTENNA -- WHAT IS IT?

Strictly speaking, an antenna is a device which converts an electric wave guided by a conductor into a free-space, unguided electromagnetic wave, and vice versa. Electrical energy is fed to the antenna via a transmission line, a conductor which passes electrical energy from one point to another. A matching device is usually required to ease the abrupt transition between the guided and the free wave. The wave guided by the line is radiated into space by the antenna (Figure 1).

All antennas follow the general law of reciprocity and can extract electromagnetic waves from space and convert them into electric waves capable of being detected by a radio receiver.

The range of frequencies over which the antenna functions efficiently, and over which a reasonable match between the guided and the free waves can be made, is termed the bandwidth of the antenna and is a function of antenna and matching system design. If the transition is smooth and the system design such that the wave characteristics do not undergo a sudden shift, the bandwidth of the antenna may be quite large. But if the transition is abrupt, a region of discontinuity exists in the system and a portion of the guided wave is reflected back down the transmission line, much in the manner that an ocean wave is reflected when it hits a sea wall. The reflected wave is compensated for by the matching device which creates equal and opposite reflection conditions to smooth the transition.

Designing an antenna to operate on one frequency is a fairly simple exercise but designing an antenna to work over a band of frequencies is much more complex. The antenna and matching system must be structured so that the antenna characteristics which change with respect to frequency do not upset the receiver or transmitter connected to it.

The operating bandwidth of an antenna is relative and one way of specifying it is to define the maximum limit of reflected energy at any operating frequency. This limit may be expressed as a voltage standing wave ratio (VSWR) or, more simply, SWR. This term is an expression of the ratio of the amplitude of the reflected voltage on the transmission line to the amplitude of the direct voltage. This interesting subject is discussed at length later in this handbook. Other expressions of operating bandwidth concern themselves with antenna efficiency and variations in the radiation pattern of the antenna.

THE RADIO WAVE -- WHAT IS IT?

It has been said that a radio wave is not a thing, such as the Empire State building, but a way in which things behave. Once you have specified the behavior, little more can be said about the radio wave. This interesting and elusive concept was derived in the late 1880's by James C. Maxwell, a brilliant student of the natural sciences. The existence of electromagnetic waves had been hinted at by Faraday and others, but the attempt to relate them to the various laws of electricity derived by Ampere, Ohm and Faraday was a failure until Maxwell bridged the gap with a breath-taking concept of nature that encompassed electricity and magnetism and predicted electromagnetic radiation!

Maxwell's famous equations picture the interplay of energy between electric and magnetic fields which is self-maintained, with the energy radiating outward into space from the point of origin. The equations express the continuous nature of the fields and define how changes in one field bring about changes in the other. The compound disturbance described by the equations of Maxwell was proven by Hertz who generated Maxwell's waves in 1888, years before the word "radio" was coined.

THE "OSCILLATING DOUBLET"

Maxwell's equations provide the link between electron flow in a conductor and electromagnetic waves radiating in space. In

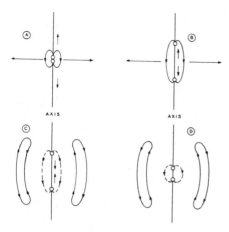

Fig. 2 The "Oscillating Doublet". Energy radiation takes place from charges moving sinusoidally with respect to each other (A and B). Separation of charges causes an electric field, shown as lines of force in plane of the page. When charges move together (C), the field closes upon itself in the polar regions. The independent electric field creates a magnetic field; both fields consitute a radiated electromagnetic wave flowing outward from the doublet (D).

addition, the equations show that the electromagnetic field provides a quantity of energy which is propagated outwards and is detached from the field of the electron flow in the conductor, or antenna.

A simplified view of this concept is the "oscillating doublet", shown in Figure 2. This imaginary bit of antenna consists of two equal electrical charges of opposite polarity closely spaced but not touching each other. When these charges are excited by an electrical force, they move apart and a regular and periodic displacement of the charges can be achieved by exciting them with an alternating current. When the charges move back and forth so that the system is in a continuous state of acceleration or deceleration called oscillation, a current flows in the doublet and the system radiates energy. The radiation of energy is based upon Maxwell's laws which state that a moving electric charge creates an electric field in space about the doublet.

Maxwell's equations further state that an electric field cannot terminate on a charge, so when the charges move together under the action of the alternating current, the field closes upon itself. The independent electric field, then, generates a magnetic field and both fields constitute a radiated electromagnetic wave flowing outward from the doublet.

Maxwell's assumption that an electric field changing in time is a form of current which sets up a magnetic field about itself, and the latter, also changing in time, sets up an electric field, was the basis for the assumption that the two interact and propagate energy into space. The electromagnetic wave thus created travels outward from the doublet, becoming weaker with distance. There is no loss of energy, it merely dissipates in

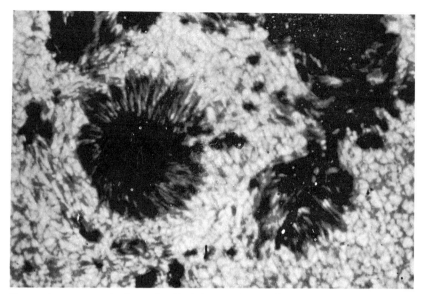

Sunspots appear to be embedded in surface of sun and may be caused by magnetic fields within the sun. These whirling masses of gas appear to move in an east-west direction. (Official NSF photo.)

area as the wave spreads. Once having been produced, the expanding wave travels and propagates itself for an unlimited time, as do the light waves reaching the Earth from stars millions of light years away from us.

What Maxwell did not know was that his wonderful electromagnetic waves could be reflected around the Earth by the as-yet undiscovered ionosphere, providing a medium for worldwide radio communication.

THE TRANSMISSION MEDIUM

High above the living map that is the surface of the earth is a twilight world, forever lit by the sunlight reflected from the thinly scattered molecules of the upper atmosphere. In this world is so little oxygen that human life would be extinguished in an instant, suffocated in a near vacuum. Yet the protective blanket of molecules that does exist shields us from the blistering hail of charged particles emanating from outer space and protects us from the scorching blast of the sun.

This is the region of space in which the atmospheric pressure is so low that free electrons and positive and negative ions exist, created from raw oxygen, nitrogen and hydrogen by the never-ending deluge of ultraviolet radiation from the sun. As the unending rain of radiation falls upon this upper atmosphere, the ionization of air molecules partially exhausts the energy content of the radiation, preventing human life from being burnt to a crisp by the deadly rays. The protection of mankind from cosmic radiation by this deep, ionized sea of air is taken for granted by most people, intent upon their terrestrial problems. Only a few scientists observe and study the undulations and vagaries of the ionized layer, which is forever being lashed and tormented by powerful radiation from the sun.

Of paramount importance to radio amateurs scattered over the face of the globe is this lofty, ionized blanket, for it is in the heart of this area that radio signals of certain frequencies are mysteriously reflected back to earth, permitting the amateur radio enthusiast to talk to his fellow hobbyists in all corners of the world.

In the early days of radio, little was known about the existence of this rarefied, ionized region of our atmosphere. Amateur radio was limited to little more than line-of-sight transmission in the spectrum of 200 to 1000 meters. Chained to a wave travelling along the surface of the earth, occasional long distance contacts by the amateur were the exception, rather than the rule. After World War 1 amateur operation in the unexplored 200 meter region showed promise of long distance communication by unthought-of means, culminating in the famous trans-Atlantic tests of 1921 when 30 pioneer American amateur stations were heard in Scotland.

During the next few years, as amateurs tuned their transmitters to shorter wavelengths, long distance records were made and broken overnight. It was found that, when using the extremely short wavelengths of 20 and 10 meters, world-wide communication could be held over a daylight path, a feat heretofore thought impossible. What was causing the mysterious skip of the high frequency signal; a skip that seized the signal of the amateur, carried it through the unknown atmosphere and then deposited it thousands of miles away, still intelligible and often of wondrous strength? It was the ionized layer of air, of course. High above the earth, acting as a mirror-reflector, this tenuous layer accomplished the impossible. Radio signals which rapidly withered and became whispers after a few hundred miles of travel across the tortuous landscape of the earth, suffered little attenuation on their lightning trip up to the ionized reflector, there to be bounced back to the eager ears of some fellow amateur, thousands of miles away.

Thus, to start the study of beam antennas we do not start with solid, earthy substances, such as wire, insulators, cable,

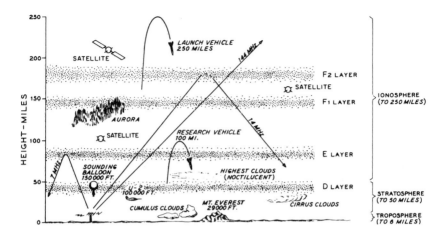

Fig. 3 The Earth's atmosphere is composed of three layers, the lowest being the troposphere, or weather layer. The stratosphere is next, a constant-temperature layer extending to a height of about 40 miles (70 km). Above this is the ionosphere (ion layer), a region which reflects radio waves. This layer extends to a height of about 250 miles (400 km).

tubing; for these are only the tools to make more effective use of this mysterious and unseen gift of nature. In the beginning, we turn to the ionosphere.

THE IONOSPHERE

The upper reaches of the atmosphere of the earth, commonly called the ionosphere, may be thought of as an onion whose skin is placed layer upon layer. The layers, however, have no abrupt gradations or edges, but blend uniformly and gradually with each other, changing with air density and altitude. This is the region which man is piercing today by means of various space probes and satellites (Figure 3).

During the hours of night, when the area is shielded from the furnace of the sun by the body of the earth, the layers coagulate into a single blanket known as the F-layer which hovers 150-250 miles (241-402 km) above the earth. Protected from the outburst of ultra-violet radiation from the sun, the F-layer is weakly ionized. The higher frequency radio signals easily penetrate the F-layer and are lost in space, never to return to earth. Lower frequency radio signals, however, are reflected from the F-layer during the night hours. Thus, as one tunes his receiver across the radio spectrum during the dark hours, a noticeable thinning out of the stations is apparent as the higher frequencies pass across the dial. Transmissions from stations on those frequencies are passing through the night-time F-layer, perhaps to be heard on the moon, or Mars, but escaping reflection to the ears of listeners on the earth.

During the daylight hours when the ionosphere is exposed to the full force of the ultraviolet radiations from the sun, the onion-like strata form again, each layer having its own particular density of ionization. The lowest of these daytime layers is the D-layer, a mere 30-50 miles (48-80 km) above the earth. This is a region of relatively dense atmosphere. The ionization of this layer is directly affected by the quantity of sunlight that falls upon it. The ionization is greatest around noontime and quickly drops to nothing when the sun hides itself behind the earth. The D-layer contributes little or nothing to long distance communication; on the contrary, it is a region of absorption of radio signals of the lower frequencies and is the principal reason that daylight communication on the 160 meter and 80 meter amateur bands is confined to relatively short distances.

Pulsing above the D-layer at a height of 50-80 miles (80-128 km) is the second definable region of ionized atmosphere called the E-layer. The intensity of ionization of this second layer follows the sunlight as does the ionization of the D-layer. This E-layer also absorbs a certain portion of the low frequency radiations, but on a smaller basis than the D-layer. Waves of 7 MHz to 10 MHz are reflected back to earth by this second layer of the "onion".

Approximately 150-200 miles (241-321 km) above the sunlit side of the earth is the region of the F2-layer, the most useful of the many ionized layers. Located in a plane of low atmospheric pressure the re-ionization process of this layer is low, and not nearly so dependent upon the location of the sun as are the actions of the lower layers, which are buried in a thicker sea of air. Ionization gradually decreases in the F2-layer as the sun sets, reaching a minimum just before the next sunrise. Unlike the D-layer and the E-layer, the F2-layer remains partially ionized during the evening hours, permitting long distance communication during these times on medium frequencies. The 40 meter DX-operator who combs the band during the small hours of the morning pays homage to the F2-layer.

During daylight hours, the F2-layer may split asunder, forming a subordinate layer designated the F1-layer. This skin of the onion adds little to the efficiency of the sky mirror, but serves as an additional absorber of energy that is reflected from the F2-layer.

Fig. 4 MUF is relatively constant during the summer months. Long distance contacts on lower bands are limited to static and high signal absorption in the ionosphere. Higher frequencies may be open 24 hours a day during higher, summer portion of the sunspot cycle. During winter months, the MUF drops to a low value at night, and tends to reach a broad maximum about noon.

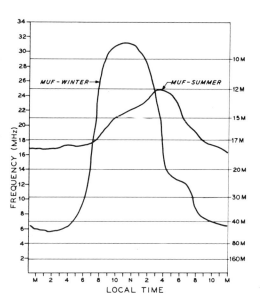

The locations and the idiosyncracies of these mysterious layers were established over the years by scientists working with special radio equipment designed to probe and expose the secrets of the layers. Pulsed signals were projected upwards toward the ionosphere and the time interval the signal took to reach a particular layer and be reflected back to earth was noted. This technique exposed the height of the layer which reflected the signal and the degree of ionization of the layer. By varying the frequency of the pulsed signal the secrets of each layer could be examined separately. The highest frequency at which a vertically projected signal would return to earth is termed the critical frequency. It may be considered to be the maximum usable frequency (MUF) for a zero length path between two adjacent earth points.

IONOSPHERIC VARIATIONS - THE MUF

Nothing is still in nature. The earth changes position with respect to the sun and the moon. The sun moves about within the galaxy. The galaxy whirls through interstellar space. It is natural, then, to surmise that the actions of the ionosphere change yearly, daily and hourly. For so they do. During the winter months in the Northern Hemisphere, the elliptical orbit of the earth brings this planet to its closest point to the sun in the yearly cycle.

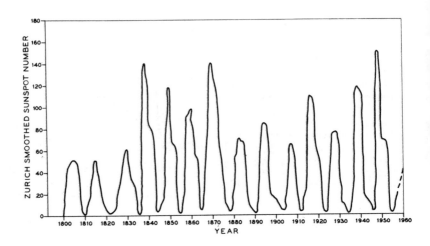

Fig. 5 The sunspot cycle has been observed by scientists for over 150 years. About 45 years ago, it was noticed that periods of radio communication via higher frequencies coincided with greater sunspot numbers. For example, 10 meters is not open for long distance communication unless the sunspot number exceeds 40 or 50. Pity the poor 10 meter amateur who experiences another period of sunspot inactivity such as that of 1800 to 1835!

The intense bombardment of the upper atmosphere by the ultraviolet radiations of the sun produces strongly ionized layers. These layers reflect radio waves of high frequency that would easily pass through the weakly ionized layers of the summer months when the earth swings past the orbital range farthest from the sun. Because the axis of the earth is tilted from the perpendicular to its orbit, the winter nights are long compared to the twilight hours of summertime. The extended winter periods of darkness allow greater time for the various layers of the ionosphere to de-ionize and pass larger portions of the radio spectrum into outer space.

The effect of these seasonal and daily fluctuations in the ionosphere are illustrated in the MUF graph of Figure 4. The maximum usable frequency for an east-west path across the United States is shown for summer and winter conditions. During the long summer days when the earth is at the outermost reaches of its orbit, ionization of the upper air is relatively constant over a 24-hour period and the MUF varies over a restricted range of frequencies.

The winter days bring the earth closer to the sun, increasing the level of ultraviolet radiations impinging upon the atmosphere; the long winter nights allow a longer period of de-ionization. As a consequence the MUF reacts in a more violent manner in winter, dropping to low levels at night and then increasing to a maximum figure during daylight hours.

These gyrations of the ionosphere are particularly noticeable on the 40, 30 and 20 meter bands. During the daylight hours the amateur bands are alive with signals. The MUF advances during the morning and the 15, 12 and 10 meter bands are open for long distance contacts. As the afternoon progresses and the sun starts to set, the 10 meter band will see the MUF drop first. Shortly thereafter the 12 and 15 meter bands will become quiet, followed by the 20 meter band. If the MUF drops to a low enough value during the evening hours (indicating a low level of ionization of the layers) even the 40 meter band will grow quiet, except for occasional long-skip signals that have been reflected back to earth by some unusual layer discontinuity.

As the summer months approach, the maximum peak of MUF drops, leaving the 15, 12 and 10 meter bands useless. The intensity of ionization is not great enough to create the mirror-reflector necessary to reflect these high frequencies except at erratic intervals. At the same time, however, the shorter hours of night prevent a complete de-ionization of the reflector and consequently the MUF does not drop to the low levels noticed during the winter months. The 20, 30 and 40 meter bands remain usable for long distance work during the hours of the night, and on occasion the DX-operator who returns from a late movie will find the 15, 12 and 10 meter bands alive with signals late into the night.

This picture of the MUF pattern is necessarily simplified, as other gigantic forces are at work continuously, kneading and distorting the ionized layers from hour to hour and year to year. The most noticeable of these forces is the so-called sunspot cycle.

THE SUNSPOT CYCLE

Long before the Declaration of Independence was signed, certain scientists had observed a long term variation in the number of storms seen on the face of the sun. Observed through a darkened lens, these gigantic storms appeared as small dark spots, slipping in and out of view as the rotation of the sun carried them across the face of the disc. The spots would wax and wane in number, the maximum groupings gathering every eleven years or so.

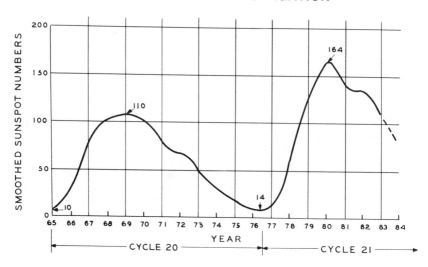

Fig. 6 Sunspot count for cycles 20 and 21. Many newly licensed amateurs have never operated during the low portion of a sunspot cycle, such as occurred in 1977. At the peak of a cycle, as in 1980, MUF is high enough to support long distance communication on the 6 meter band on a regular basis, especially in tropical areas of the world.

Through the years the daily number of observed sunspots was duly recorded, and monthly averages were taken. Properly interpreted, these monthly averages produced a smoothed sunspot number which could be plotted into a yearly chart (Figure 5). With the advent of radio and the discovery that long distance transmission was virtually dependent upon ultraviolet ionization of the upper atmosphere, close attention was paid by radio engineers to this 11-year phenomenon. It was found by careful study that the ultraviolet emanations from the sun followed the sunspot cycle closely. When violent whirlpools of radiation were visible upon the surface of the sun, ionization of the atmosphere of the earth was heavy and radio conditions were good. The MUF was high and long distance contacts on 10 and even 6 meters were possible.

As the sun storms subsided, the degree of ionization of the atmosphere dropped, and radio conditions generally became poorer. The 10 and 15 meter bands became useless, and 20 meters became spotty and erratic. Amateurs grumbled and moved to the lower frequency bands for long-distance communication, waiting for the sunspot cycle to reassert itself again.

The phases of the sunspot cycle are shown in Figure 6. A minimum occurred during 1976, dropping slowly from the previous peak. During the lean years of solar activity, the 6, 10, 12 and 15 meter bands were virtually devoid of signals, inhabited mainly by wandering ignition noise popping forlornly across the empty bands. Hardy souls would sometimes get on the bands for occasional north-south openings, mindful of the prosperous years of bountiful high frequency activity induced by radiation storms taking place on the surface of the sun over 93,000,000 miles away.

The 20, 30 and 40 meter bands were subject to great periods of ionospheric punishment; distant signals were weak and watery. Long distance contacts were, of course, possible but for long periods of time no DX signals of consequence were heard. When the sun set, the hf amateur bands became practically useless except during the short summer evenings. The long distance voice of amateur radio became a mere murmur.

Only the 80 and 160 meter bands were an exception to these gloomy happenings. Often, on a winter evening during a year of minimum sunspot activity, the MUF would drop as low as two or four megacycles. The local rag-chews and traffic nets, normal denizens of the 80 meter band, would fade out and the thrilling signals of intercontinental stations would break through. The staid, stable 80 meter band would become a hotbed of distant signals, for a few short hours, that would put 20 meters to shame.

THE NEW SUNSPOT CYCLE

As the sunspot cycle inexorably increases, radio conditions on 40, 30 and 20 meters begin to improve. The 40 meter band stops "going dead" during the hours of darkness, and the daylight hours show a definite improvement in 20 meter long distance contacts. Sporadic signals from the tropical zones start to show up on the 15 meter band, and the north-south path begins to open regularly on this band. Slowly the 10 meter band awakens. The first sign is the fall opening of the north-south trans-equatorial path. American amateurs suddenly discover the erstwhile dead band bristling with South American amateurs. On a good day, a lone South African amateur may make an appearance for a short period of time.

Grandly and predictably, the sunspot cycle approaches a new peak. Ten meters is now "open" during the cooler months, with phenomenal signals from all parts of the world to delight the amateur. Indeed, in the tropical areas having high MUF the band is bursting with signals 24 hours a day, all year long.

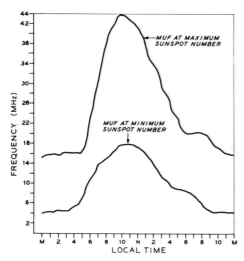

Fig. 7 MUF for a typical east-west path during the low period of the sunspot cycle rarely rises over 18 MHz. At the peak of the cycle, the MUF may climb over 50 MHz. During 1986 thru 1989, frequencies over 18 MHz will be relatively useless for regular ionospheric-reflected long distance communication.

Fifteen meters, too, has changed from a shy actor to a DX veteran. Twenty, 30 and 40 meters are wide awake with long distance DX skip. Signals from Asia and Africa compete with other loud signals from Australia and rare South Pacific islands. True, occasional angry outbursts from the solar generator that is the sun obliterate the amateur bands for short periods of time, but this is a small price to pay for the DX opportunities during the years of maximum MUF.

A comparison of the MUF for maximum and minimum periods of the sunspot cycle is interesting. The tremendous difference in the maximum usable frequency for these two periods is shown in Figure 7.

The sunspot cycle goes on, as it has for millenia past. Soon the MUF barometer starts to drop once again, and amateur radio must prepare for a battening of the hatches and a reefing of the sails as the new lows of the MUF approach.

SHORT-TERM IONOSPHERIC VARIATIONS

Other important forces are at work on the ionosphere. Ionosphere storms, sudden ionospheric disturbances and sporadic E-layer ionization are but a few. However, these are second-order effects when compared with the 11-year cycle. A shorter 28-day cycle of ionospheric events caused by the rotation of the sun also has an effect on radio transmission.

Variations from the expected normal ionospheric skip transmission are believed to be caused by bursts of ultraviolet and other forms of radiation from the sun. This radiation is thought to come from sudden flare-ups and storms on the face of the sun that coincide with sharp increases in measured solar radiation. The storms are accompanied by the emission of electrified particles which bombard the atmosphere of the earth. The flare-ups are tremendous cosmic explosions which occur suddenly and with no warning. Shortly after such a disturbance the MUF drops sharply, even to a near blackout of high frequency reception. Such a phenomenon is called a sudden ionospheric disturbance (SID). The SID starts abruptly and lasts over a period of perhaps half an hour to several hours. High frequency radio communication is disrupted by an extreme increase in atmospheric absorption of radio signals and a severe decrease in the ability of the ionosphere to reflect radio signals back to earth. As the SID results from radiation from the sun, only radio paths either partially or completely in the daylight areas of the world are affected. The lower frequencies are the first to drop out and the last to return to service as the absorption affects the lower frequencies most severely. A strong SID will drop out all high frequency signals as well as the normal background noise, and the amateur turning on his receiver during such a disturbance may well think his equipment is inoperative! Sudden ionospheric disturbances of this type occur most often during periods of high sunspot activity, and become few and far between during the lower portions of the sunspot cycle.

THE IONOSPHERIC STORM

The storms on the sun can often be seen with the naked eye, through a piece of dark glass, appearing as small dark spots on the surface of the sun. Some sunspots are nearly always present even though not always visible without magnification. The solar flare-ups may be seen as tremendous bursts of flame at the edge of the sun, shooting millions of miles above the disc. If you look for these spots and flares, take great care to use special dark glasses, since permanent blindness can result from inadequate eye protection.

The ionospheric storm is caused by bombardment of the earth's atmosphere by subatomic solar particles. The particle cloud is generated by flare-ups but follows the ultraviolet radiations at somewhat slower speed, creating a delayed but longer lasting ionospheric and magnetic disturbance. The solar particles reach the earth from one to four days after a flare-up has occurred. The ionization of the ionosphere is markedly reduced by the particles so that radio waves normally reflected from the layer will penetrate the ionosphere and no longer return to earth.

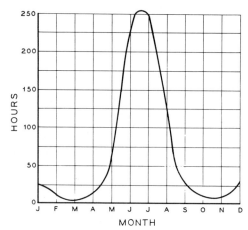

Fig. 8 Sporadic-E openings on higher frequency bands tend to peak during summer months. Openings up to 1400 miles (2300 km) are common in the U.S. and Canada. An increase in sporadic-E propagation is observed during periods of low sunspot activity.

During a severe ionospheric storm the combination of absorption and weakened reflection produces a radio blackout during which period long distance transmission and reception are impossible to many areas of the world, and the MUF drops by as much as fifty percent. As in the case of the SID, the ionospheric storm occurs generally during periods of high sunspot activity, beginning in the high latitudes and expanding into the temperate zones of the earth as the storm grows. The effects of the storm are noted in areas of daylight and darkness alike.

Radio propagation often improves sharply just before a radio blackout. It is therefore to the advantage of the DX operator to monitor the high frequency bands during the period following a sudden ionospheric disturbance. Suddenly improved conditions often indicate a forthcoming ionospheric disturbance.

SPORADIC-E PROPAGATION

Quite frequently irregular "clouds" of very high ionization are found at E-layer height in the ionosphere. They are thought to be caused by shearing forces in the upper atmosphere. This sporadic-E layer often achieves a density sufficient to support communications on frequencies considerably higher than those normally being reflected by the ionosphere. Sporadic-E reflection is often quite localized and spotty, producing only erratic skip openings, while at other times the clouds cover a large area up to one hundred miles (170 km) across. The clouds may shift very rapidly in a westerly direction and disappear and reappear in a short period of time. They occur both at night and during daylight hours and tend to peak during the summer months (Figure 8). Sporadic-E propagation is common

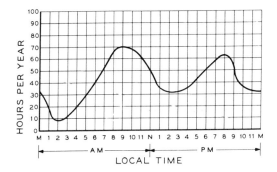

Fig. 9 The most likely times for Sporadic-E openings to take place are between 8-11 a.m. and 6-8 p.m., local time.

on the 20 through 10 meter bands and is noticeable to a lesser extent on the 50, 144 and 220 MHz bands. This form of propagation is possible a high percentage of the time near the equator, and much less frequently near the poles; it seems to be more intense during periods of low sunspot activity. Propagation openings tend to occur during the early morning and later afternoon hours, especially during auroral displays (Figure 9). The percentage of time that sporadic-E propagation appears in the United States on the various amateur bands is shown in Figure 10.

Sporadic-E skip on the 6 and 10 meter bands may be predicted by noting that as the skip distance decreases on 15 or 10 meters, the MUF reflected by the sporadic-E cloud is increasing. For example, when minimum skip distance on 10 meters is down to about 400 miles, this is an indication that sporadic-E short-skip openings will probably appear on the 6 meter band. In the same vein, when the 15 meter band is open for short-skip contacts of 350 miles or so, chances are good that both 10 and 6 meters are open for sporadic-E contacts.

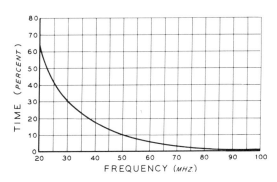

Fig. 10 Percentage of time Sporadic-E propagation occurs during the summer months at frequencies below 100 MHz.

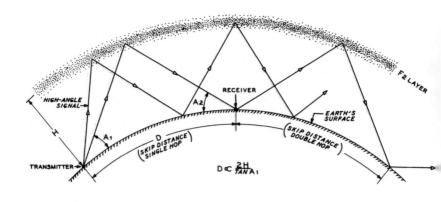

Fig. 11 Single-hop transmission takes place up to distances of about 2500 miles (4000 km). Beyond this distance, the angle of radiation (A1) approaches zero, and communication takes place by multiple-hop transmission. Silent (skip) zones between the hop points may be noted. The signal may also reach a distant point by the "long path", opposite in bearing to the greater circle path by 180 degrees. If both paths are open, a strong echo will be heard on the signal.

THE ANGLE OF RADIATION

Since long distance signals reflect from the ionized sky mirror much like a billiard ball rebounding after striking the cushion of the table, certain assumptions may be made that have been proven valid by theory and practice. The first assumption is that there is an optimum angle for the wave to approach the ionized layer to permit the reflected signal to reach a designated point. The second assumption is that the wave may be reflected from the layer not only once but twice, and perhaps several times, in its journey around the globe.

Figure 11 illustrates a simplified single-hop transmission of a radio signal by ionospheric reflection. . The vertical angles of departure and arrival of the signal are indicated by A_1 and A_2. The great-circle distance between the two points is noted by D. The effective height of the reflecting layer is H. As H changes, the vertical angles A_1 and A_2 also change. As the distance D grows, A_1 and A_2 decrease to maintain the path. A distance D is finally reached at which these vertical angles approach zero, and single-hop transmission becomes impossible.

Beyond this distance, multiple-hop transmission takes place. This <u>skip distance</u> is of the order of 2,500 miles for F_2-layer reflection. It can be seen from Figure 11 that the optimum angle of radiation of the signal for one path may not necessarily be the correct angle for a different path. It is also evident that the number of hops that the signal takes on its trip around the earth affects the optimum vertical angle of radiation.

There is no one best radiation angle for general amateur communication. The "best" angle is a function of many interdependent variables and changes from day to day and from hour to hour, a helpless captive of the whims of the gigantic reflecting mirror, quivering in the upper atmosphere.

Certain generalized statements may be made, however, which provide a workable basis for selecting the best angle of radiation for long-distance communication. The optimum angle of radiation decreases as the operating frequency is raised. A range of operating angles chosen for 40 meter operation may be too high for optimum operation on the 10 meter band. Thus the optimum angle of radiation is a function of the amateur band in which the operator is interested.

The term angle of radiation of an antenna may be taken to mean the angle above the horizon of the axis of the main lobe of radiation. With practical amateur antennas the radiation pattern is not a knife-edge of energy, nor is it even as sharp as the light beam from an automobile headlight. Rather, it is a bulbous lobe, occupying a large area in front of the antenna array. Beam widths of 40 to 80 degrees are common where parasitic arrays are used. Thus it can be seen that the beam antenna "sprays" a wide area of the ionosphere with the emitted signal, insuring that even with large changes in layer height and large variations in transmission path, a certain amount of the radio signal will be emitted at or near the desired radiation angle.

If the antenna were suspended in free space, the main lobe of radiation would be directly in line with the main axis of the antenna. When the antenna is located in proximity to the surface of the earth, a conflict takes place between the direct wave from the antenna and the wave that is reflected from the surface of the earth. A phase (time) difference occurs between these two waves causing cancellation or reinforcement at various angles above the horizontal. The cancellation or reinforcement is dependent upon the difference in path length between the direct and reflected signals and upon the phase difference between the waves caused by the reflection.

By varying the height of the antenna above the reflecting ground, the vertical angles of the cancellation and reflection patterns may be readily changed. Ground reflection patterns have been developed by which the free space pattern of the

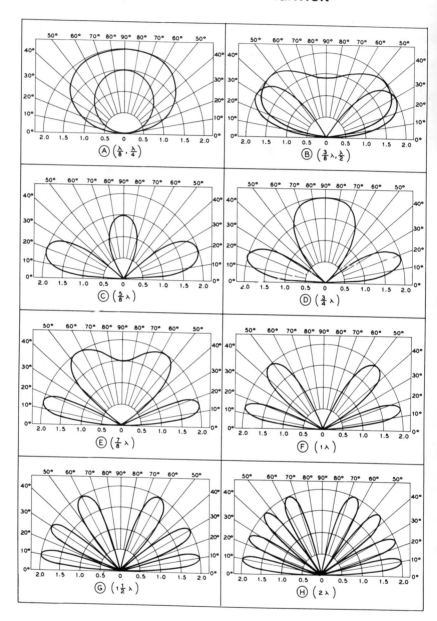

Fig. 12 Ground reflection patterns for a horizontal antenna at various heights above ground are shown. Graphs are multiplying factors applied to the vertical radiation pattern of the antenna to establish a picture of the actual vertical radiation field. The reinforcement and cancellation of the wave at certain vertical angles changes with antenna height. The actual pattern of a real-life antenna varies from these representations because the earth beneath it is not uniform and is not a perfect conductor.

※   ※   ※

antenna can be modified to show the true vertical pattern of the antenna at any chosen height above ground (Figure 12).

GROUND REFLECTION PATTERNS

The ground reflection patterns of Figure 12 assume the earth is a smooth reflecting surface, which it is not. The actual reflection patterns encountered in practice bear only a rough resemblance to these idealized patterns. The effect these patterns have upon the radiation performance of a parasitic beam when superimposed upon the typical free-space pattern of the beam is shown in Figure 13.

These ground reflection patterns indicate only what forms the radiation lobes may take, assuming that the antenna radiates energy equally well at all vertical angles. The parasitic beam antenna does not do this; rather, it confines most of its radiation to a single, broad forward lobe with a minimum of energy radiated to the top, back and sides of the antenna. Because of this, certain lobes that show up in the ground reflection patterns do not appear when the final beam pattern is derived from a fusing of these two radiation patterns. The final pattern will not be symmetrical since the beam tends to suppress radiation from its back side.

The high angle lobes shown in Figures 12C, D and E will be greatly suppressed, since the antenna radiates little energy that is reflected at high angles from the surface of the earth. In addition, the low angle radiation below 10° that may be seen in Figures 12G and H is usually absorbed by the ground, so that radiation below 5° or less is absent from practically all antennas. It is interesting to note that tilting the antenna from a horizontal plane will not lower the angle of radiation. On the contrary, all tests to date prove conclusively that tilting the parasitic array more than a few degrees from the horizontal tends to raise the pattern of radiation, thus negating the effects of height on the array.

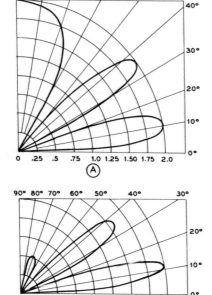

Fig. 13 The vertical field pattern of a horizontal dipole 1¼ wavelengths high is shown at (A). A greater portion of radiated energy is at angles above 35°. The pattern of a three element Yagi beam at the same height above ground is shown at (B). The high angle lobe is almost completely suppressed; the intermediate lobe is reduced in strength.

A typical set of reflection patterns for a two or three element parasitic beam at various heights above the ground is shown in Figure 14. It can be seen at once that the high-angle lobes are partially suppressed and more energy is being placed in the important, low-angle lobes. Less energy is being wasted in high-angle radiation than by a dipole of comparable height.

One interesting myth is exploded by the patterns of Figure 14. The use of a parasitic array does not necessarily lower the angle of radiation, as compared to a dipole. The angle of radiation is a function of the height of the antenna above the reflecting surface of the ground. It is true that more power is radiated at a low angle when a parasitic beam pattern is compared to the pattern of a dipole, but the axis of the main lobe above the horizontal is substantially the same in both cases.

DERIVING BEAM PATTERNS

The classic reflection patterns for a dipole antenna above a perfectly conducting ground plane are shown in Figure 12. To obtain equivalent patterns for a beam antenna, these plots are used as multiplying factors applied to the basic radiation pattern

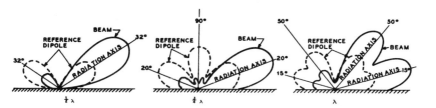

Fig. 14 Effect of ground conductivity on the vertical radiation angle lobe of a Yagi array is shown for three antenna heights. The beam patterns are compared to a reference dipole pattern at each height. Note that the angle of radiation of the main lobe of each antenna is the same for equal heights.

of the beam. If, for example, a beam has a strong radiation lobe in one direction, a greatly reduced radiation lobe to the rear, and very little radiation in the vertical plane, and is placed one and one-quarter wavelengths above the ground, the ground reflection pattern shown in Figure 12D would be altered in the manner shown in Figure 14.

In real life, amateur antennas are not situated above a perfectly conducting ground plane. The earth is not smooth and is a lossy conductor. The reflecting surface is imperfect and ground reflection is not as clear-cut as the images of Figure 14 imply. The pattern lobes are distorted and the nulls are incomplete, as shown in Figure 15.

Measurements conducted on long-distance signals received over a period of years, however, indicate that optimum regions of vertical radiation do exist for the various amateur bands, as shown in Figure 16. This graph shows that for most of the time, the majority of signals arrive at a distant receiver at a common angle of radiation. At various times, however, the angle of signal arrival can, and does, fall outside these generalizations. Thus, because of the irregularity of the earth and the vagaries of the ionosphere, only broad assumptions can be drawn as to the "optimum" vertical angle of signal radiation and reception. It varies with path length, ionospheric conditions, time of year, and from day to day and hour to hour.

ARRAY HEIGHT ABOVE GROUND

So much for theory. What's the final word on antenna height? More and more amateurs are being hampered by building codes and lot restrictions and in many areas the good old days of "the best height is the greatest height" are gone forever.

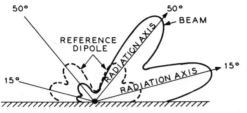

Fig. 15 Vertical elevation pattern for a three element Yagi beam at height of one wavelength compared to the pattern of a reference dipole at the same height above ground.

As far as 20 meters and above is concerned, it must be said that passable results can be obtained with beams as low as 25 to 30 feet (7.5 to 9 meters) above the ground. If the antenna is not surrounded by power lines and telephone cables, most beams can do a satisfactory job on short range single-hop contacts at this low elevation. Unfortunately, a low transmitting antenna often brings it into close proximity with nearby television and stereo receiver antennas and the chances of interference are enhanced when the amateur antenna is located at or near the same elevation as the TV or stereo antenna, and close to it.

The improvement noted in raising a beam antenna from 25-30 feet to 45-50 feet (13 to 15 meters) is often startling, and cannot be fully explained by a study of the optimum radiation angles. Other factors, such as the proximity of houses and utility wires, often mask the performance of an otherwise good antenna, and when the antenna is cleared of these damaging influences it performs in the intended manner. As the antenna is raised further in height, a point of diminishing returns is reached as soon as the cost of the supporting structure begins to overshadow the results gained by the added height. This point varies from pocketbook to pocketbook, and from one location to another.

Experience has shown that a very high beam antenna (100 to 150 feet, 30 to 45 meters) may be excellent for very long distance work, but it is inferior for close-in communications. (It doesn't do much good to be very loud in Outer Mongolia where there are few hams and relatively weak in Europe and North America where the majority of amateurs are located.)

THE "BEST" ANTENNA HEIGHT?

As with other things in life, the "best" antenna height is a compromise. Interested in rag-chewing and occasional DX? For the higher frequency bands, an antenna height of 35 to 45 feet (10 to 13 meters) is acceptable. Long distance DX? A higher antenna will certainly help. How about 45 to 50 feet (13 to 15

BAND	RANGE OF OPTIMUM ANGLE OF RADIATION	"OPTIMUM" ANTENNA HEIGHT
7 MHz	12° – 40°	ABOVE 45'
14 MHz	10° – 25°	ABOVE 40'
21 MHz	7° – 20°	ABOVE 38'
28 MHz	5° – 14°	ABOVE 34'

Fig. 16 Optimum vertical angle of radiation for 7 thru 28 MHz bands lies between 5° and 40° for long distance communication. Antenna heights greater than 40 ft (12 m) are recommended on these bands to limit high angle radiation and to enhance low angle radiation from a horizontally polarized antenna.

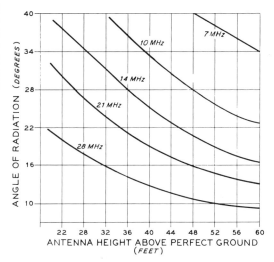

meters)? A serious DX contest operator who wants to slug it out with the many outstanding DXers on the air? He can benefit from antenna heights of 50 to 85 feet (15 to 26 meters). The ultimate? How about 90 to 100 feet (27 to 30 meters)?

On the other side of the argument, it has been noted many times that if the beam antenna is too high, it will "overshoot" the target area. At W6SAI, for example, optimum antenna height for contacts to Western Europe seems to be about 50 feet (15 meters). Going up to 75 feet (22 meters) seems to make the signals more "watery" most of the time. But signal reports from Central Asia are better when the antenna is at 75 feet. As a result, the W6SAI crank-up tower usually sits at about 50 feet. ("For my location and my operating habits, that height suffices," - W6SAI... "I leave my crank-up tower at 45 feet most of the time, even though it goes to 65 feet." - W2LX.)

TO SUM IT UP - MINIMUM ARRAY HEIGHT

As a "rule of thumb", a <u>minimum</u> height of 30 feet (9 meters) is suggested for 10 and 12 meters, 35 feet (10 meters) for 15 and 18 meters, and 40 feet (12 meters) for 20 meters. You may not have the most potent signal on the band, but experience shows those heights will work well for most amateur communications. In any event, comfort can be taken from the thought that the amateur with the tallest tower and the biggest antenna is not always the loudest signal at any given point on the earth. The vagaries of the ionosphere are a great equalizer of signal strength and a good operator with a weaker signal often comes out on top!

For continuing good results, optimum use must be made of the best antenna location at hand. The highest gain array consistent with cost and space requirements should be placed at the loftiest site possible. Only then will the antenna installation do justice to its transmitting and receiving equipment. In the present era of fierce competition, it is the antenna installation that usually separates the men from the boys. The amateur using a well located beam antenna, operating with a low standing wave ratio on the feedline, stands head and shoulders above his competitors using dipole antennas or poorly adjusted beam antennas. A good antenna always returns the money, time and labor invested in it with dividends of increased operating pleasure and reliable contacts.

Chapter 2

The Yagi Beam Antenna

The Yagi parasitic beam antenna is a simple object composed of pieces of tubing, critically cut and spaced; it is deceptively guileless in appearance. Where does the gain come from, what magic properties have the extra elements, and with no connection to the antenna, how can they possibly generate or create a power gain when brought near a dipole? Good questions, and ones not easily answered nor understood.

THE BEAM ANTENNA PRINCIPLE

The basic theory underlying beam antennas of any type was first stated by Lord Rayleigh (England) in 1877 long before radio transmission was known. As applied to antennas, his Reciprocity Theorem states:

> If a voltage is applied to the terminals of antenna A and the induced current measured at the terminals of another antenna B, then an equal current will be found at the terminals of antenna A if the original voltage is applied to the terminals of antenna B.

This classic theorem was later expanded into the concept of mutual impedence between two coupled antennas which dealt with the ratio of voltage induced in a parasitic element by a given current flowing in the exciting antenna.

The action of the parasitic elements can be mathematically stated by the use of the mutual impedance concept, but it is a highly complex situation. A simpler explanation of parasitic action may be derived from the physical concept of signal interception. The Reciprocity Theorem tells us that an antenna acts

An early wire-and-insulator three-element Yagi beam at W6PKK. This 10-meter array amazed amateurs with strong signal it provided when most stations were using dipoles. Beam was delta-matched and fed with twisted-pair transmission line.

in the same fashion whether transmitting or receiving energy, so for simplicity a receiving antenna is used for illustrative purposes.

SIGNAL INTERCEPTION AND RERADIATION

A radio wave travels unhindered through any dielectric medium such as the atmosphere of the earth. Upon meeting free electrons, it imparts energy to the electrons. Such an action as this takes place in the ionosphere where the radio waves are reflected back to the surface of the earth. This transfer of energy always takes place whenever the radio wave meets a conducting material, such as a metallic surface or an ionized layer of air. A conducting material may be thought of as any substance having a surplus of free electrons that are easily removed from the parent atom. Two materials having a surplus of free electrons and which are good conductors are copper and aluminum.

When the radio wave meets a conductor, the free electrons in the conductor move in a direction that corresponds to the electric-vector direction of the radio wave. If the conductor happens to be a piece of horizontal wire and the radio wave is so polarized that the electric-vector direction of the wave is also horizontal, the electrons move <u>along</u> the wire. In other words, a current flows in the conductor.

This action takes place regardless of the length of the conductor. If we imagine the radio wave to be a short pulse,

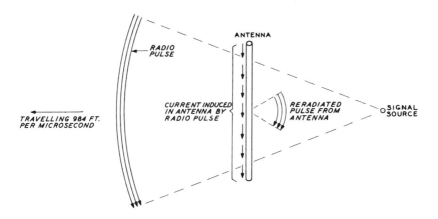

Fig. 1 Energy reflected from a conductor that intercepts a radio wave may be visualized by assuming the conductor is excited by a short pulse of energy from a point source. Current is induced in the conductor by the pulse and electron movement reradiates a portion of the energy back into space.

and examine the wire just after the pulse has passed by, we find that the current induced in it by the pulse of radio frequency energy is still flowing. This sequence of events is shown in Figure 1. The induced pulse of current gradually diminishes in amplitude because of the impedance offered by the wire to the flow of current.

The impedance the wire offers to the flow of current is mainly caused by two factors: The first is the ohmic resistance of the wire. Part of the induced radio energy pulse is dissipated as heat created in the wire by the resistive loss of the conductor. The second factor is far more subtle and unusual. The electrons moving in the wire actually reradiate radio energy back into space. Energy from the pulse is dissipated as a radio wave back into the dielectric medium surrounding the conductor. Generally speaking, any conducting medium that extracts radio energy from space reradiates a portion of that energy back into space. Armed with these highly important concepts, we may now turn to a dipole antenna and observe how it functions.

THE RESONANT DIPOLE ANTENNA

If a termination (or load) is connected to an antenna that is energized by a passing radio wave, a certain amount of power is extracted from the wave and dissipated in the load. The current flowing into the load may be thought of as the sum of many individual currents flowing in the antenna, induced by the radio

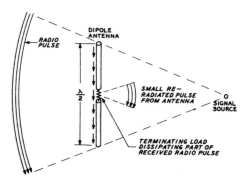

Fig. 2 When conductor is terminated by resistive load, part of intercepted radio pulse is dissipated in load; the remaining portion is reradiated back into space. Greatest amount of intercepted power occurs when conductor is resonant and load is equal to the feedpoint resistance of conductor. Load is placed at point of maximum current in the conductor.

wave acting along the length of the antenna. When all the individual induced currents are in phase at the load the maximum amount of power is extracted from the radio wave. The condition of proper phasing is called resonance. Resonance is established when the length of the antenna bears a certain relationship to the frequency of the intercepted wave. In a simple antenna, a resonant condition is usually found at multiples of one-quarter wavelength (1/4, 1/2, 3/4 wavelength, etc.). The one-half wave resonance point is the one commonly used in parasitic arrays and the one with which we are concerned.

With any type of electrical power source, whether it be a storage battery, a generator or a receiving antenna, maximum power is delivered to a load when the load impedance is equal to the generator impedance. In this condition, the generator and load are said to be matched. A simple one-half wave dipole terminated by a load resistance is shown in Figure 2.

To obtain the most efficient transfer of energy from the antenna to the load resistance, the system must meet two requirements: The first requirement is that the antenna must be resonant. The second is that the load resistance must equal the radiation resistance of the antenna. In other words, the system must be matched. Radiation resistance of an antenna may be defined as that value of resistance which, when substituted for the antenna, will dissipate the same amount of power as is radiated by the antenna. The actual value of radiation resistance of any antenna is determined by the configuration and size of the antenna, and the proximity and character of nearby objects. As in the case of the generator, the matched antenna delivers a portion of the power extracted from the passing wave to the terminating load and reradiates into space the remaining portion of the power that is not dissipated by the dc resistance of the antenna system.

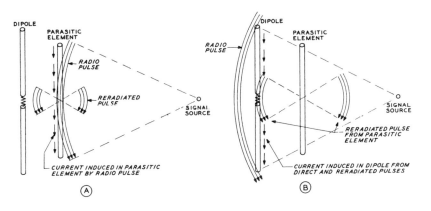

Fig. 3 A parasitic element in front of a dipole reradiates most of the intercepted radio pulse (A). Terminated dipole receives energy directly from pulse, and also from reradiation from parasitic element (B). Proper tuning of parasitic element insures that reradiated energy reaches the resonant dipole in phase with the direct radio pulse.

THE PARASITIC ELEMENT

A resonant rod or wire reradiates a large portion of the radio energy it intercepts if it is not connected to a load. Such a rod or wire is called a parasitic element. Figure 3 shows a parasitic element placed near a dipole. The dipole is properly terminated by a load resistor. The parasitic element is placed between the dipole and the radio signal source. The signal is first intercepted by the parasitic element, which extracts energy from the radio wave and reradiates it. The dipole is now exposed to the original radio wave plus the reradiated wave from the parasitic element, which reaches the dipole a fraction of a radio cycle later. If the reradiated wave from the parasitic element reaches the dipole at the proper instant, it will reinforce a wave received directly by the dipole.

The phase-timing of the wave reradiated from the parasitic element is determined by the physical separation between the dipole and the parasitic element, and by the length of the parasitic element. Under proper conditions, one-half of the reradiated wave from the parasitic element is captured by the dipole. As the spacing between the parasitic element and the dipole is changed, the length of the parasitic element must be altered to retain the proper phase relationship between the two elements. Since the intensity of the intercepted field surrounding the

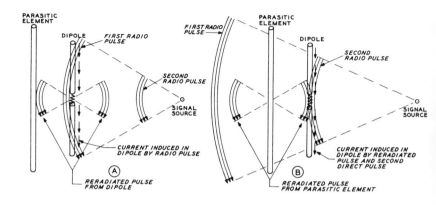

Fig. 4 A parasitic element placed behind a dipole reradiates both direct pulse and pulse reflected from the dipole. Phase-timing of reradiated wave is determined by element spacing and tuning of the parasitic element.

parasitic element decreases at increasing distances from the dipole, the effect the parasitic element has on the dipole also decreases as the distance between the dipole and the parasitic element is increased.

As the parasitic element is brought closer to the dipole, it exerts greater effect on the dipole and a maximum of the reradiated energy is captured by the dipole. As the spacing between the two elements passes a certain critical minimum point, other important forces tend to neutralize the proximity of the parasitic element and its effectiveness declines rapidly. Element spacing in parasitic arrays is covered later in this handbook.

DIRECTOR AND REFLECTOR ELEMENTS

When the parasitic element is placed between the dipole and the received signal source and is tuned so as to enhance the signal captured by the dipole, the parasitic element is termed a director.

A parasitic element may be placed "behind" a dipole as shown in Figure 4 and still exert a profound effect upon the dipole. In this case, the radio wave is first intercepted by the dipole, a part of the wave is dissipated in the load impedance and a part of it is reradiated. The parasitic element is now exposed to the original radio wave plus that portion of the wave that is reradiated from the dipole. The parasitic element extracts energy from both waves and reradiates nearly all of it.

If the length of the parasitic element is correct, and the spacing between it and the dipole is correct, the reradiated wave from the parasitic element reinforces the direct wave received by the dipole. Such an element is called a reflector.

A simple dipole is equally receptive to radio waves received from either side of it. A single parasitic element placed near the dipole makes it more receptive to waves received in one direction. The phasing of the parasitic element that increases the gain of the dipole in one direction decreases its gain in the opposite direction. Thus, the parasitic element produces a more or less unidirectional beam pattern. An array of this type is termed a two element parasitic beam.

There is a situation wherein the two element beam performs as a bidirectional antenna, the parasitic element working both as a director and as a reflector, but the tuning adjustments of the elements for this particular case are difficult to achieve in practice.

TWO OR MORE PARASITIC ELEMENTS

It is entirely practical to construct a parasitic array that uses two or more parasitic elements. Multiple directors are commonly used with a single reflector. The signal gain of such a multi-element parasitic beam is appreciably higher than the gain of a two element array, but the multi-element beam is more cumbersome and more frequency sensitive than the two element array. Antennas employing more than two parasitic elements are often used on the high frequency bands. These are discussed later in this handbook.

FEED POINT RESISTANCE

Radiation resistance, as defined earlier in this chapter, is that value of resistance which, when substituted for the antenna, dissipates the same amount of power as is radiated by the antenna. In order to match any antenna to a transmission line or other feed system, it is important to know the value of the radiation resistance of the antenna at the point of attachment of the transmission line. This is called the feedpoint resistance. For a simple half-wave dipole the feed point resistance at the center is about 72 ohms when the dipole is located one-half wavelength above a good ground surface. The actual change in feed point resistance of the dipole, as the height is varied above the ground, is shown in Figure 5.

When one or more parasitic elements are placed near the dipole, the feedpoint resistance of the antenna is lowered from a nominal 72 ohm value to a value nearer 20 ohms. This new lower

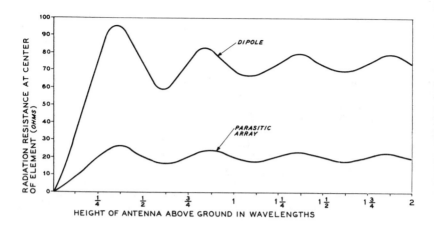

Fig. 5 The feedpoint resistance of a dipole varies about the mean value of 72 ohms as height above ground is varied. The feedpoint resistance of the driven element of a Yagi beam is of a lower value and varies about the mean value of 20 ohms. Fluctuations are less acute than those of the dipole.

feedpoint resistance is a function of the number of parasitic elements, their spacing from the driven element and the tuning and phasing of each element. The variation in feedpoint resistance as the height of the beam antenna above ground is changed is much less than the variation noted in the case of the dipole.

ANTENNA DIRECTIVITY

Before power gain is discussed, antenna directivity should be considered. This concept is important as antenna gain comes about by altering the directivity of an antenna. The directivity is the ability of the antenna to concentrate its radiation in a specific direction, as compared to a theoretical isotropic antenna which has no directivity and does not exist in real life. In many cases, the common dipole is taken as a reference source. In any case, directivity is stated for free space conditions, a fictitious situation as all real antenna interact with the surface of the earth.

Directivity of a beam antenna can be related to real life by comparing it with a dipole antenna placed at the same height above ground as the test antenna, or substituted for the test antenna in the same position. Directivity and power gain tests can be made in this fashion provided the numerous environmental factors affecting antenna performance are taken into consideration. Confusing results and incorrect comparison ratios are often the outcome of such tests.

ANTENNA GAIN -- MUCH ADO ABOUT SOMETHING

Fast horses, expensive cars, vintage wine, antenna gain and other exotic aspects of life seem to exert a fascination among enthusiasts that is a mystery to the casual observer. Since fundamental knowledge about these subjects seems to be shrouded in folklore, they offer endless opportunities for speculation and rumor. Nonexperts often conclude that these are topics invoked by the learned to mystify the humble.

Antenna gain, however, is of intense interest to all radio communicators, and well it might be. Antenna gain costs money, takes up space, and takes time to create. Antenna advertisements extoll the virtues of high gain and other interesting features. So it is important to understand the meaning and limitations in the expressions of antenna gain that abound in the literature and that fill the amateur bands with occasional controversy.

Power gain is the term used to express the power increase in the desired direction of a specific antenna as compared with a standard antenna. The comparison antenna for scientific tests is the isotropic radiator which radiates equally well in all directions. This antenna does not exist except as a mathematical concept since all practical antennas radiate better in one direction than in another and most of them exhibit gain over an isotropic radiator. A dipole, for example, has a power gain of 2.14dB over an isotropic antenna.

Most amateur antennas are referenced in power gain to a dipole (not to an isotropic radiator) and gain expressed in this manner is abbreviated dB, or occasionally dBd. If the antenna gain is referenced to an isotropic radiator on the other hand, the gain is abbreviated dBi.

Thus a beam antenna can, for example, have a gain figure of 6 dB referenced against a dipole and a second gain figure of 8.14 dBi when referenced against an isotropic radiator. It is easy to confuse the two scales of measurement and some "hard sell" members of the antenna manufacturing community take advantage of the resulting confusion by not specifying which reference is being used in their advertisements and specification sheets.

As trivial as an isotropic radiator sounds, the concept is very important. In your mind's eye, picture an isotropic radiator as a very small light bulb - a flashlight bulb will do. Imagine that this bulb is at the very center of a large sphere.

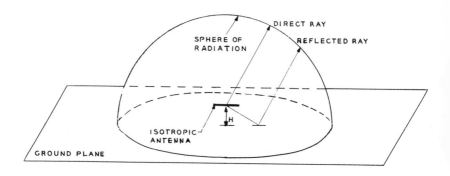

Fig. 6 The effect of ground on an isotropic antenna can be visualized by placing the antenna above a metallic plate. One-half of
the radiation sphere about the antenna is illuminated, the other
half being represented by the ground plane. Since the same amount
of power is radiated in half the sphere volume, the radiated field
is doubled. In addition, ground plane changes normal radiation
pattern of the antenna by reflecting and focusing the radiated
energy.

It illuminates the inner surface of the sphere equally at all
points. This is a good approximation of an isotropic radiator.

Now, remove the little bulb and replace it with a long, thin
bulb that approximates a dipole antenna. You will find that the
inner surface of the sphere is illuminated quite brightly off the
sides of the bulb but very weakly off the ends. This bulb, in
other words, has directivity. And if you place a polished
reflector behind the bulb, you can focus a great amount of light
in one direction at the expense of light in another direction,
which is what a beam antena does.

This fanciful picture represents the isotropic antenna, the
dipole and a simple beam antenna in free space, a situation
which hardly exists in real life.

To examine the antenna near the earth, in your mind's eye
cut the sphere in half horizontally and substitute a metallic plate
for the missing half of the sphere. Mount the isotropic antenna
at the center point of the plate, as shown in Figure 6. Now,
only half the sphere is illuminated, the other half being represented by the "ground" sheet. Since the same amount of power
is radiated in half the volume, the radiated field is doubled, or
increased by 3 dB. In addition, the presence of the ground
plane beneath the antenna changes the normal space radiation
pattern by reflecting and focusing the radiated energy. If the

ground plane is infinite and very smooth, the energy can be doubled at best, or cancelled under the worst circumstances. Thus, the overall effect of the ground is to boost the radiated field by 3 dB because of the elimination of half the sphere about the antenna, plus adding a possible 3 dB more to the gain figure due to ground reflection.

REAL-LIFE ANTENNA GAIN

Every amateur is interested in antenna gain. It costs time and money to have it and those who do are louder on the air than those who don't. The problem, then, is to define antenna gain so one antenna can be compared with another under realistic conditions.

Antenna gain may be calculated with the aid of a computer, or it may be measured directly with an operative model antenna. Both techniques are in use today and the problem in correlating data from the two techniques is complex, confusing and sometimes open to question.

A search of the technical literature over the past 40 years reveals a bewildering collection of antenna gain measurements and computer-derived gain figures. The authors disagree among themselves and in some instances the authors contradict themselves as they tell their stories.

The problems are many. If the computer program is in error, the data derived will be in error. And the techniques used to make direct "on the air" comparisons between two antennas are vague. Finally, the experimenters often have different goals in mind when they conduct their investigations. To complicate matters, test techniques are not standardized and it is difficult to completely scale an antenna so that the test model (and the surrounding environment) is equal in all respects to the real thing.

It is no wonder, then, that specific gain data are hard to compile for the Yagi antenna types used by amateurs. It is not difficult to zero-in on gain figures that are a consensus of a number of tests. Such a compromise number is often more nearly correct in real life than either the computer-derived data or those taken from measurements made on an antenna range.

P.T. BARNUM IS ALIVE AND WELL
AND WRITING ANTENNA ADVERTISEMENTS

Computer measurements relating to gain are universally compared to an isotropic antenna in free space, something that is unrealistic and unobtainable. To convert the computed figure to

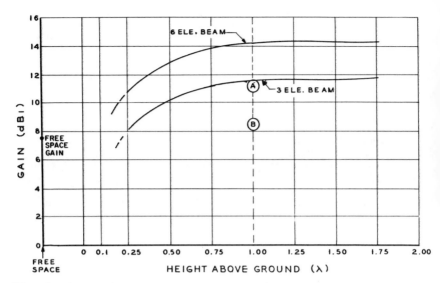

Fig. 7 Measured antenna gain is a function of the height of the antenna above ground. Shown are computed curves for 3- and 6-element beams at various heights. Antenna range measurements of 6-element beam (A) shows actual gain figure of about 11 dB. Measurement of representative 3-element beam (B) shows gain figure of about 8.5 dB. Free space gain figure for 6-element beam is about 7.5 dB. Many factors render real-life gain figures less than the theoretical gain, as explained in the text.

one that is more meaningful, 6 dB is sometimes added to compensate for the effect of the earth and signal reflection from it. This provides the maximum theoretical gain obtainable from the antenna under investigation.

The question, then, is how much of this "free" 6 dB is realizable in the average amateur installation? About half (3 dB) is gained because the antenna "illuminates" only a half-hemisphere in real life and a portion of the ground reflection gain is commonly achieved even though the reflecting surface may be rough and covered with objects such as buildings, power lines, cars, etc.

Measured antenna gain is also a function of the height of the antenna above the earth. Shown in Figure 7 are computer-derived gain curves for a three and a six element beam at various heights above a perfect ground plane. Above one wavelength high, the theoretical maximum gain figures for the antennas are 11.54 dB and 14.22 dB, respectively. How do these computations compare with measurements made with similar antennas tested on an antenna range?

Range data varies considerably depending upon test procedures and antenna placement but, generally speaking, a nominal value of 8.5 dB gain has been recorded for the three element array and a figure of about 11 dB has been noted for the six element configuration.

Many factors render the real-life gain figure less than the theoretical gain. Inherent antenna loss, the presence of objects in the near-field of the antenna, ground conductivity, the unevenness of the ground, the fact that gain is usually measured near ground level and the main lobe of the beam is elevated above that -- these factors and more obscure the actual gain figure of the array.

Antenna gain, much like the speed of the aforementioned race horses, miles-per-gallon figures for an automobile, and the "music power" of a stereo amplifier, is an elastic term that brings joy to the believers in the "hard sell" technique. These terms are much abused -- so much so that advertised antenna gain figures are not accepted for publication in some amateur magazines.

Gain figures for the antennas described in this handbook are not computer-derived, they are taken from actual measurements. In all cases the gain is referenced to a dipole, so all figures are identified by the symbol dB. This figure is conservative and smaller than the computer-derived figure. This is a realistic approach as it provides information that is related to true-life conditions, where the antenna is not at the center of a hollow hemisphere or suspended over an infinite copper sheet!

THE DECIBEL (dB)

Power gain and front-to-back ratio of beam antennas are usually expressed in terms of decibels. The usual amateur view of the decibel is generous, since liberal-reading "S-meters" of modern communication receivers are bountiful in the indication of signal strength. This is understandable, but the reader is warned not to use the inflated "S-meter" decibel in place of the more universally accepted one, which is defined as:

> One decibel equals ten times the common logarithm of the power gain over a specific reference level.

The decibel (dB) is not a unit of power, but a ratio of power levels. In antenna practice the decibel may be used as an absolute unit by fixing an arbitrary level of reference. If this reference level is taken as the power figure of a dipole, another antenna may be said to have "so many decibels power gain (or loss) compared to the dipole". In this sense, a representative three element beam may be said to have a power gain of 8 dB. (Decibels can be used to express voltage ratios as well as power ratios, and this practice is usually followed in low level audio applications.)

THE IMPORTANCE OF POWER GAIN

It has been determined by experiment that a power change of one decibel is just audible over an average radio transmission path. A power increase of two decibels is the minimum that is really worthwhile to undertake, since the result of power changes of less than this value can be accurately measured only under closely controlled conditions not usually found outside laboratories, and cannot be heard by the ear.

A power change of 4 to 5 dB achieved by going from a dipole to a small beam antenna is very worthwhile and is readily apparent in signal reports received. Best of all, antenna gain is usable on reception as well as transmission and a good beam helps to pull weak signals up into readability.

Substitution of a large, high gain beam antenna for a dipole or a ground plane antenna produces startling results. It can make the difference between no signal at all and a strong, readable signal. This fact was brought home forcefully some years ago when an amateur in northern California erected a 40 meter, three element Yagi antenna -- the first in the area. Other unhappy amateurs soon found out that the beam owner could work European amateurs on 40 meters in the late afternoon and get good reports when other amateurs using dipoles and ground plane antennas could not even hear the European signals!

In summation, then, power gain is "the name of the game" and quickly separates "the men from the boys" in active DX competition. Thus it may truly be said that the beam antenna is the key to success in the fascinating game of working DX.

THE FRONT-TO-BACK RATIO

The power gain of a parasitic antenna may be thought of as taking the power radiated to the sides and rear of the array and squirting it out the front of the array. Of great interest to the user of a beam antenna is the amount of power that still escapes from the back side of the array (Figure 8). The ratio of the power radiated in the forward direction of the beam as compared

Fig. 8 Power gain of an antenna array may be thought of as taking radiated power from back and sides of array and squirting it out the front of array. Front-to-back ratio of beam is measure of power radiated in the forward direction compared to that radiated in the reverse direction. The ratio varies widely both with angle of arrival of the signal from the rear of array and height of the array above the ground.

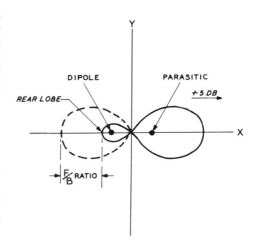

to that radiated in the opposite direction is termed the front-to-back ratio of the antenna. Ratios of the order of 5 to 30 dB may be obtained from parasitic arrays adjusted to provide maximum gain figures. Front-to-back ratios measured on amateur antenna installations vary widely from the above figures as a result of wave reflection from the ground and nearby objects.

Computer studies of the front-to-back ratio (F/B ratio) show that maximum ratio is obtained only at a single frequency and that in theory the ratio is extremely high. While forward gain adjustments to a Yagi are rather uncritical, adjustment for best F/B ratio is quite critical and operation of the antenna only a small percentage away from the design frequency reduces the ratio severely. In addition, the true F/B ratio is often obscured by unwanted reflection from nearby metallic objects, power lines and other surfaces. A signal reflection from a hill to the rear of the antenna can destroy the F/B ratio of a beam under certain circumstances.

Because of the difficulty of measuring the true F/B ratio of a beam, most amateurs accept whatever ratio they achieve under conditions of maximum signal gain and do not try to adjust their array for this elusive quality.

ANTENNA POLARIZATION

By custom and convenience, most high frequency antennas are horizontally polarized, that is, the radiating elements are parallel with the horizon. It is entirely possible for the beam antenna to be so mounted that the radiation is vertically polarized; the parasitic elements are then in a vertical position. Regardless of the plane of polarization, the high frequency wave returned to the earth from the ionosphere usually has random polarization as the wavefront is distorted by the action of reflection from a non-homogeneous surface. Thus, in most cases the orientation of the antenna has little effect upon the received signal.

The electrical characteristic of the ground beneath and in proximity to the antenna array, however, has a more pronounced effect upon a vertically polarized array than upon a horizontal one. Radiation from the vertical array is severely reduced by deficiencies in the ground system. When the earth is less than a perfect conductor, it may be considered a lossy dielectric that can cause undue loss of radiated power, especially at low and medium angles of radiation. An important factor, therefore, in the choice of horizontal versus vertical polarization appears to be the condition of the ground in the vicinity of the antenna. Unless a good reflecting surface such as a salt marsh, a body of water, or a set of long copper radial wires is at hand, horizontally polarized antenna elements are recommended for best hf performance.

THE LAW OF REASON

The reader is reminded that the Law of Reason (otherwise known as "common sense") applies equally well to all forms of beam antennas as it does to other facets of daily life. On occasion an unorthodox form of antenna gains wide publicity as a "break-through" in performance, providing the lucky user (or more likely the buyer) untold advantages of greater power gain, enhanced front-to-back ratio, or otherwise promising performance outclassing the usual forms of antennas widely used by numerous amateurs. Extreme caution should be exercised in accepting such claims, especially if the performance characteristics of the antenna in question seem to have been generated in the advertising department rather than the engineering department of the manufacturer!

THE PHYSICAL CONCEPT OF POWER GAIN

The physical concept of power gain is illustrated in Figure 9, showing the illumination of a sphere by a directional antenna placed within it. An isotropic (nondirectional) radiator illuminates the interior of the sphere in a uniform manner. The power gain of any antenna is the ratio between the surface area of the sphere illuminated by the isotropic radiator and that portion illuminated by the directional antenna. Since the field pattern of a practical directional (beam) antenna is not clear-cut but blends into nothingness at the extremities, the actual pattern is defined as that elliptical, illuminated portion of the

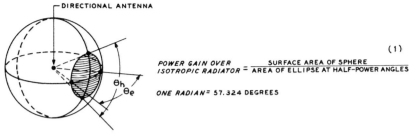

$$\text{(1)}$$

$$\frac{\text{POWER GAIN OVER}}{\text{ISOTROPIC RADIATOR}} = \frac{\text{SURFACE AREA OF SPHERE}}{\text{AREA OF ELLIPSE AT HALF-POWER ANGLES}}$$

ONE RADIAN = 57.324 DEGREES

THE AREA OF A SPHERE IS EQUAL TO : 4π SQUARE RADIANS $\qquad$ (2)

THE AREA OF AN ELLIPSE (OR A CIRCLE) IS EQUAL TO: πAB SQUARE RADIANS (3)

WHERE A AND B ARE ONE-HALF THE LENGTH AND WIDTH, RESPECTIVELY, OF THE ELLIPSE EXPRESSED IN RADIANS.

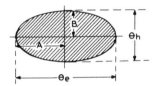

Θ_e AND Θ_h REPRESENT THE HALF-POWER BEAM WIDTHS IN THE ELECTRIC AND MAGNETIC PLANES, RESPECTIVELY. THE ELECTRIC PLANE IS GENERATED IN THE SAME PLANE AS THE RADIATOR ELEMENT, WHILE Θ_h IS GENERATED IN THE PERPENDICULAR PLANE.

A IN RADIANS $= \dfrac{\Theta_e}{114.59}$ $\qquad$ *B IN RADIANS* $= \dfrac{\Theta_h}{114.59}$ $\qquad$ (4)

THEREFORE : $\quad G = \dfrac{4\pi}{\pi \dfrac{\Theta_e \; \Theta_h}{(114.59)^2}} = \dfrac{52525}{\Theta_e \; \Theta_h} = \begin{array}{l}\text{POWER GAIN OVER}\\ \text{ISOTROPIC RADIATOR}\end{array}$ $\qquad$ (5)

SINCE A HALF-WAVE DIPOLE HAS A GAIN OF 1.64 OVER AN ISOTROPIC RADIATOR, THE GAIN OF A DIRECTIONAL ANTENNA OVER A HALF-WAVE DIPOLE MAY BE EXPRESSED AS :

POWER GAIN $(G) = \dfrac{52525}{(1.64)\,\Theta_e \; \Theta_h} = \dfrac{32027}{\Theta_e \; \Theta_h}$ $\qquad$ (6)

Fig. 9 Illustration of how power gain is ratio between surface of an imaginary sphere illuminated by an isotropic radiator and remainder of the sphere. On polar plot of a beam antenna, included angle of the illuminated area is taken between "minus 3 dB" power points on plot. Power gain can be computed when beam width is known.

sphere which lies between the half-power angles of the radiator field. On the usual polar plot of a beam pattern, these angles are for the "-3 dB" power points.

The power gain of any antenna over a dipole may be computed from Figure 9 when the beam width (expressed in degrees) in the cross sections of the plane of radiation are known. Formula (6) is one well worth noting, as it provides a quick method for determining power gain over a dipole antenna when the half-power beam widths are known (see page 52).

The preceding calculations have assumed that no power is spent in backward radiation or in spurious lobes that may actually exist in a directional antenna. If the spurious lobes are 15 dB or more below the strength of the main lobe, the formulas are quite accurate. Even if unwanted lobes are down only 10 dB, the calculation of gain will be correct within two- or three-tenths of a decibel.

It should be noted that directivity alone does not always provide a true picture of power gain. Radiation efficiency may at times be an important factor, since an antenna can have excellent directional characteristics but at the same time be crippled by poor radiation efficiency. If much of the transmitter power is absorbed and converted to heat in the antenna structure, the actual power gain may be considerably less than the directivity pattern would indicate.

EFFECTIVE APERTURE

Effective aperture is closely associated with directivity and power gain. In a simplified analogy it may be thought of as the frontal area from which the receiving antenna will extract signal power from the radio wave. Sometimes this concept is referred to as capture area (Figures 10 and 11). On the other hand, physical aperture is a measure of the area physically occupied by the antenna system, and may be smaller or greater than the effective aperture. Some antennas, such as the parabolic dish type, have an effective aperture somewhat smaller than their physical size, while others such as high-Q parasitic arrays have an effective aperture considerably larger than their physical size. The ratio between the effective and the physical apertures indicates what order of power gain can be expected from an antenna of given size. The higher the ratio, the higher the gain per unit size of the antenna, although other factors such as bandwidth and spurious lobes must be taken into consideration when choosing an antenna.

IF THE POWER GAIN OF AN ANTENNA SYSTEM IS KNOWN, THE EFFECTIVE APERTURE MAY BE CALCULATED FROM:

$$A_{eM} = \frac{1.64 G}{4 \pi} = 0.13 \ G' \tag{7}$$

WHERE G' IS THE POWER GAIN OVER A HALF-DIPOLE.

FROM (7), THE EFFECTIVE APERTURE OF A HALF-WAVE DIPOLE IS EQUAL TO 0.13 SQUARE WAVELENGTHS. THE APERTURE IS ELLIPTICAL, AND MEASURES APPROXIMATELY 3/4 X 1/4 WAVELENGTH.

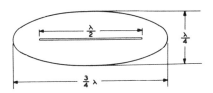

IT MAY BE MORE CONVENIENT TO FIND THE EFFECTIVE APERTURE IN SQUARE FEET, IN WHICH CASE THE FORMULA BECOMES:

$$A_{eM} \ (SQ. \ FT) = \frac{G f^2}{7,586,000} \tag{8}$$

WHERE G IS THE GAIN OVER A HALF-WAVE DIPOLE AND f IS THE FREQUENCY IN MEGACYCLES.

THE FOLLOWING FORMULAE MAY BE USED TO CALCULATE THE ACTUAL DIMENSIONS OF THE APERTURE:

--WHEN THE APERTURE IS CIRCULAR (OR ELLIPTICAL), SUCH AS WOULD BE THE CASE WHEN USING 2 STACKED YAGIS:

$$A_h = 2 \sqrt{\frac{A_{eM} \ \theta_h}{\pi \ \theta_e}} \qquad A_e = 2 \sqrt{\frac{A_{eM} \ \theta_e}{\pi \ \theta_h}} \tag{9}$$

WHERE A_h IS THE APERTURE WIDTH IN THE "h" PLANE, AND A_e IS THE APERTURE WIDTH IN THE "e" PLANE.
A_h AND A_e ARE EXPRESSED IN WAVELENGTHS.

--WHEN THE APERTURE IS RECTANGULAR (OR SQUARE), SUCH AS WOULD BE THE CASE WHEN USING MANY PHASED DIPOLES:

$$A_h = \sqrt{\frac{A_{eM} \ \theta_h}{\theta_e}} \qquad A_e = \sqrt{\frac{A_{eM} \ \theta_e}{\theta_h}} \tag{10}$$

Fig. 10 Effective area (capture area) may be visualized as frontal area from which an antenna extracts signal power from the radio wave. Yagi antennas have an effective capture area considerably larger than their physical size. The ratio between effective and physical apertures can determine power gain of the array. Capture area of a dipole is considered to be about 0.13 square wavelength.

EXAMPLE: *CALCULATE THE PHYSICAL SIZE OF THE ELLIPTICAL APERTURE GENERATED BY A 2-YAGI ARRAY.*

HALF-POWER BEAM WIDTH IN THE "e" PLANE IS 20 DEGREES.
HALF-POWER BEAM WIDTH IN THE "h" PLANE IS 10 DEGREES.

EFFECTIVE APERTURE
OF
2 STACKED YAGIS

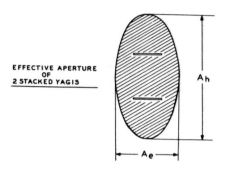

THE POWER GAIN OVER A HALF-WAVE DIPOLE, $G = \dfrac{32027}{10\,(20)} = 160.1$ (22.05 DB)

EFFECTIVE APERTURE, $A_{eM} = 0.13\,(160.1) = 20.8\ \lambda^2$

SINCE THE APERTURE IS ELLIPTICAL, WE WILL USE THE FORMULA (9)

$$A_e = 2\sqrt{\dfrac{20.8\,(10)}{\pi\,(20)}} = 3.62 \text{ WAVELENGTHS}$$

$$A_h = 2\sqrt{\dfrac{20.8\,(20)}{\pi\,(10)}} = 7.26 \text{ WAVELENGTHS}$$

AT 144 MEGACYCLES, A_e *IN FEET* $= \dfrac{3.62\,(984)}{144} = 24.7 \text{ FEET}$

$$A_h \text{ IN FEET} = \dfrac{7.26\,(984)}{144} = 49.6 \text{ FEET}$$

--TO CONVERT A_h, *(OR* A_e*) FROM WAVELENGTHS TO FEET:*

$$A_h \text{ IN FEET} = \dfrac{A_h \text{ IN WAVELENGTHS} \times 984}{\text{FREQUENCY IN MEGACYCLES}}$$

Fig. 11 An example of gain and aperture calculation for two Yagi beams. Data in Fig. 9 gives antenna gain derived from E and H plane beamwidths; Fig. 10 provides information on elliptical apertures. This hypothetical array provides a power gain of about 22 dB over a dipole.

Fig. 12 The arrays in a stack should be spaced so that apertures just "touch." This allows maximum gain consistent with minimum stacking distance. Overlap of apertures may lead to spurious side lobes and reduced front-to-back ratio. High gain Yagis must be spaced up to several wavelengths apart to prevent overlap of apertures.

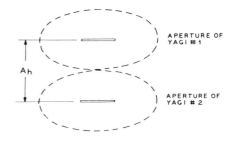

APERTURE OF YAGI # 1

A_h

APERTURE OF YAGI # 2

SPACING BETWEEN ARRAYS AS DETERMINED BY APERTURES

One of the important reasons for determining effective aperture size is that it provides a key to the distance used to space antennas when stacking two or more in an array. A simple rule of thumb is to make the spacing such that the effective apertures just "touch" one another as shown in Figure 12. If the antennas are spaced closer than this, the effective apertures overlap, and power gain is reduced. The higher the gain figure of the individual antennas, the larger the effective aperture, thus calling for increased spacing between bays. Dipoles may be spaced one-half wavelength in an array without overlap of apertures, whereas high gain Yagis used in an array must be spaced up to several wavelengths apart to prevent overlap of apertures.

Two 3-element parasitic beams may be stacked one-half to five-eighths wavelength apart in the vertical plane with negligible aperture overlap. The gain of such a stacked array will approximate three decibels over the power gain of a single beam. A power gain of nearly 20 decibels over a dipole may be achieved by stacking up to 32 beams in a 4 x 8 configuration. In addition, it is possible to "sandwich" (or interleave) stacked beams to form a "Christmas tree" as shown in the illustration. This "tree" consists of stacked 20, 15 and 10 meter arrays on a 110-foot steel mast. At the center of the stack is a single three element 40 meter beam and mounted atop the structure is an extended fourteen element 2 meter beam. For good measure, a tri-band beam is mounted below the 40 meter beam.

"Christmas Tree" Yagi array of ex-W2BDS consisted of stacked beams for all amateur bands between 40 and 2 meters. A 5-element tri-bander was placed at center of stack for comparative purposes.

PARASITIC BEAM PATTERNS

Both polar and elevation patterns of multielement Yagis have been measured and plotted using model antennas operating in the 500 to 1000 MHz range. Measurements performed on hf amateur beams have shown similar patterns.

The polar pattern of a representative, horizontally polarized Yagi is shown in Figure 13. The pattern width is 69 degrees, measured at the half-power points. These points are the spots on the beam pattern where the power gain figure is reduced one-half, or 3 dB, from the maximum figure obtained at the nose of the pattern. Superimposed on this plot is the polar pattern of a reference dipole. The beam has a forward power gain of about 5.3 dB over the dipole, and the rear lobe of the beam pattern is reduced about 12 dB compared against the forward lobe. A two element beam would provide a plot such as this.

The polar pattern of a four element Yagi is shown in Figure 14. The polar pattern width is about 50 degrees at the half-power points. The beam has a forward gain of about 8 dB over a reference dipole, and the rear lobe is suppressed approximately 18 dB compared to the forward lobe. The forward lobe of both beams is quite broad so that precise aiming of the array is

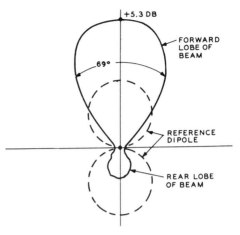

Fig. 13 Polar plot of a field pattern of a horizontally polarized 2-element Yagi. Forward lobe has beamwidth of 69° measured at half-power (-3 dB) points on plot. Power gain over a comparison dipole is about 5.3 dB; the rear lobe is reduced about 12 dB below the forward lobe.

not too important. However, the polar pattern of the thirteen element vhf Yagi shown in Figure 15 has a forward beam width of only 27 degrees. Appreciably more aiming care is required with this array than with smaller ones having very wide lobe patterns.

THE PROXIMITY EFFECTS OF NEARBY OBJECTS

In common with other antennas, the Yagi is sensitive to objects located in the vicinity of the antenna. Figure 16 shows the polar plot taken of the SWR on the transmission line of a five element Yagi rotated through 360 degrees. The beam is located atop a 40 foot (12 m) high tower. To the northwest of the tower is located a high voltage transmission line. When the beam is swung in that direction, the SWR rises to 2-to-1. At the same time, the loading of the transmitter changes significantly.

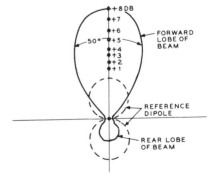

Fig. 14 Polar plot of a 4-element Yagi has half-power beamwidth of about 50°. Beam has forward gain of about 8 dB over a dipole and front-to-back ratio of 18 dB. Nose of beam pattern is quite broad making precise aiming of beam unnecessary.

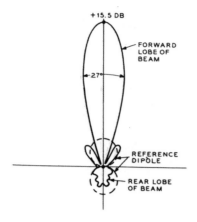

Fig. 15 Polar plot of a 13-element vhf beam shows beamwidth of 27° as measured at the half-power points. Large in size as this beam is, the horiziontal pattern is still quite broad.

A tall tree is located about 40 feet southwest of the tower. The SWR measurements rise slightly when the beam is aimed at the tree and also rise a small amount when the beam is pointed at the house next door. A range of distant hills about 100 feet high and 600 feet to the northwest of the tower causes no change in measured SWR when the beam is aimed in that direction.

It can be observed that the absorption and reflection of rf power from nearby conductors, such as the power line, can cause havoc with antenna adjustment and operation. The transmitted signal can also be routed along the wires, causing TVI at ranges quite beyond the usual primary blanketing range of the transmitter. It is therefore a good idea to keep a beam antenna at least 40 to 50 feet (12 to 15 m) away from overhead wires so as to keep intercoupling between wires and antenna to a mini-

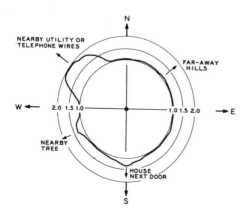

Fig. 16 The Yagi antenna is sensitive to conducting objects in the near field, as shown in plot of SWR of a 3-element hf array. Utility wires raise SWR figure to 2-to-1 when antenna points in a north-west direction.

Parasitic arrays for different frequencies can be stacked one above the other. Elements may also be interlaced on one boom. Shown here is a 21 MHz array stacked over a 14 MHz array. Stacking distance is 10 feet (3 m).

mum. The proximity of trees, bushes and houses seems to have less effect upon the operation of the antenna than do utility wires and power poles. Even though a house contains a collection of electrical wiring, metal lath, pipes and gas lines, this collection of metal is restricted in area and has less effect on the operation of the beam antenna than do the long, extended utility wires.

The electrical height of a beam antenna is often altogether quite different than the physical height. A parasitic array mounted atop a forty foot tower may still be many feet below surrounding trees, buildings and utility wires. A small increase in the physical height of an antenna in such a situation will often cause an apparent increase in signal strength that is difficult to attribute to the modest change of elevation. Every effort should be made to raise the beam antenna to a height sufficient to place it well in the clear, above nearby metallic objects and trees. Arrays located close to rooftops are often detuned by the proximity of metal rain gutters and electrical wiring located in the roof and attic of the house. It is well to make a close examination of the attic area before attempting to erect an antenna array a few feet above the roof of the house.

STACKING ANTENNA ARRAYS OF DIFFERENT FREQUENCIES

In some instances it is desirable to stack parasitic arrays for each of two different bands, such as 20 and 15 meters. Many amateurs have tried placing the two antennas on the same tower, one above the other, or perhaps interlaced on the same supporting boom. If this is done, only one rotation mechanism is required to turn the two arrays.

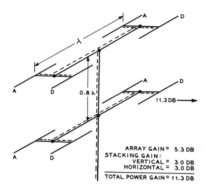

ARRAY GAIN= 5.3 DB
STACKING GAIN:
VERTICAL = 3.0 DB
HORIZONTAL = 3.0 DB
TOTAL POWER GAIN= 11.3 DB

Fig. 17 Identical Yagi arrays for the same band may be stacked horizontally, vertically, or both. Maximum gain for vertical stacking for hf beams up to six elements occurs at spacings of about 0.5 to 0.7 wavelength. Stacking gain for two arrays is about 3 dB. Horizontal stacking provides additional gain.

In the earlier discussion of signal interception and reradiation it was stated that any conducting medium that extracts radio energy from space reradiates a part of that energy back into space. It was also stated that two such conducting mediums placed close together would exert an influence on each other. These forces and influences are still present to an extent when one or both of the conducting mediums is in a nonresonant state. It is therefore logical to assume that the placing of one beam antenna in proximity to another (even though they may be tuned to widely separated frequencies) would have an effect on both of the antennas. By judicious spacing and positioning, however, the proximity effect may be reduced to such a value that the deterioration of efficiency of one or both of the two antennas may be considered insignificant.

Experience has shown that different hf Yagi beams may be interlaced. Examples of these designs are shown later in the handbook. In the case of stacking dissimilar arrays, it has been determined that all elements should lie parallel to one another. Spacing between the beams is not critical, provided it is greater than about one-third the boom length of the larger array.

STACKING IDENTICAL PARASITIC ARRAYS

Two identical parasitic arrays for the same frequency range may be stacked both vertically and horizontally (Figure 17) to provide additional gain in the same manner that dipoles may be stacked. It must be kept in mind, however, that to realize any worthwhile increase in directivity and gain the two arrays must be spaced sufficiently far apart to insure that the mutual coupling between the two arrays remains at a low value. Maximum increase of the gain figure for vertical stacking occurs at a spacing of about 0.5 to 0.7 wavelength, and the stacking gain obtained over the gain figure for a single parasitic array is about 3 dB.

The stacking distance must increase in proportion to the power gain of each array. Two thirteen element 144 MHz parasitic arrays exhibited maximum stacking gain at a vertical spacing of two wavelengths. It may be imagined that each parasitic antenna has a "capture area" of space over which it exerts considerable influence. The higher the gain of the array, the larger this capture area. Care must be taken in the stacking process to prevent the individual capture areas of each antenna from overlapping and thus dropping the maximum gain figure of the configuration.

A gain figure of about 3 dB is obtained when parasitic arrays are stacked side by side as shown in Figure 17. The spacing between the centers of the arrays should be on the order of 1 wavelength to achieve this additional gain figure.

MINIATURE BEAMS

An interesting addition to the parasitic beam antenna family is the miniature beam. This antenna takes the form of a two or three element parasitic array, utilizing short, electrically lengthened elements in place of the more usual half wave elements. In some instances, very close spacing between the elements is used to make the beam compact in terms of the operating frequency. In many cases the use of a miniature beam permits operation on the 20 meter band where the "wing spread" required by a full size 20 meter parasitic array is not compatible with the limited antenna area.

Certain handicaps must be accepted by the user of a miniature beam. The rule that "one never gets something for nothing" applies to beam antennas as well as to more common objects. In order to obtain the benefits of small physical size, the user of a miniature beam must sacrifice both antenna gain and operational bandwidth.

The drop in antenna gain is caused by the fact that a portion of the active elements of the array that normally would contribute to the radiated field is compressed into a loading coil or stub whose radiation field is quite small. In addition, certain extra rf losses in the loading coils further reduce the operational efficiency of the elements. The loading coils must be high Q before any appreciable power gain is obtained from a miniature beam antenna. An efficient two element miniature parasitic beam antenna has a gain figure of 3 dB or so. If loading coils of low Q are employed in the array, the gain may easily vanish, and the array show less radiated field than a simple dipole.

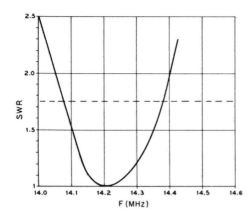

Fig. 18 SWR curve of a 20 meter "minibeam" shows that bandwidth is sacrificed when array is reduced in size. For operation with a trans-mitter having a maximum permissible SWR limit of 1.75-to-1, bandwidth of beam is about 300 kHz.

The SWR bandwidth of a typical two element miniature 20 meter beam is shown in Figure 18. It can be observed that the bandwidth of the miniature array is less than one-half the bandwidth of a full size two element beam. For operation over the whole 350 KHz of the 20 meter band with a reasonable value of SWR on the transmission line, it is necessary to tune the miniature beam to the high frequency end of the band and then add short, removable "outriggers" to the tips of the elements to tune the array to the low frequency end of the band. The front-to-back ratio of a good two element miniature beam com-pares favorably with that of a conventional beam, being on the order of 10 to 15 dB.

As far as can be determined, the addition of a third loaded element to the array to form a three element miniature beam improves neither the gain figure nor the F/B ratio of the config-uration.

LINEAR LOADING

"Lossy" loading coils may be eliminated and linear loading elements substituted in their place in a compact beam (Figure 19). A compact 40 meter beam employing this principal can reduce the "wingspread" from 67 feet (20 meters) to 44 feet (13.4 meters). As shown in the illustration, the element is folded back on itself to produce an electrical equivalent of a resonant half-wavelength. The total length of an element in this particular antenna is approximately 90 feet (27.4 meters) with the center portion folded back upon itself, resulting in an overall physical length somewhat shorter than the usual half wave element.

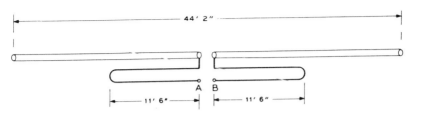

ig. 19 Loading coils, unless exceptionally high-Q, add consider-
ble resistance loss to antenna element. Because of the difficul-
y in constructing a weatherproof high-Q coil, it is more practi-
al to replace coil with wire element folded back along antenna.
he "wingspread" of a half-wave element may be reduced to 60% of
ull size by this method without introducing appreciable loss.

The outer portions of the element are made of sections of
self-supporting aluminum tubing, while the folded portions are
made of #12 AWG hard-drawn copper wire suspended beneath the
element by means of small insulating blocks. The complete
element is quite light in weight and has low wind resistance.

The SWR bandwidth of a compact beam of this configuration
compares favorably with the bandwidth of a full-size equivalent
beam antenna. The 40 meter two element version, for example,
has an SWR of less than 2/1 across the complete band.

THE OFF-CENTER LOADED ELEMENT

A computer study shows that placement of the loading coil
or stub in an element is critical. While center loading is effective, off-center placement of the loading coil improves element
efficiency and bandwidth even though more inductance is required in the coil to establish element resonance. For optimum
performance, the loading coils should be placed midway down the
arms of the element.

Shown in the photograph on the next page is a four-element
log-periodic Yagi (LPY) beam for the 40 meter band utilizing
stub-loaded elements. The stubs are placed in the middle of the
element arms and are folded back against the element towards
the center of the array. The "wingspan" of the beam is reduced
to about 65 percent of a full-size array by this technique without apparent loss in power gain or front-to-back ratio. Maximum
element length is 47 feet (14.3 m) and boom length is 42 feet
(12.8 m).

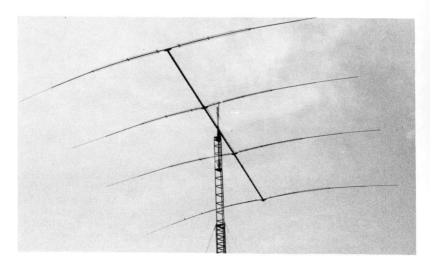

Bandpass LPY Yagi beam for 40 meters. A low value of SWR is achieved across the whole 7 MHz band. Elements are mounted on a 42 foot (12.8 m) boom. Longest element is 47 feet (14.3 m). Each element makes use of linear loading. The loading starts near the center of each element half and each loading stub is folded back along the beam element. Antenna is built by KLM, PO Box 816, Morgan Hill, CA 95037.

All elements are fixed in length but minor tuning adjustments may be made by means of moveable shorting bars at the ends of the stubs. Bandwidth of this compact 40 meter beam is very good, with the SWR remaining below 1.5-to-1 across the band. The array uses a two element log-periodic structure in conjunction with a parasitic reflector and director. (Antenna design by KLM.)

FEEDPOINT RESISTANCE OF A MINIBEAM

With portions of the beam elements wound up into coils, the feedpoint resistance of the antenna drops rapidly. The feedpoint resistance (composed of the radiation resistance plus the loss resistance of the coils) runs about 60 percent of the value encountered in a full-size beam. Coil loss tends to raise the feedpoint resistance, and a high value indicates high coil loss.

Chapter 3

The HF Yagi

EARLY HISTORY

The basic principles of a Yagi beam antenna made of parasitically excited elements had been generally known since the time of Marconi. It was not until the Yagi-Uda experiments in 1926, however, that concise knowledge was gained of the operation of this remarkable antenna.

The Yagi-Uda (more commonly referred to as the Yagi) beam antenna consists of a driven dipole element with additional linear elements in the near-field that are excited by the dipole. Adjustment and spacing of the parasitic elements produces considerable power gain over the normal radiation of the dipole. No electrical connections are made between the driven element and the parasitic elements.

The original Yagi design was first applied to shortwave point-to-point and broadcast antennas about 1928. Finally, in 1935 a classic article by the late M.P. Mims, ex-W5BDB, appeared in QST magazine, giving construction details and tuning information for a two element, 20 meter rotary Yagi antenna.

The "signal squirter" of W5BDB was the first rotary beam to catch the fancy of the amateur operator, starting the trend toward the use of rotary Yagi arrays on the hf and vhf bands. The three element beam was popularized on the 10 meter amateur band about 1938. When aluminum tubing became freely available after World War II, the Yagi appeared in increasing numbers on 20 meters and some daring experimenters even built giant Yagi antennas for 40 meters! And on the vhf/uhf bands, the use of multi-element Yagis quickly became imperative for serious long distance work as high in frequency as 450 MHz.

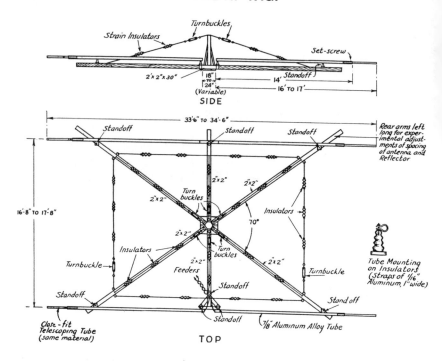

The famous 1935 "signal squirter" 20-meter beam of ex-W5BDB caught the fancy of yesterday's DX operator because of the "punch" of the two element array. Built of hard-to-get aluminum tubing mounted on a wood frame, the Yagi was fed with a twisted-pair transmission line. Several years later, it was discovered that close element spacing gave appreciably higher gain than this wide-spaced design. (Drawing from QST, December, 1935.)

YAGI PARAMETERS

The hf Yagi beam is particularly forgiving with regard to overall dimensions when only a small number of elements are used. It has been possible for builders to get good results from an array that has been pre-cut to somebody's idea of the perfect antenna. For many years "secret dimensions" have floated around the amateur world and magic results have been claimed for unorthodox designs based upon hope and a little bit of luck.

Recently computer studies and accurate field tests run on antenna ranges have removed some of the mystery previously employed in the design and construction of the Yagi antenna.

At the same time, greater insight has been gained into the effects of element diameter and taper, mounting hardware and feed systems. All of these parameters are discussed in this handbook.

The hf Yagi antennas described herein are modeled after a basic design centered at the mid-point of the frequency range in use, and make use of elements of uniform diameter, uniformly spaced along the boom. In all cases (except that of the two-element director design) a single reflector is used since additional reflectors have not proven to be of any benefit. In addition, except for very long vhf Yagis, unequal spacing of director elements does not provide improvement over the basic design.

The handbook designs are based upon an element diameter of one inch (2.54 cm) with no taper, and a center design frequency of 14.17 MHz. Power gain is expressed in decibels (dB) and is referenced to a <u>dipole</u>. These data can be scaled to other operating frequencies, as explained later.

Generally speaking, the length of a reflector element in a Yagi beam is close to a free space half-wavelength, the driven element is resonant at the design frequency and the director is somewhat shorter than resonant length. Power gain and front-to-back ratio qualities of the Yagi are achieved by adjustment of the length and spacing of the parasitic elements. An impedance match to the transmission line is obtained by changing the length (resonance) of the driven element. Fortunately, driven element and parasitic adjustments are not interlocking.

BASIC ELEMENT LENGTH

The half wavelength in space of an electromagnetic wave is:

$$\text{Length (feet)} = \frac{492}{f(\text{MHz})} \text{ , or length (meters)} = \frac{150}{f(\text{MHz})}$$

The length of a half-wave resonant conductor in space is slightly less, depending only upon the diameter of the conductor. The required shortening from the theoretical value is represented by a <u>scaling factor, K</u>, as shown in Figure 1. A dipole for 7 MHz made of No. 12 wire (diameter = .081"), for example, has a length-to-diameter ratio of about 10,000. The K factor (from the chart) is 0.97. A practical wire antenna of No. 12 wire, however, must be supported by end insulators which have a small capacitive loading effect, tending to shorten the dipole even more. Experience has shown that a K factor of 0.96 duplicates the general case (492 x 0.96 = 472):

THE HF YAGI

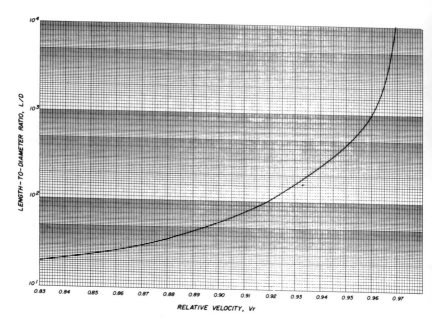

Fig. 1 Graph of the relative phase velocity (K-factor) of a cylindrical antenna element as a function of the length-to-diameter ratio. (By H.F. Tolles, after Schelkunoff and Friis.)

$$\text{Wire dipole length (feet)} = \frac{472}{f(MHz)}, \text{ or } \frac{143.87}{f(MHz)} \text{ (meters)}$$

The length of the 7 MHz wire dipole, then, is:

$$\text{Length (feet)} = \frac{472}{7.0} = 67.42 \text{ feet, or } 20.55 \text{ m.}$$

TUBING ELEMENT LENGTH

In the case of the Yagi beam, the elements are generally made of tubing instead of wire and the K factor is smaller. For 1-inch (2.54 cm) tubing used as a standard design in this handbook, the length/diameter ratio at 14.17 MHz is 417 and the K factor is close to 0.95. The length of a 20 meter tubing dipole, supported at the center, then, is:

Length (feet) $= \dfrac{467}{14.17} = 32.96$ feet, or $\dfrac{142}{14.17} = 10.05$ m.

The Yagi can be designed for any frequency, but it is common practice on most amateur bands to choose the center of the band as the design frequency. In theory, the Yagi is a single-frequency device and electrical performance deteriorates when the antenna is operated off-frequency. In practice, the Yagi can operate efficiently over a narrow frequency range either side of the design frequency with no significant deterioration of the important electrical characteristics.

Because of the width of the 10 and 6 meter bands, it is usual to design an array for operation either at the low or the high frequency ends of the band as a practical design will not encompass the whole band.

DESIGN FREQUENCIES

The design frequencies chosen for the hf antennas described in this handbook are: 7.15, 10.12, 14.17, 18.11, 21.22, 24.94, 28.6, 29.2 and 50.1 MHz. Vhf design information is provided in a later chapter. Experience has shown that these design frequencies permit good beam antenna operation over a large portion of the amateur band with no serious deterioration in gain or F/B ratio at the band edges.

FREQUENCY SENSITIVITY OF THE YAGI

The driven element and the parasitic elements of the Yagi antenna are frequency sensitive. Proper operation of the antenna depends upon spacing and tuning of the elements. If the Yagi antenna is operated at other than the design frequency, all tuning and phasing adjustments change. Amateur hf operation is a "region" technique as opposed to a "spot frequency" technique, thus it becomes of great interest to determine the operational characteristics of a parasitic array used at a frequency a few percent removed from the design frequency.

At the design frequency, the driven element is self-resonant and presents a resistive load to the transmission line and transmitter. As the transmitter frequency is moved away from the design frequency, the antenna presents a more and more reactive load to the transmitter. At the same time, the feedpoint resistance of the driven element slowly changes (Figure 2). As these parameters change, the SWR on the transmission line changes.

A maximum permissible SWR limit line can be drawn over the antenna plot (Figure 3). This limit is usually specified by the

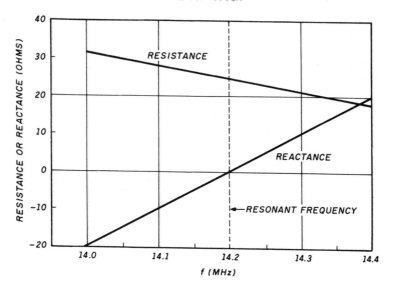

Fig. 2 Feedpoint resistance and reactance of typical Yagi antenna vary as transmitter frequency is shifted above and below design frequency (14.20 MHz). Antenna resistance changes slowly but reactive component changes rapidly when antenna is operated off resonant frequency. As parameters depart from normal value at resonant frequency, SWR on transmission line rises, as discussed in the text.

transmitter manufacturer. In this example, operation of the antenna at the hf end of the band exceeds the permissible value of SWR. Either the antenna must be readjusted for better performance at the hf end of the band, or some sort of matching network must be placed between the transmitter and the antenna to lower the SWR the transmitter "sees" to an acceptable value. Either technique will work well, but it is easier to do the latter than the former.

At the band edges it is important that the parasitic elements still function in normal fashion. This requires that the operational frequency of the antenna never approach the self-resonant frequency of the parasitic elements. Under normal conditions, then, the parasitic elements are self-resonant outside the band edge limits.

ELEMENT TAPER

It was discovered about 1935 that a tapered broadcast tower required a different height for resonance than one having a

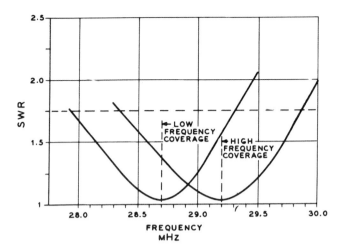

Fig.3 Some solid state transmitters have a maximum value of antenna SWR they are capable of matching. In this example, the maximum limit is 1.75-to-1. If this antenna is adjusted to resonance at 28.7 MHz, it will cover the range from 28.0 to 29.3 MHz within the SWR limit. For operation at the high frequency end of the band antenna resonant frequency is adjusted to 29.2 MHz.

uniform cross section. The tapered tower, in fact, had to be longer than the uniform tower. Amateurs have found this to be true, to their sorrow, where tapered beam elements cut to "standard" dimensions had to be lengthened by as much as ten percent to achieve resonance after the beam was finally put in place and tested.

Mechanical considerations and wind resistance require that most hf beam elements have a taper from center to each tip and such elements are usually made of telescoping tubing. Thus the effect of taper enters into hf beam designs.

The taper effect can be understood if the average diameter of the element is taken as the standard. The thicker portion of the element (the center) has a larger diameter than standard and hence less inductance per unit of length. This portion of the element must be lengthened to reestablish resonance. The tip of the tapered element, on the other hand, is at a point where little current flows and the diameter-to-inductance ratio is unimportant. However, since the ends of the antenna are at a high voltage point the capacitance effect is diminished for a small diameter element so--once again--the element must be lengthened to reestablish resonance.

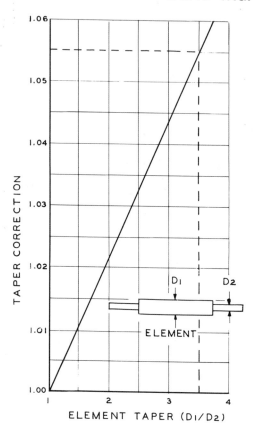

Fig. 4 The taper affects overall element length. Once the basic length has been determined from the Tables in this chapter, length must be increased to correct for element taper. For example, if the taper (D1/D2) is 3.5, the element length correction factor is 1.055.

When many telescoping tubing diameters are used to make up a tapered element, calculation of the effective electrical length can become quite complex. However, a close approximation of the taper factor can be made by comparing the ratio of center element diameter to tip diameter. The graph of Figure 4 illustrates this approximation. Standard data for hf beam antennas may be adapted for any reasonable taper ratio by this procedure. In the case of most vhf beams, however, the elements have no taper and this approximation does not apply.

EFFECT OF ELEMENT SUPPORT

The boom-to-element mechanical clamping system has a minor effect upon element length in the hf region. In the case of a 20 meter element U-bolted with saddles to a flat plate, which in turn is U-bolted to the boom, the average reduction in element length is about 5/8" (1.6 cm) and the effect is progressively

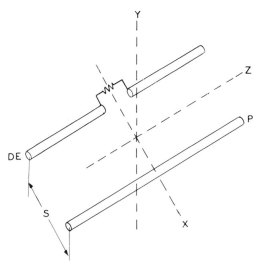

Fig. 5 The 2-element Yagi beam can use parasitic element either as a reflector or a director. In either case, power gain over a dipole is about 5.2 dB and front-to-back ratio is close to 10 dB for practical values of element spacing. Feedpoint resistance runs about 28 ohms. In this illustration, X-Z is the horizontal plane and antenna polarization is horizontal.

less on the lower frequency bands. Thus, for all practical purposes, the effect of element support hardware may be neglected in the hf bands. In the vhf region the effect of mounting hardware is significant and is discussed in detail later in this handbook.

THE TWO ELEMENT YAGI BEAM

The simplest and most compact Yagi is the two element beam (Figure 5). Length of the parasitic element may be adjusted so that it acts either as a reflector or a director.

When the parasitic is a reflector (longer than the driven element) a maximum theoretical gain of about 5.2 dB over a dipole is achieved at an element spacing between 0.10 and 0.15 wavelength. The front-to-back (F/B) ratio runs about 10 dB. A summary of the beam characteristics is given in Figure 6. At the shorter boom length bandwidth is reduced and the SWR on the transmission line rises quite rapidly as the beam is operated off-frequency. In addition, the reflector length should be increased about 1% over the given value to maintain the gain at

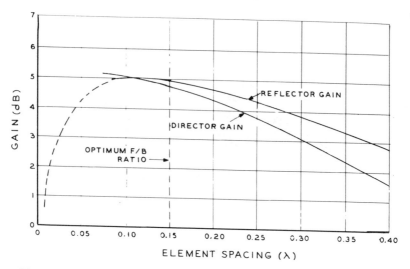

Fig. 6 Operating characteristics of a 2-element Yagi beam. Maximum gain and best front-to-back ratio occur when element spacing is less than one-quarter wavelength. An infinite combination of spacing and lengths exists; a compromise must be made between bandwidth in one case, and gain and front-to-back ratio in the other.

the low frequency end of the band. In the case of a narrow band, such as the 10,18 or 25 MHz bands, this alteration is not necessary.

When the parasitic element is a director (shorter than the driven element) the same gain figure and front-to-back ratio given for the reflector case is achieved at about 0.15 wavelength spacing. Thus the characteristics of the two element beam do not depend greatly upon whether the parasitic element is a reflector or a director. In either case, the feedpoint resistance is very close to 28 ohms at the design frequency. The general formulas for untapered elements are:

Reflector case:

$$\text{Reflector length (feet)} = \frac{492.4}{f\,(\text{MHz})}, \text{ or (meters)} = \frac{150.1}{f\,(\text{MHz})}$$

$$\text{Driven element length (feet)} = \frac{460.5}{f\,(\text{MHz})}, \text{ or (meters)} = \frac{140.4}{f\,(\text{MHz})}$$

TABLE 1- 2-ELEMENT COMPUTER-OPTIMIZED YAGI

BAND	REFLECTOR		R-SPACING		DRIVEN ELEMENT		DRIVEN ELEMENT		D-SPACING		DIRECTOR	
(FREQ)	FEET	METERS	FEET	METERS	FEET	METERS	FEET	METERS	FEET	METERS	FEET	METERS
40M (7.15)	68'10"	20.98	16'6"	5.04	64'11"	19.79	68'7"	20.9	10'10"	3.31	64'7"	19.68
30M (10.12)	48'8"	14.82	11'8"	3.56	48'7"	14.82	48'5"	14.76	7'8"	2.34	45'5"	13.85
20M (14.17)	34'9"	10.59	8'4"	2.55	32'6"	9.91	34'7"	10.54	5'6"	1.67	32'4"	9.8
17M (18.11)	27'2"	8.29	6'6"	1.99	25'4"	7.73	27'0"	8.25	4'3"	1.30	25'2"	7.7
15M (21.22)	23'3"	7.07	5'7"	1.7	21'7"	6.58	23'1"	7.04	3'8"	1.11	21'5"	6.54
12M (24.94)	19'9"	6.02	4'9"	1.45	18'4"	5.58	19'8"	5.99	3'1"	0.95	18'2"	5.5
10 LO (28.60)	17'3"	5.25	4'2"	1.26	15'11"	4.86	17'1"	5.22	0'33"	0.83	15'10"	4.8
10 HI (29.20)	16'10"	5.14	4'1"	1.23	15'7"	4.76	16'9"	5.11	0'32"	0.81	15'6"	4.72
	$L_R = \dfrac{492.4}{f(MHz)}$		$S_R = \dfrac{117.6}{f(MHz)}$		$L_{DE} = \dfrac{460.5}{f(MHz)}$		$L_{DE} = \dfrac{490.2}{f(MHz)}$		$S_D = \dfrac{77.9}{f(MHz)}$		$L_D = \dfrac{457.7}{f(MHz)}$	

Table 1   Practical design information for the 2-element Yagi beam. One-inch diameter (2.54 cm) tubing is used for the standard design with a K-factor close to 0.95. Elements are supported at the center and no correction is applied for mounting hardware. Dimensions are given to the nearest inch or centimeter. Apply the factor given in Figure 4 for tapered elements.

Director case:

$$\text{Director length (feet)} \quad = \frac{457.7}{f\,(MHz)}, \text{ or (meters)} = \frac{138.8}{f\,(MHz)}$$

$$\text{Driven element length (feet)} \quad = \frac{490.2}{f\,(MHz)}, \text{ or (meters)} = \frac{149.35}{f\,(MHz)}$$

In either case:

$$\text{Spacing (R - DE)} = \frac{117.6}{f\,(MHz)} \qquad \text{Spacing (DE-D)} = \frac{77.9}{f\,(MHz)}$$
$$\text{(feet)} \qquad\qquad\qquad\qquad \text{(feet)}$$

   The general design information for two element beams with untapered elements is given in Table 1. Apply the factor given in Figure 4 for tapered elements.

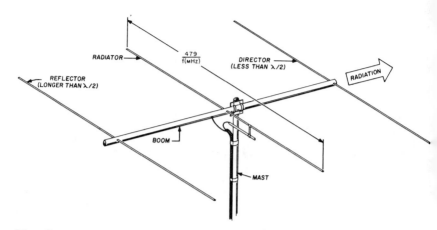

Fig. 7   The 3-element Yagi beam employs a single parasitic reflector and director. Gain is a function of element tuning and boom length. Equal reflector and director spacing to driven element is used. Remarks given under Table 1 apply to this design. For the general case, power gain is over 7.4 dB and front-to-back ratio runs 15 to 20 dB. Feedpoint resistance runs between 16 to 28 ohms for boom lengths 0.2 to 0.5 wavelength.

THE THREE ELEMENT YAGI BEAM

If two parasitic elements are placed near a dipole, one on each· side, the resulting array is a three element beam (Figure 7). One parasitic element is shortened with respect to the driven element to act as a director and the other element is lengthened to act as a reflector. A uniform, nearly unidirectional pattern is obtained having better front-to-back ratio and gain figure than are obtained from a two element beam.

Gain of the three element beam is a function of boom length when the parasitics are adjusted for maximum gain (Figure 8). With a 0.45 wavelength boom, a power gain of about 7.8 dB over a dipole is achieved. Good gain is realized at shorter lengths and at the popular boom length of 0.3 wavelength, the gain runs about 7.4 dB. The F/B ratio as a function of boom length is approximated in Figure 9. Best ratio is obtained with a fairly short boom and 0.25 wavelength long seems to be a good choice.

The frequency response of a representative hf three element Yagi antenna is shown in Figures 10 and 11. The first

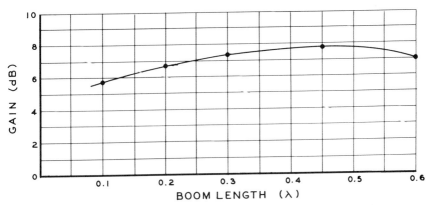

Fig. 8 Power gain of a 3-element Yagi beam varies from 6.5 to 7.8 dB over a dipole when parasitic elements are adjusted for maximum gain. When tuned for optimum front-to-back ratio, power gain is about 0.7 dB less. Ground reflection provides appreciably higher power gain than indicated by free-space calculations.

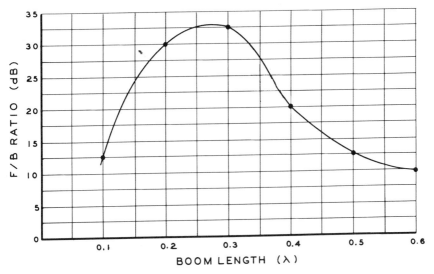

Fig.9 The front-to-back ratio of a 3-element Yagi beam can reach a maximum figure of about 33 dB near the design frequency. The ratio curve for other boom lengths resembles this example. Front-to-back ratio increases as element spacing decreases and drops off as boom length is increased. Maximum f/b ratio is hard to attain in practice.

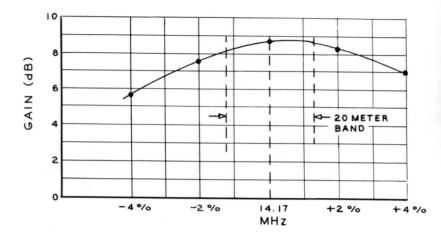

Fig. 10   Gain curve of a 3-element Yagi beam is fairly constant about the design frequency, with maximum gain achieved at the higher frequency end of the band.

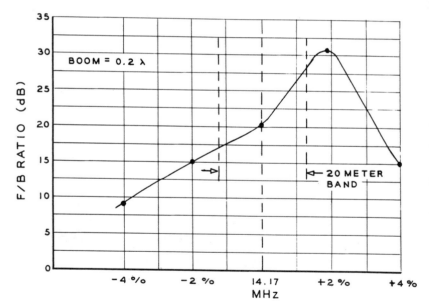

Fig. 11   Front-to-back ratio response of a 3-element Yagi beam peaks near high frequency end of the band. In the general case, the points of maximum gain and maximum front-to-back ratio occur above the design frequency of the array.

illustration shows that the gain curve is fairly constant about the design frequency, with maximum gain achieved at the high frequency end of the band. The F/B ratio peaks at over 30 dB outside the high frequency end of the band. In real life, the gain curve is more to be trusted than is the front-to-back ratio curve.

When the beam antenna is in the presence of ground, the front-to-back ratio depends upon the arrival angle of the signal from the rear of the array, being different for a low arrival angle than for a high angle. Amateurs have learned this to their dismay after adjusting their beams for a good front-to-back ratio on a local signal and finding the ratio poor or nonexistent on a strong, distant signal arriving from the same direction but at a different arrival angle. The consensus is that a three element Yagi beam with a boom length of 0.2 to 0.3 wavelength will exhibit a front-to-back ratio of about 15 to 20 dB, the better ratio occurring when the boom is shorter.

The feedpoint resistance of a three element Yagi beam varies with height above ground, as does that of any other antenna. Generally speaking, for heights greater than 0.5 wavelength the three element beam shows a feedpoint resistance ranging from about 16 to 28 ohms for boom lengths from 0.2 to 0.5 wavelength.

THE MULTI-ELEMENT YAGI BEAM

Additional parasitic directors may be added to a three element hf Yagi beam to increase the power gain. Antenna gain is roughly proportional to the boom length of the multi-element Yagi provided a sufficient number of directors are spaced along the boom. Choice of boom length is critical for best performance and gain increases with boom length. The F/B ratio, moreover, also seems to be a critical function of boom length.

Long Yagi beams with boom lengths up to five wavelengths have been designed for vhf/uhf service, providing power gains as high as 15 dB. For very long Yagi designs, as the boom length is increased, the optimum director spacing also increases. And in this instance, director lengths can be individually optimized for maximum gain. The design of multi-element Yagis is considered in the vhf section of this handbook.

THE COMPUTER-OPTIMIZED YAGI DESIGN

Computer studies by the late James Lawson, ex-W2PV, and others have provided important data for the multi-element Yagi, taking into account element length, spacing, element diameter, taper, and mounting hardware. Many studies are based upon

TABLE 2- 3-ELEMENT COMPUTER-OPTIMIZED YAGI

BAND	REFLECTOR		DRIVEN ELEMENT		DIRECTOR		R-SPACING		D-SPACING	
(FREQ)	FEET	METERS	FEET	METERS	FEET	METERS	FEET	METERS	FEET	METERS
40M (7.15)	69'0"	21.10	66'5"	20.26	63'4"	19.32	18'10"	5.76	20'6"	6.27
30M (10.12)	48'9"	14.87	46'11"	14.31	44'9"	13.65	13'4"	4.07	14'6"	4.43
20M (14.17)	34'10"	10.62	33'6"	10.21	32'0"	9.76	9'7"	2.92	10'0"	3.05
17M (18.11)	27'3"	8.32	26'3"	8.07	25'0"	7.62	7'5"	2.27	8'1"	2.47
15M (21.22)	23'3"	7.09	22'4"	6.82	21'4"	6.51	6'4"	1.94	6'11"	2.11
12M (24.94)	19'9"	6.03	19'0"	5.80	18'2"	5.53	5'5"	1.65	5'11"	1.79
10 LO (28.60)	17'3"	5.26	16'7"	5.06	15'11"	4.83	4'9"	1.44	5'2"	1.57
10 HI (29.20)	16'11"	5.16	16'3"	4.96	15'6"	4.73	4'7"	1.41	5'0"	1.53
6M (50.10)	9'10"	3.00	9'6"	2.89	9'0"	2.75	2'8"	0.82	3'0"	0.89
	$L_R = \dfrac{493.6}{f\,(MHz)}$		$L_{DE} = \dfrac{475}{f\,(MHz)}$		$L_D = \dfrac{453}{f\,(MHz)}$		$S = \dfrac{135}{f\,(MHz)}$		$S = \dfrac{147}{f\,(MHz)}$	

Table 2 Practical design information for the 3-element Yagi beam. One-inch diameter (2.54 cm) tubing is used for the standard design with a K-factor close to 0.95. Elements are supported at the center and no correction is applied for mounting hardware. Dimensions are given to the nearest inch or centimeter. Apply the factor given in Figure 4 for tapered elements.

National Bureau of Standards measurements carried out at the Sterling, Virginia, and Table Mountain, Colorado, antenna test ranges. The results of these investigations form the basis for the computer-generated programs of Yagi performance.

THE OPTIMIZED THREE ELEMENT YAGI BEAM

This close-spaced Yagi design is excellent for all amateur bands between 40 and 6 meters. The antenna is quite compact, being built on a boom about 0.3 wavelength long. Computed forward gain is 7.4 dB over a dipole and the front-to-back ratio is better than 20 dB at the design frequency.

The general formulas for untapered elements are:

$$\text{Director length (feet)} = \frac{453}{f\,(MHz)}, \text{ or (meters)} = \frac{138.3}{f\,(MHz)}$$

$$\text{Driven element length (feet)} = \frac{475}{f\,(MHz)}, \text{ or (meters)} = \frac{144.6}{f\,(MHz)}$$

$$\text{Reflector length (feet)} = \frac{493.6}{f\,(MHz)}, \text{ or (meters)} = \frac{150.5}{f\,(MHz)}$$

$$\text{Spacing: (R - DE)} = \frac{135.7}{f\,(MHz)} \quad \text{DE - D} = \frac{141.7}{f\,(MHz)}$$
(feet)

The general design information for three element beams with untapered elements is given in Table 2. Apply the factor given in Figure 4 for tapered elements.

THE OPTIMIZED FOUR ELEMENT YAGI BEAM

The four element computerized Yagi design shows that a substantial increase in gain can be achieved over the three element model, but the F/B ratio of the four element design is much poorer than that of the smaller beam unless the spacing between the director elements is increased. For example, when all elements are spaced 0.15 wavelength, the F/B ratio is approximately 10 dB at the design frequency. When the director spacings are increased to 0.25 wavelength, the F/B ratio increases to about 27 dB at the design frequency. This emphasizes the fact that placing four elements on a relatively short boom boosts the gain, but at the expense of the front-to-back ratio. Increasing boom length restores the F/B ratio while holding gain at the same high level.

The Yagi design summarized in Table 3 provides a power gain of about 9.1 dB over a dipole with a F/B ratio of better than 27 dB at the design frequency. Reflector spacing is 0.2 wavelength and director spacings are 0.25 wavelength. This requires a 48'6" (14.8 m) boom at 14 MHz.

The general formulas for untapered elements are:

$$\text{Director length (feet)} = \frac{455.8}{f(MHz)}, \text{ or (meters)} = \frac{138.93}{f(MHz)}$$

$$\text{Driven element length (feet)} = \frac{471.3}{f(MHz)}, \text{ or (meters)} = \frac{143.65}{f(MHz)}$$

$$\text{Reflector length (feet)} = \frac{484}{f(MHz)}, \text{ or (meters)} = \frac{147.52}{f(MHz)}$$

TABLE 3 - 4-ELEMENT COMPUTER-OPTIMIZED YAGI

BAND	DIRECTORS		DRIVEN ELEMENT		REFLECTOR		0.25 SPACING		0.20 SPACING	
(FREQ)	FEET	METERS	FEET	METERS	FEET	METERS	FEET	METERS	FEET	METERS
40 M (7.15)	63' 9"	19.43	65' 11"	20.1	67' 8"	20.63	34' 4"	10.49	27' 6"	8.40
30 M (10.12)	45' 0"	13.73	46' 7"	14.19	47' 10"	14.58	24' 3"	7.41	19' 5"	5.93
20 M (14.17)	32' 2"	9.80	33' 3"	10.14	34' 2"	10.41	17' 4"	5.29	13' 10"	4.24
17 M (18.11)	25' 2"	7.67	26' 0"	7.93	26' 9"	8.15	13' 7"	4.14	10' 10"	3.32
15 M (21.22)	21' 6"	6.55	22' 2"	6.77	22' 9"	6.95	11' 7"	3.53	9' 3"	2.83
12 M (24.94)	18' 3"	5.57	18' 10"	5.76	19' 5"	5.92	9' 10"	3.00	7' 10"	2.41
10 LO (28.6)	15' 11"	4.86	16' 5"	5.02	16' 11"	5.16	8' 7"	2.62	6' 10"	2.10
10 HI (29.2)	15' 7"	4.76	16' 2"	4.92	16' 7"	5.05	8' 4"	2.57	6' 9"	2.06
6 M (50.1)	9' 1"	2.77	9' 4"	2.87	9' 8"	2.94	4' 10"	1.50	3' 10"	1.20

$$L_D = \frac{455.8}{f(MHz)} \qquad L_{DE} = \frac{471.3}{f(MHz)} \qquad L_R = \frac{484}{f(MHz)} \qquad S = \frac{246}{f(MHz)} \qquad S = \frac{197}{f(MHz)}$$

Table 3 Practical design information for the 4-element Yagi beam. One-inch diameter (2.54 cm) tubing is used for the standard design with a K-factor close to 0.95. Elements are supported at the center and no correction is applied for mounting hardware. Dimensions are given to the nearest inch or centimeter. Apply the factor given in Figure 4 for tapered elements.

0.25 wavelength spacing (ft) = $\frac{246}{f(MHz)}$, or (meters) = $\frac{74.98}{f(MHz)}$

0.20 wavelength spacing (ft) = $\frac{197}{f(MHz)}$, or (meters) = $\frac{60.05}{f(MHz)}$

Apply the factor given in Figure 4 for tapered elements.

THE OPTIMIZED SIX ELEMENT YAGI

A computer study shows that the addition of a third director to form a five element Yagi provides little advantage. The use of four directors to form a six element array, however, is beneficial. Computed forward gain is nearly 10.5 dB over a dipole and the front-to-back ratio at the design frequency is

TABLE 4 - 6-ELEMENT COMPUTER-OPTIMIZED YAGI

BAND	DIRECTOR		DRIVEN ELEMENT		REFLECTOR		SPACING	
(FREQ)	FEET	METERS	FEET	METERS	FEET	METERS	FEET	METERS
40 M (7.15)	61' 8"	18.80	66' 0"	20.12	68' 2"	20.78	20' 7"	6.29
30 M (10.12)	43' 7"	13.28	46' 8"	14.22	48' 2"	14.68	14' 7"	4.45
20 M (14.17)	31' 1"	9.48	33' 4"	10.15	34' 4"	10.48	10' 4"	3.17
17 M (18.11)	24' 4"	7.42	26' 1"	7.95	26' 10"	8.20	8' 2"	2.48
15 M (21.22)	20' 9"	6.33	22' 3"	6.79	22' 11"	7.00	6' 11"	2.12
12 M (24.94)	17' 8"	5.39	18' 11"	5.77	19' 6"	5.96	5' 10"	1.80
10 LO (28.6)	15' 4"	4.70	16' 6"	5.03	17' 0"	5.19	5' 2"	1.57
10 HI (29.2)	15' 1"	4.60	16' 2"	4.93	16' 8"	5.09	5' 0"	1.54
6 M (50.1)	8' 9"	2.68	9' 5"	2.87	9' 9"	2.97	2' 11"	0.90

$$L_D = \frac{440.94}{f(MHz)} \qquad L_{DE} = \frac{472}{f(MHz)} \qquad L_R = \frac{487.4}{f(MHz)} \qquad S = \frac{147.6}{f(MHz)}$$

Table 4 Practical design information for the 6-element Yagi beam. One-inch diameter (2.54 cm) tubing is used for the standard design with a K-factor close to 0.95. Elements are supported at the center and no correction is applied for mounting hardware. Dimensions are given to the nearest inch or centimeter. Apply the factor given in Figure 4 for tapered elements.

better than 35 dB. Because of the current distribution in the elements, reflector and director spacings can be reduced to about 0.15 wavelength with no ill effects. This design requires a 52.5 foot (16 m) boom at 14 MHz (Table 4).

The general formulas for untapered elements are:

Director length (feet) $= \dfrac{440.9}{f(MHz)}$, or (meters) $= \dfrac{134.39}{f(MHz)}$

Driven element length (feet) $= \dfrac{472.6}{f(MHz)}$, or (meters) $= \dfrac{144.05}{f(MHz)}$

$$\text{Reflector length (feet)} = \frac{487.4}{f(MHz)}, \text{ or (meters)} = \frac{148.56}{f(MHz)}$$

$$\text{Element spacing (feet)} = \frac{147}{f(MHz)}, \text{ or (meters)} = \frac{44.80}{f(MHz)}$$

Apply the factor given in Figure 4 for tapered elements.

ELEMENT DIAMETERS

The recommended element diameters for these antennas range from 1.25" (3.18 cm) to 0.875" (2.22 cm) at 14 MHz, and 0.75" (19 mm) to 0.4375" (11.1 mm) at 29.2 MHz. The 20 meter diameters also apply to the 40, 30 and 17 meter bands. The 10 meter diameters apply to the 15, 12 and 6 meter bands. Within these broad limits, element diameter is not critical. In all cases, the tapering data given in Figure 4 applies.

SCALING HF YAGI ANTENNA DESIGNS

It may be desired to build a Yagi antenna to operate at some frequency removed from an amateur band. The designs shown in this chapter can be <u>scaled</u> to another frequency by the following ratio:

$$\text{New dimension} = \frac{\text{original dimension x original frequency}}{\text{new frequency}}$$

For example, a 14.15 MHz element measures 33.07' (10.08 m) long. What will its length be when scaled to 10.1 MHz?

$$\text{New dimension} = \frac{33.07 \times 14.15}{10.1} = 46.33' \text{ (14.12 m)}$$

In scaling to a frequency reasonably close to an amateur band, the variation in diameter-to-length ratio of an element may be ignored.

DESIGN EXAMPLE FOR A THREE ELEMENT YAGI

It is desired to build a three element Yagi for operation at 20 MHz using the formulas in Table 2. The elements are made of telescoping tubing that tapers from 1.25" (3.18 cm) at the center to 0.5" (1.27 cm) at the tips. Average element diameter is 0.875", which is within the limits established for the data.

Basic element dimensions are:

$$L_D = \frac{461.5}{10} = 46.15 \text{ ft } (14.07 \text{ m})$$

$$L_{DE} = \frac{478}{10} = 47.8 \text{ ft } (14.57 \text{ m})$$

$$L_R = \frac{492}{10} = 49.2 \text{ ft } (15 \text{ m})$$

$$S = \frac{141.7}{10} = 14.17 \text{ ft } (4.32 \text{ m})$$

Element taper factor is $\frac{1.25"}{0.5"} = 2.5$

From Figure 4, the taper correction for a factor of 2.5 is 1.03. The final element dimensions are:

L_D = 46.15 x 1.03 = 48 ft (14.63 m)
L_{DE} = 47.8 x 1.03 = 49.7 ft (15.15 m)
L_R = 49.2 x 1.03 = 50.7 ft (15.45 m)
S requires no taper adjustment

CHANGING DECIMAL FOOT TO INCHES

When a hand calculator is used to compute antenna dimensions the resultant is expressed as a decimal figure (example: 49.7'). Most measuring tapes and rulers are marked in feet and inches. The following table can be used to convert a decimal foot to equivalent fractions of an inch.

Dec.Foot		Inch	Dec.Foot		Inch
.10	=	1 1/8	.55	=	6 1/2
.15	=	1 3/4	.60	=	7 1/8
.20	=	2 1/4	.65	=	7 3/4
.25	=	3	.70	=	8 3/8
.30	=	3 3/8	.75	=	9
.35	=	4 1/8	.80	=	9 1/2
.40	=	4 5/8	.85	=	10
.45	=	5 1/4	.90	=	10 5/8
.50	=	6	.95	=	11 1/4

Example: 49.7' = 49'8 3/8"

Changing Decimal Feet to Meters: Feet x 0.3048 = Meters

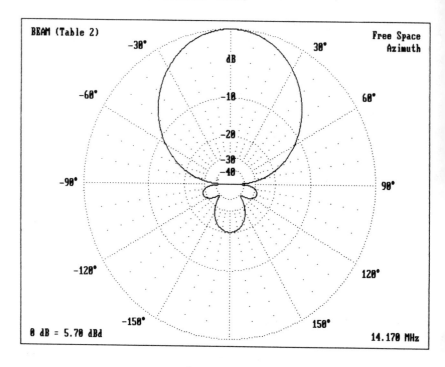

Fig. 12 Azimuth pattern plot of Yagi beam described in Table 2. At design frequency the front-to-back ratio is about 20 dB with small side lobes at 110 degrees from axis of main lobe. Design was formulated on MININEC antenna program (K6STI).

Chapter 4

The Multiband Beam Antenna

PART 1 - THE DECOUPLING PRINCIPLE

The parasitic beam antenna is a frequency-sensitive array capable of operation over a narrow range comprising approximately plus or minus one percent of the design frequency. Detuning the parasitic elements of the beam widens the operating range somewhat at the expense of antenna gain. Efficient operation of the simple parasitic beam on more than one amateur band, therefore, is out of the question as the frequency separation between bands is a large percentage of the operating frequency of the antenna. Accordingly, some form of switching must be used to decouple (disconnect) sections of the antenna elements if it is desired to operate a resonant parasitic array at widely separated portions of the radio spectrum.

The concept of decoupling traps was first proposed in 1940 to make a multi-frequency, hf receiving antenna for aircraft communication. This idea was put to use in a novel three band Yagi antenna by Chester Buchanan, W3DZZ, in 1953. Decoupling traps were used in all elements to achieve 20, 15 and 10 meter operation.

Considerable success is achieved in manufacturing practical multi-band parasitic beam antennas that use automatic decoupling traps of the form shown in Figure 1. These arrays utilize the high impedance of a parallel resonant circuit to isolate or decouple unwanted portions of the antenna. The decoupling devices are placed in the element at the proper points to isolate the center portion of the element, allowing it to resonate at some chosen operating frequency, F3. A second set of decouplers is placed in the element to isolate a somewhat longer center portion at a lower frequency, F2. The complete element, including the decoupling traps, resonates at a third lower frequency, F1.

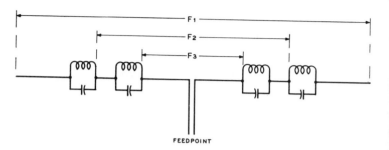

Fig. 1 Representative three-frequency dipole element. Resonant decoupling traps disconnect portion of active element when antenna is operated near frequency of trap. Inner set of traps are resonant at frequency F3; outer traps are resonant at F2. Entire element is resonant at F1.

The three operating frequencies may bear no relationship to one another and need not be harmonically related. Theoretically, an antenna element could be made to resonate on any number of frequencies by the addition of a sufficient quantity of decoupling traps.

Many popular multiband beam antennas for amateur use are designed using the decoupling trap concept, with the great majority of arrays built for use in the 14-21-28 MHz bands. Another design operates in the 7 and 14 MHz bands, and a few "trap" beams have been built that function on the 6 and 2 meter bands.

THE DECOUPLING TRAP

The simplest form of decoupling trap consists of a parallel tuned circuit resonant at the operating frequency of the transmitter (Figure 2). This device presents a high impedance at the terminals at its resonant frequency. At that frequency, the current flowing through the inductor is equal in magnitude and opposite in phase to the current flowing through the capacitor, consequently the resultant current flowing through the trap is only that amount passing through the loss resistance. If this resistance is sufficiently high, the trap is equivalent to an open circuit, or open switch. Therefore, at or near the resonant frequency of the trap the outer sections of the antenna element are effectively decoupled, and the center portion of the element resonates at a frequency determined by its physical length plus any residual effect contributed by the presence of the decoupling traps.

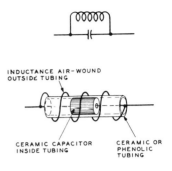

Fig. 2 Parallel resonant trap must be waterproof and have reasonably high value of efficiency. One form of construction places capacitor in phenolic tube with inductor wound over tube. Coil should be made of aluminum wire when aluminum elements are used to reduce electrolytic corrosion. Trap capacitor must be able to withstand peak rf voltage developed at end of dipole element.

At some lower operating frequency resonance is again established in the multiband antenna system, the F3 traps acting in the manner of a loading coil, with the major portion of the antenna current flowing through the trap inductor and a smaller portion flowing through the capacitor and the loss resistance. A second set of decoupling traps permits the antenna element to resonate at the next lower operating frequency, F2. The whole element resonates at the lowest operating frequency F1. Thus, the traps act either as an open circuit isolating the outer portions of the antenna, or as loading coils connecting the outer sections of the element to the center portion of the antenna. By its mere proximity, the resonant trap exhibits some capacitance to the active portion of the antenna even when the trap resembles an open switch. As a result, the electrical length of the active portion of the antenna between the traps is somewhat shorter than the normal resonant length. In addition, the loading effect of the traps in the overall active element shortens element length. The multiband beam therefore has shorter element dimensions on any operating frequency as compared to a conventional parasitic array of the same frequency. The amount of element shortening depends upon the inductance-to-capacitance ratio of the decoupling trap.

A resonant coaxial section may be used for a decoupling trap as shown in Figure 3. The short, coaxial section is resonant at the highest operating frequency, F3; the center section is resonant at the next lower operating frequency, F2; and the longer, inner section is resonant at the lowest operating frequency, F1. The impedance between the tip of each outer section and the adjacent inner tube is extremely high, thus effectively decoupling each element from the adjoining one. A simpler version of this concept is shown in Figure 4, where the coaxial sections are replaced by linear elements made of wire. This multiband system may be visualized as three dipoles con-

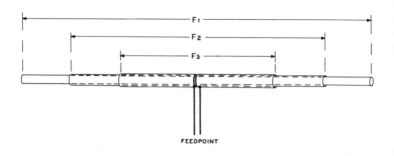

FEEDPOINT

Fig. 3 A resonant coaxial section may be used in place of capaci-tor-inductor trap. Three concentric elements exhibit very high selectivity making adjustment difficult. Physical complexity of design makes it impractical for everyday use.

nected in parallel at the feed point. Only a few feet of separation is required at the ends of the resonant elements.

PRACTICAL DECOUPLING TRAPS

A practical multiband antenna is a series of engineering compromises as the factors contributing to an efficient, low loss decoupling trap are at odds with the need for a compact, waterproof unit capable of operating in an outdoor environment. Commercial decoupling traps usually have the capacitor arranged about the coil so as to form a protective waterproof shield. This arrangement results in a practical, long-life assembly with somewhat less than optimum electrical characteristics. Accordingly, most multiband beam antennas exhibit smaller bandwidths and lower gain figures than those achieved by single band arrays of the same general size and configuration. This is the price that

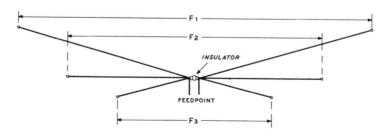

Fig. 4 Three dipoles connected in parallel at feedpoint form a simple triband driven element for inexpensive multiband antenna.

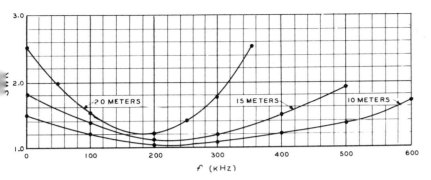

Fig. 5 Typical SWR curves for 20-15-10 meter triband Yagi beam.
Bandwidth is least on the lower two bands as elements are short
in terms of a half-wavelength.

the beam owner must pay for the luxury of multiband operation
with a single antenna! In any event, the amount of power lost
in the decoupling traps is not a great penalty judging from the
number of "tribander" beams in use and the potent signals
coming from them! Representative SWR curves for a 20-15-10
"tribander" are shown in Figure 5.

A unique double trap assembly is shown in Figure 6. This
configuration is used in some commercial multiband antennas.
Two traps are placed back to back inside an aluminum outer
housing. The inductors are wound on grooved insulating forms
with the housing serving as a common resonating capacitor for
both inductors. Plastic end cups seal the assembly against dirt
and moisture.

THE COAXIAL TRAP DESIGN

What constitutes an efficient trap? The trap is a parallel
resonant tuned circuit that provides a very high impedance
between its terminals at the design frequency. At frequencies
below resonance, the trap approximates a series inductance,
physically shortening the antenna. Conventional designs specify
a high-Q inductor and a high voltage capacitor, the combination
being resonant at the design frequency. Tests indicate that a
satisfactory trap requires a resonant frequency impedance of
10,000 ohms, or higher, otherwise the trap allows interaction
between the element sections and complicates antenna adjustment.
In addition, experience has shown that a coil Q (selectivity
figure) of about 150 provides a reasonable compromise between
cost and performance.

It must be remembered, however, that as losses approach

Fig.6 Representative dual trap assembly is inclosed in aluminum housing. Two inductors are wound on grooved form. The housing serves as resonating capacitor for both inductors. Plastic end cups protect traps against the weather.

zero, circuit Q approaches infinity and a zero-loss trap would be useful only at one frequency. The property of the trap that provides isolation is impedance and the property of the trap that restricts bandwidth (the operating range) is coil Q. Thus, high-Q in an antenna trap may not be the most desirable feature because of the bandwidth restriction of the trap.

Trap experiments by Gary O'Neil, N3GO, point the way to combine medium-Q and high impedance in a simple design (Figure 7). In this configuration a length of coaxial line is connected as

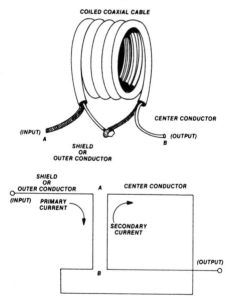

Fig. 7   The transformer coupled trap of N3GO. The trap acts as a 1-to-1 transformer, reverse connected. Primary and secondary currents oppose each other at resonance, providing a high impedance. Trap has low Q which provides good bandwidth (wide operating range).

Fc (MHz)	Form Length (In)	Form Length (cm)	Coax Length (In)	Coax Length (cm)	Number turns	Effective Length (In)	Effective Length (cm)
3.750	6.0	15.2	123.06	312.6	19.8	120	305
7.150	4.2	10.7	70.70	179.6	10.9	65	165
10.075	3.6	9.1	53.70	136.4	8.0	48	122
14.175	3.2	8.1	41.47	105.3	6.0	36	92
18.118	3.0	7.6	34.80	88.4	4.9	29	74
21.225	2.8	7.1	31.24	79.3	4.3	26	66
24.940	2.8	7.1	28.09	71.3	3.7	22	56
28.850	2.6	6.6	25.61	65.0	3.3	20	51

FIG.8 – Dimensions for constructing traps
for frequencies between 3.75 and 29 MHz

a balun transformer (A). Current injected into the primary from a source induces a secondary current. Reverse-connecting the windings causes primary and secondary currents to oppose each other, greatly reducing the overall current flow through the trap at resonance. The capacitance of the coaxial line provides the trap capacitance and the coiled line provides the inductance. The proximity of the conductors, moreover, provides magnetic coupling that accounts for the transformer action mentioned previously. Tests of this design show a much lower Q (greater operational bandwidth) than a conventional trap but with a comparable impedance at resonance, implying similar loss characteristics. The combination of high impedance and low Q contribute to a noncritical design that does not require accurate tuning to function well. Trap data for the hf bands is given in Figure 8.

The problem of assembling an efficient, waterproof decoupling trap is formidable. That is the main reason few homemade triband beams are heard on the air. Simple traps, however, can be made for a wire antenna as the trap is not required to support a tubing element.

BUILD A TRIBAND BEAM ANTENNA?

The mechanical problems inherent in building a multiband trap beam have discouraged all but the stoutest home builders from attempting a project of this magnitude. Commercially

C,3COI°

"Be careful, its a trap"

(Courtesy RSGB and G3COI)

available multiband beams in kit form have solved the tough
environmental and stress problems by the use of a special trap.
The coil is wound on an insulator that is also the element support and the coil shield serves as the resonating capacitor.   The
ends of the assembly are sealed by plastic, waterproof caps.

Triband beams perform well, as any amateur can confirm
after listening to some of the more prominent contest and DX
operators who employ this type of antenna.   No doubt about it:
the trap beam is an important contribution to amateur radio
communications and is here to stay.   But construction is not to
be taken lightly.   The mechanical complexity is too great for the
average experimenter.   Good beam kits have solved this problem.

PART 2 - OTHER DECOUPLING SYSTEMS

THE LINEAR DECOUPLING TRAP

A quarter-wave portion of transmission line may replace the
parallel tuned decoupling trap (Figure 9).   This design uses a
portion of the antenna element as one side of a transmission line
section.   The center portion of the antenna (F2) is resonant at
the highest operating frequency and the complete element (F1) is
resonant at the lowest operating frequency.   A high impedance
exists between points 1 and 2 of the linear trap when the trap is
a quarter wavelength long at the operating frequency.   For
example, linear stubs a quarter wavelength long at 10 meters can
be attached to a 10 meter dipole to decouple it from the balance
of the structure which is made long enough to resonate in some
lower frequency amateur band.

As in the case of the parallel-tuned trap, the linear trap
adds inductive loading to the element at the lowest frequency of

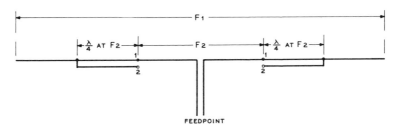

Fig. 9 Linear decoupling traps incorporated in a dipole provide resonance at a higher frequency. High impedance at points 1 and 2 decouple the antenna tips. Linear trap adds loading at the lowest operating frequency reducing the physical length of the overall element.

operation, thus reducing the physical length below that normally expected for resonance. If the decoupling stub has an air dielectric and a velocity factor near unity, the physical length of the stub is very close to an electrical quarter wavelength and the whole system may resonate at a lower frequency than desired. To establish resonance at the desired lower frequency of operation, the overall length is reduced by shortening the center section the required amount. Resonance is established at the higher frequency by adding short loading wires at the ends of the center section.

THE CHOKE DECOUPLER

It is possible to achieve dual frequency operation with a single antenna element by using relatively high inductance coils as decoupling chokes (Figure 10). At the higher frequency of

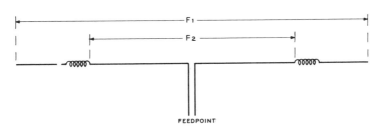

Fig. 10 Dual frequency operation of an element is accomplished with high inductance coils used as decoupling chokes at the higher frequency of operation. Coils act as loading inductors at the lower operating frequency. High Q of the coils reduces operating bandwidth on the lower band and tip sections are very short.

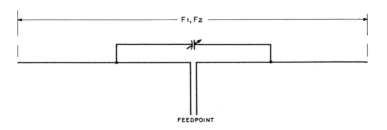

Fig. 11 Center resonant decoupler establishes dipole resonance on two widely different frequencies. At the lower frequency, the element is loaded by the parallel resonant circuit which presents a capacitive reactance at the higher operating frequency.

operation, F2, the coils act as high impedance rf chokes, severely limiting the current flow in the outer tips of the antenna. At the lower frequency of operation, F1, the coils serve as loading inductors, resonating the overall system to the desired operating frequency. By virtue of the relatively high coil inductance, the tip sections of the radiator are extremely short and a small change in tip length results in an appreciable change in the lower resonant frequency of the system. The decoupling coils may be wound on common plastic electrical conduit tubing obtainable at any large electrical supply house.

At the higher frequency of operation, the Q of the system is reasonably low and a SWR curve comparable to an equivalent single band element is obtained. At the lower frequency, the relatively high Q of the loading coils sharpens the response of the system. Reducing the number of turns in the loading coil and increasing the length of the tip sections broadens the passband, but may necessitate adjusting the length of the inner portion of the antenna to re-establish resonance at the higher frequency.

THE CENTER RESONANT DECOUPLER

An unusual form of decoupling device is shown in Figure 11. The complete antenna element is self-resonant at the highest frequency of operation. At some lower resonant frequency the element is center-loaded by a parallel tuned circuit composed of the center of the element, a capacitor connected across the element, and the connecting leads of the capacitor. The element (which is more than one-half wavelength long at the highest frequency) presents a capacitive reactance across the tuned

The broadband log periodic antenna design is frequency-independent over the range determined by the longest and shortest elements. Large L-P antennas are capable of operation over the 3 to 30 Mhz spectrum.

circuit at the lowest frequency of operation. This reactance, plus the reactance of the parallel capacitor, are sufficient to resonate with the inductance of the center loop at the lowest operating frequency. At the highest frequency of operation, the tuned circuit exhibits a capacitative reactance which is nullified by lengthening the element a slight amount.

PART 3 - THE BROADBAND LOG PERIODIC BEAM

The log periodic (L-P) beam antenna is an adaptation of the popular Yagi beam which retains the gain of the Yagi while providing better bandwidth performance. The parasitic beam provides the greatest gain per unit area of any of the popular antennas, but as the gain increases with the number of elements, operational bandwidth becomes more restricted. At 10 meters, for example, where the band is wide in terms of the frequency, it is difficult to obtain a good match, and good front-to-back ratio over the whole band with a Yagi. As discussed earlier, a typical 10 meter, three element parasitic beam has an operational bandwidth of about 800 kHz, as defined by the SWR limit on the feedline. At the outer limits of frequency, moreover, the front-to-back ratio of the beam suffers and the gain decreases.

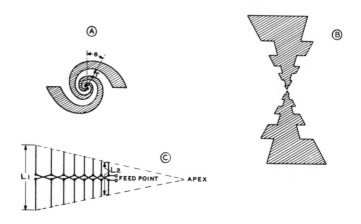

Fig. 12 Log periodic antenna designs. (A) Balanced, planar log
periodic spiral antenna structure is electrically similar to a
dipole. Fed at the center points, the antenna is defined in
terms of angle θ and exhibits a relatively constant feedpoint
resistance and radiation pattern over a wide range of frequencies. (B) Planar, log periodic antenna design whose geometry re-
peats periodically with respect to the logarithm of the frequency. If the antenna structure is folded back upon itself, the
radiation pattern becomes undirectional. (C) Dipole elements
replace the "teeth" of antenna B to form a log periodic beam
array. The antenna is fed at the apex with a balun and a coaxial
line.

The restricted bandwidth of any antenna may be improved
by applying the equiangular principle to the design. That is, if
the shape of the antenna can be specified entirely by angles,
antenna performance is substantially independent of frequency.

THE L-P EQUIANGULAR PRINCIPLE

A frequency-independent antenna, of which the log periodic
array is an example, is a structure that exhibits the same performance at different frequencies by virtue of the fact that the
antenna has no critical dimensions that are frequency sensitive.
A simple frequency-independent antenna described by angles is
shown in Figure 12A. The shape of this dipole antenna, when
expressed in terms of the operating frequency, is the same for
any frequency. Practical antennas of this design are limited in
size and thus limit the frequency-independent characteristic. To
be truly frequency-independent, the spiral dipole would have to
start at a small point and expand to infinity. Practically, the

antenna requires a feedpoint at the center and has outer length limits. As a result, a practical equiangular dipole has frequency limits that are defined by the physical, not the electrical, limitations.

THE LOG PERIODIC ANTENNA

A modified form of frequency-independent antenna is shown in Figure 12B. This is a planar structure with the design repeated periodically with respect to the logarithm of the frequency. It is known as a log periodic antenna. The design shown is flat, and is considered to be a dipole. If one side of the antenna is folded back about the feedpoint to form a three dimensional structure, the structure provides power gain and front-to-back ratio, and is considered a beam antenna.

This design can be further simplified, as shown in Figure 12C. The toothed structure is replaced by dipole elements. This is a log periodic dipole antenna and is a popular design for tv and fm receiving antennas. Radiation is toward the apex when used for transmitting and versions of this antenna are used by amateurs on the vhf bands. The frequency limits of the antenna are those at which the outer elements are about one-half wavelength long.

The dipoles are fed at the center point from a balanced transmission source in such a manner that successive dipoles have a 180 degree phase reversal between them. A broadband structure is thus formed, with most of the radiation coming from those elements in the vicinity of a half-wavelength long at the operating frequency. Gain and bandwidth bear a definite relationship to the length and the included angle of the antenna.

Unfortunately, some of the elements in a log periodic antenna of this type are inactive; the active elements move along the structure as the frequency of operation is changed. At the lowest operating frequency, the longest elements have the most current in them and, as the operating frequency is raised, the center elements become active and have the greatest current. At the upper frequency limit, the shortest elements have the greatest current in them, with the longer elements relatively inactive. Thus, a log periodic antenna this type must be considerably longer than a parasitic Yagi of equivalent gain.

THE LOG PERIODIC YAGI (LPY) BEAM

The log periodic principle may be applied to the Yagi antenna to expand the bandwidth of this popular design, without appreciable loss of gain. Log periodic driven elements are added to the Yagi parasitic elements to provide the desired bandwidth

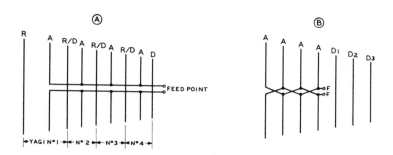

Fig. 13 The log periodic yagi (LPY) beam antenna (A). The array is made up of a series of end-fire Yagi beams, each fed from a common transmission line. The inbetween elements are parasitics, each one serving the dual function of director and reflector for the adjacent larger and smaller driven elements. (B) The LPY bandpass array makes use of a log periodic structure having the frequency characteristics of a bandpass filter. Note that the feedline is transposed between the driven elements.

and are fed in the same manner as the simple log periodic antenna. The number of fed-elements determines the bandwidth.

A basic log periodic Yagi array is shown in Figure 13A. The antenna is made up of a series of interlaced end-fire Yagis, with each driven element fed from a common, balanced transmission line. Unlike the driven elements in a log periodic dipole array, those of the LPY design are fed in a non-transposed manner. The inbetween elements are parasitics, and log periodic performance is obtained by making each parasitic element serve the dual function of director and reflector for the adjacent longer and shorter driven elements. Practical LPY antennas having power gains of about 9 dB are built for vhf work, but the length is long considering the power gain obtained from a simple Yagi beam.

THE LPY BANDPASS ANTENNA

An interesting version of the LPY antenna is the LPY bandpass array, which provides a greater power gain per unit of length than the interlaced design. This antenna makes use of a log periodic dipole structure with the frequency characteristics of a bandpass filter. A number of parasitic elements, trimmed to cover the appropriate frequency range, are used to enhance the power gain of the log periodic bandpass array (Figure 13B). A frequency response of such an antenna designed for the 6 meter

Fig. 14 The gain vs frequency plot of six meter LPY beam antenna. The original LPY structure was designed for color tv reception which required good passband characteristics and adjacent channel protection. Many modern tv antennas are modeled after this design.

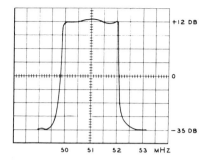

band is shown in Figure 14. The LPY bandpass beam antenna is easy to build, simple to adjust and provides good power gain considering the overall length of the structure.

PART 4 - INTERLACED BEAM DESIGNS

Individual Yagi beams for two or more bands can be placed on a single boom, with the elements interlaced and spaced to provide a minimum of interaction between the beams. This is a cut-and-try procedure as no specific information exists on the technique of element interlacing. Even so, many different interlaced arrays are on the air and some practical designs are shown in this section.

Generally speaking, the high frequency parasitic elements are placed in front of the lower frequency elements and separate feed systems are used. A single feedline can be connected to either antenna by means of a coaxial relay mounted on the boom of the array, or separate feedlines can be run from the interlaced antenna to the station.

Amateur antenna experimenters have tackled the interlaced beam problem and have developed interesting antennas. Shown in Figure 15 is a simplified trap antenna used by KH6OR (Hawaii) which employs interlaced parasitic elements for 15 and 20 meter operation. Full size parasitic elements are employed and only two traps are used for the driven element. The antenna is constructed on a 20-foot aluminum boom in the general manner described later in this handbook. The length and position of the parasitic elements on the boom are adjusted so that a minimum of interaction exists between the elements. The driven element employs two gamma matching sections in parallel, each adjusted to one amateur band. The matching sections are fed by a single 50 ohm coaxial line.

The original decoupling traps in this beam antenna employed fixed vacuum capacitors which, unless obtained on the surplus

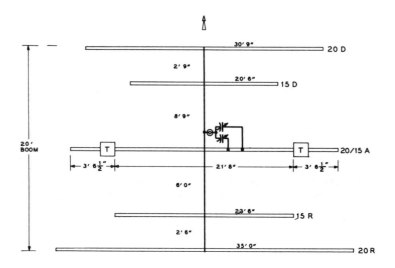

Fig. 15   The KH6OR dual band Yagi array for 20 and 15 meter
bands. Full size parasitic elements are used in conjunction with
two traps in the driven element. Two gamma match systems are
used and the beam is fed with a single coaxial line. Traps are
tuned to 21 MHz. Conventional gamma dimensions given in chapter
7 are used. Design is resonant at 14.3 MHz and 21.3 MHz. Elements are made of 1-1/4" diameter tubing with telescoping end
sections. Traps are made of a 25 pF capacitor in parallel with 6
turns of no. 6 aluminum wire, 3" (7.6cm) diam. and 2" (5cm) long.

market, are prohibitively expensive for the average amateur. A
substitute capacitor may be made up of two 50 pF, 7.5 kVdc
zero temperature coefficient ceramic capacitors connected in
series and placed within a waterproof phenolic tube. The trap
inductor is wound of aluminum wire and affixed to the capacitor
assembly with homemade clamps. After assembly, the traps are
placed in a location clear of nearby metallic objects and dipped
to a frequency of 21.0 MHz. The gamma matches are adjusted
for minimum SWR on the transmission line on each band. The
original KH6OR gamma matches were built of concentric aluminum
tubes with a dielectric made of portions of a defunct plastic
"hula-hoop".   Representative   gamma   dimensions   are   listed
elsewhere in this handbook.

THE W4KFC INTERLACED YAGI FOR 15 AND 10 METERS

Shown in Figure 16 is a practical and tested twin beam
designed by Vic Clark, W4KFC, for 15 and 10 meter operation.

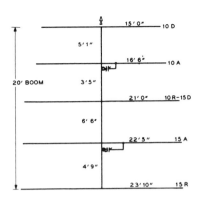

Fig. 16   The W4KFC twin beam for 15 and 10 meter bands utilizes a common element as a 10 meter reflector and a 15 meter director. Beam is built on a 20 foot (6m) boom and has two gamma match systems. A single coax line can be used with a switching relay mounted on the boom.

A similar configuration could be used for 15 and 12 meters or 12 and 10 meters with normal element lengths. The design consists of two three-element Yagis mounted on a single 20 foot (6.1 m) aluminum boom. The 10 meter array is placed in front of the 15 meter array, and one common element element serves as a compromise parasitic director for the 15 meter beam and a parasitic reflector for the 10 meter beam.

Each driven element is fed with a gamma matching system and separate transmission line and each gamma is adjusted independently of the other matching device. Gamma dimensions are given in Chapter 7. Since the gammas are single frequency systems, there is little possibility of interlocking adjustments. As far as can be determined from on-the-air tests, power gain and front-to-back ratios are entirely comparable with separate three-element Yagi arrays.

INTERLACED YAGIS FOR 20/15 AND 15/10 METERS

Shown in Figures 17 and 18 are two popular interlaced arrays designed to fit on a 20 foot (6.1 m) aluminum boom. The 20/15 meter assembly is tuned to center frequencies of 14.25 MHz

Fig. 17   Interlaced Yagi design for 20 and 15 meter bands uses a 20 foot (6m) boom and two gamma matches. Design frequencies are 14.25 MHz and 21.2MHz. Low transmission line SWR is achieved on both bands.

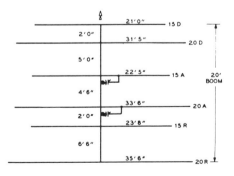

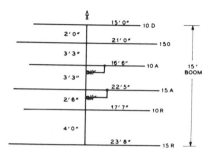

Fig. 18 Interlaced Yagi design for 15 and 10 meter bands uses a 15 foot (4.6m) boom. Single transmission line can be used if a co-axial relay is mounted on the antenna boom.

and 21.2 MHz. The SWR on the 50 ohm coaxial line remains below 1.4-to-1 over the 20 meter band and below 1.5-to-1 over the 15 meter band. Separate gamma matching systems and feedlines are used. The 15/10 meter array has a SWR of below 1.4-to-1 across the 15 meter band and below 1.5-to-1 over a span of 700 kHz in the 10 meter band.

A similar interlaced design for 20 and 10 meters is shown in Figure 19. In this case, it is necessary to insulate the parasitic elements from the boom to preserve a good front-to-back ratio.

INTERLACED BEAM COMBINATIONS

Interlaced Yagi arrays may be built for almost any combination of bands provided the builder takes care that spurious resonant frequencies do not appear in the assembly, arising from element-boom resonance. This problem may be avoided by insulating all elements from the boom. It is often easier to adjust separate driven elements than to use a single trapped element. Tri-band interlaced arrays for 20, 15 and 10 meters have been constructed but adjustment must be done on a cut-and-try basis. Sufficient test equipment must be at hand to thoroughly check out operation and to determine if the inactive elements are degrading the beam pattern.

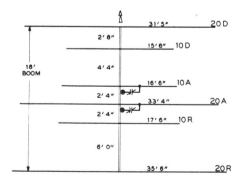

Fig. 19 Interlaced Yagi design for 20 and 10 meter bands uses a 15 foot (4.6m) boom. Elements are insulated from the boom to prevent unwanted spurious resonances. Dipoles may be replaced with a single trapped element.

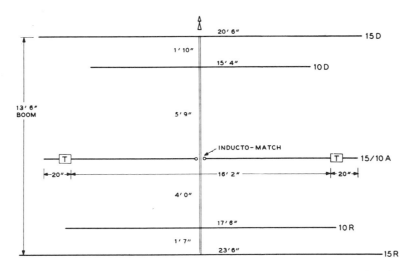

Fig. 20 The W6SAI interlaced beam for the 15 and 10 meter bands. The traps are resonant at 28.0 MHz and elements are adjusted for resonance at 21.3 and 28.7 MHz. Traps are 5 turns of no.8 aluminum wire, 3 inches (7.6 cm) diam. and 3 inches long. The capacitor is 25 pF at 15 kV. (Two 50 pF ceramic units in series). Antenna provides good power gain and front-to-back ratio.

THE W6SAI COMPACT INTERLACED BEAM FOR 15/10 METERS

The decoupling trap principle is employed to construct a compact two-band beam for 10 and 15 meters, as shown in Figure 20. Interlaced, full-size parasitic elements are used, in conjunction with a trapped driven element. Boom length is only 13'6" (4.11 m) and the elements are positioned on the boom to provide minimum interaction between them. The parasitic elements are made of one-inch (2.54 cm) diameter aluminum tubing, while the driven element is made of 1½" (3.8 cm) diameter tubing. All elements are insulated from the boom to forestall spurious resonant frequencies involving boom-element resonance. Element tips beyond the traps are made of 3/4" (1.9 cm) diameter tubing. The traps are dipped to 28.0 MHz before installation in the dipole element.

Either a dual gamma matching system, or the inductomatch may be used with this beam antenna. While the dual gammas are somewhat easier to adjust, the inductomatch provides a better match over a wider band of operation as it is inherently a low-Q device. This is helpful when operation is contemplated over the width of the 10 meter band. If the inductomatch is used, the driven element is split at the center and the hairpin or coil placed at that point, together with a coaxial balun. Before the balun and inductor are attached to the dipole, the center point is jumpered with a loop of wire and the element is adjusted to frequency with the aid of a dip oscillator. To accomplish this, the beam is placed atop a ten foot stepladder and the length of the tips of the driven element adjusted to provide an indication of resonance at 21.3 MHz and 28.7 MHz. The traps are not adjusted at this time, as they have been set before being installed in the element.

Once the driven element has been set to frequency, the hairpin and balun are attached and a frequency run is made on the antenna, using an SWR meter in the transmission line. The length of the hairpin, or the turns in the shunt inductor, are adjusted to provide a good SWR match.

The radiation resistance of the beam is about 25 ohms on 15 meters and about 38 ohms on 10 meters. Thus, a compromise setting of the inducto-match must be found that is satisfactory for both bands. It is possible to reach a SWR of less than 1.4-to-1 at the resonant frequency on either band. The best bandwidth is achieved by adjusting the driven element as described, rather than by using the matching system to "pull" the resonant frequency of the antenna to the desired point in the band. While the latter technique works, it is always desirable to separate the tuning adjustments and the matching adjustments, for when they are combined, the operational bandwidth of the array usually suffers to some extent.

ELEMENT TAPER

The antenna designs shown in this chapter are based upon elements with little or no taper unless otherwise specified. If severely tapered elements are used, element length may have to be increased as much as ten percent. See Chapter 3 for additional information on element taper.

SIMPLE MULTIBAND BEAMS

Simple, inexpensive multiband antennas using tuned feeders and a Transmatch unit at the transmitter are shown in Figures 21 and 22. The first version covers the 20, 17, 15, 12 and 10 meter bands. It consists of a center-fed 20 meter resonant element and a single director. The director may be cut for the band of maximum interest. Thus, the array is a two-element beam on one band and a center-fed driven element on the other bands, the parasitic element not functioning on these bands.

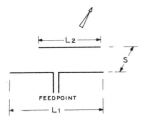

Fig. 21 This simple two-band beam has a tuned dipole as a driven element and a single band parasitic element. If fed with balanced feedline and a Transmatch, the beam will function as a single element on any band higher than the design band.

BAND (MHZ)	L1		L2		S	
DE / DIR	Feet	Meters	Feet	Meters	Feet	Meters
14 / 18	32' 8"	9.96	25' 1"	7.66	8' 2"	2.48
18 / 21	25' 6"	7.79	21' 5"	6.53	6' 11"	2.12
21 / 24	21' 9"	6.65	18' 3"	5.56	5' 10"	1.80
24 / 28	18' 6"	5.66	16' 9"	5.10	5' 2"	1.57

* * *

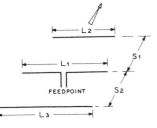

Fig. 22 A director for the "high" band and reflector for the "low band" form a simple multiband antenna. Balanced feedline and a Transmatch are used for greatest flexibility.

BAND (MHz)	L1		L2		L3		S1 = S2	
R/DE/DIR	Feet	Meters	Feet	Meters	Feet	Meters	Feet	Meters
14/18/21	32' 8"	9.96	21' 5"	6.53	35' 4"	10.77	8' 2"	2.48
18/21/24	21' 9"	6.65	18' 3"	5.56	27' 2"	8.28	6' 11"	2.12
21/24/28	18' 6"	5.66	16' 9"	5.10	23' 8"	7.28	5' 2"	1.57
24/28/50	16' 2"	4.93	9' 1"	2.77	18' 9"	5.70	4' 4"	1.31

The beam is fed with tuned feeders and a transmatch. The second beam employs two parasitic elements, one cut as a reflector for one band and the other as a director for a higher frequency band. Again, the driven element is fed with tuned feeders and a Transmatch. The antenna operates as a two element parasitic beam on two bands and has a bidirectional radiation pattern similar to a dipole on the other bands.

Stacked 10-element Yagis give K2GL's 10 meter signal a solid punch. Beams are fed with a T-match and balun to provide low SWR across the DX portion of the band.

Chapter 5

The VHF Yagi Antenna

EARLY HISTORY

Simple experiments were run with two and three element Yagi arrays in the old 56 MHz amateur band in the early "thirties" but little practical use was made of the information because of the lack of measuring equipment, aluminum tubing and low loss coaxial line.

World War II brought the Yagi into quick use for radar antennas since it was rugged and provided more gain per unit of area than any other type of beam design. At the same time, production of inexpensive, low loss coaxial cable permitted the use of multiple Yagis for high gain antenna arrays used in the early vhf radar equipment. After the war, amateurs quickly discovered that the Yagi could be built lighter and more compactly than any other high gain antenna. As a result, the Yagi could have more elements and be erected at a greater height than the more cumbersome arrays.

The price paid for these advantages is the rather narrow operational bandwidth of the long Yagi. The bandwidth depends upon the number of elements used and the array tuning. Very long Yagis have been built with multiple directors and Figure 1 shows the approximate power gain and operational bandwidth versus antenna boom length in wavelengths. The maximum practical length of a long Yagi is largely determined by the ability to physically align a large number of directors without the supporting structure interfering with antenna operation.

Since vhf Yagis are of a moderate size, much antenna design work has been done using model antennas mounted on antenna ranges. Only recently has the practical work been confirmed by computer programs. In spite of the great number of variables (number of directors, director spacing, element

Some useful dimensions for vhf antennas and transmission lines.

Frequency	50 MHz		146 MHz		222 MHz		432 MHz	
	Inches	(cm)	Inches	(cm)	Inches	(cm)	Inches	(cm)
1 wavelength [1]	236.2	(600)	80.8	(205.2)	53.2	(135.1)	27.3	(69.4)
5/8 wavelength	147.6	(375)	50.5	(128.4)	33.2	(84.4)	17.1	(43.4)
1/2 wavelength	118.1	(300)	40.4	(102.7)	26.6	(67.5)	13.7	(34.7)
3/8 wavelength	88.6	(225)	30.3	(77.0)	19.9	(50.6)	10.2	(26.0)
1/4 wavelength	59.0	(150)	20.2	(51.3)	13.3	(33.7)	6.8	(17.3)
1/2 wavelength coax [2]	77.9	(198)	26.6	(67.7)	17.5	(44.6)	9.0	(22.9)
1/4 wavelength coax [2]	38.9	(99)	13.3	(33.8)	8.7	(22.1)	4.5	(11.4)
1/2 wavelength twinlead [3]	96.8	(246)	33.1	(84.1)	21.8	(55.4)	11.2	(28.4)
1/4 wavelength twinlead [3]	48.3	(123)	16.5	(40.0)	10.9	(27.7)	5.6	(14.2)
Per cent change each MHz [4]	2		0.6		0.45		0.25	

Notes: (1) Dimensions are based on the wavelength-in-air formula 11810/F(MHz).

(2) Coaxial-cable lengths are based on the velocity factor of RG-8/U or RG-58/U, which is approximately 0.66.

(3) Twinlead lengths are based on the velocity factor of 0.82 for common TV lead-in of parallel wires with flat, solid-dielectric insulation.

(4) The dimensions given are for frequencies in the most-often used part of the bands. The dimensions *increase* as you go lower, and *decrease* as you go higher in frequency. Example: If you want to work at 51 MHz, decrease the dimensions given by 2 per cent; for 145 MHz, increase the dimensions by 0.6 per cent.

length and diameter, etc.) it is possible to design a high gain Yagi from computer-derived charts with the assurance that the antenna will work as specified.

THE NBS YAGI PROGRAM

Much of the pioneer amateur work done on long Yagis has been confirmed by an exhaustive study conducted by the National Bureau of Standards which demonstrated the interrelationship between element lengths, diameters and spacings, as well as the effect of a metal supporting structure. Some of the information in this chapter is derived from the NBS study. Those readers desiring more detail are referred to NBS Technical Note 688, December, 1976, by P. Viezbickie, available from Superintendent of Documents, U.S. Government Printing Office, Washington DC 20420, SD Catalog No. C13.46:688. Additional basic design data can be obtained in "A New Method for Obtaining Maximum Gain From Yagi Antennas", by Ehrenspeck and Poehler, IRE Transactions on Antenna Propagation, October, 1959, pp. 379-386.

VHF YAGI PERFORMANCE

It has been suggested that the gain of a long Yagi is proportional to boom length and that doubling the length would increase antenna gain by 3 dB. This goal is not achievable in practice and a computer study suggests a more modest gain-to-length relationship, as shown in Figure 1. Practical tests show

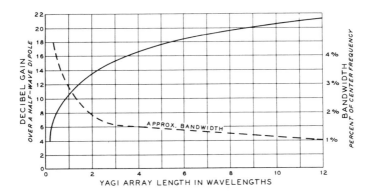

Fig. 1 Power gain and bandwidth of a long Yagi antenna are expressed in terms of array length (boom length). Practical tests show that this gain limit can be approached in arrays up to several wavelengths long. Operating bandwidth tends to decrease with increasing array length and the precision required for element measurement and assembly increases with increasing frequency.

that this gain limit can be approached in arrays less than several wavelengths long.

It should be noted that bandwidth tends to decrease with increasing array length and that the precision required for element measurement and beam assembly increases with increasing frequency. At 1296 MHz, for example, the NBS report calls for an element length tolerance of 1 mm, or less than 1/32". This points up the need for accurate physical antenna dimensions anywhere in the vhf spectrum.

Experience has shown there is no one set of "magic" measurements for the vhf Yagi antenna. Two antenna designs are discussed in this chapter; the first is a variation of the NBS design technique as adapted by Joe Reisert, Jr., W1JR, and the second a design technique perfected by Gunter Hoch, DL6WU (Germany), based upon computer studies and antenna range measurements. Other interesting antenna data also exist that approximate the results achieved with the arrays presented in this handbook.

SCALING VHF ANTENNA ELEMENTS

It is common practice to design and test a vhf Yagi at one frequency and then to scale the dimensions to another band of

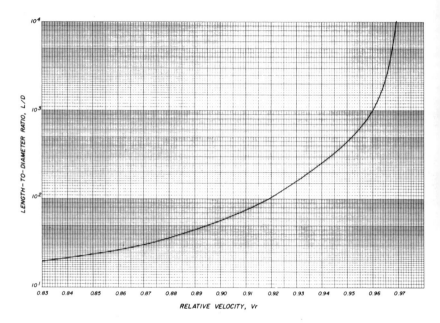

Fig. 2   The length of an antenna element is a function of the element length-to-diameter ratio.   The design of a vhf Yagi becomes increasingly difficult as operating frequency increases as structural demands require a larger-than-optimum element diameter.   Other antenna types supplant the Yagi above about 500 MHz.   (This graph is also shown in chapter 3 of this handbook.)

frequencies.   This   can   be   done   mathematically   provided   all antenna   dimensions   are   scaled   and   that   the   element   mounting system   does   not   enter   the   picture.   The   following   technique   was developed by Harold Tolles, W7ITB.

The   graph   in   Figure   2   was   derived   by   Schelkunoff   and Friis   in   1952   for   elements   approximately   a   half-wavelength   long. It   shows   that   the   relative   wave   velocity   on   any   element   is   a function of the length-to-diameter ratio:

$$\frac{l_n}{d_n} = r_n \tag{1}$$

where l_n = the length of the nth element
      d_n = the diameter of the nth element
      r_n = the length-to-diameter ratio

Once the relative wave velocity, v_{rn}, is determined from Figure 2, the free-space wavelength and <u>element length</u> are related by:

$$l_o = \frac{l_n}{v_{rn}} \text{ or } l_o = \frac{d_n r_n}{v_{rn}} \tag{2}$$

where l_n = the length of the nth element

        l_o = the free-space wavelength

For changes in an <u>element's diameter</u>, the new and old lengths can be equated by:

$$l_o = \frac{l_n}{v_{rn}} = \frac{L_n}{V_{rn}} = \frac{D_n R_n}{V_{rn}} \tag{3}$$

where L_n = the new length

        D_n = the new diameter

        V_{rn} = the new relative velocity

        R_n = the new length-to-diameter ratio

PRACTICAL EXAMPLES

<u>Length for a given diameter</u>: How long should a 3/8-inch diameter rod be when it is a one-half wavelength radiator at 150 MHz? From the standard wavelength formula, a free-space, half-wavelength radiator is 39.3429 inches long. Rearranging equation 2 yields:

$$\frac{l_o}{d_n} = \frac{r_n}{v_{rn}} = \frac{39.3429}{0.375} = 104.9$$

By moving along Figure 2, a point will be found on the curve where the length-to-diameter ratio divided by the relative velocity equals 104.9, r_n = 96.3 and v_{rn} = 0.918.

From equation 1, the rod length then becomes:

$$
\begin{aligned}
l_n &= d_n \times r_n \\
&= (0.375)(96.3) \\
&= 36.12 \text{ inches}
\end{aligned}
$$

<u>Change of diameter</u>: Assume that a one-half wavelength element is 391-1/8 inches long, and that its diameter of 1.5

inches should be increased to 2.0 inches for added strength. What should the new length be? By equation 1:

$$r_n = \frac{l_n}{d_n} = \frac{391.125}{1.5} = 260.75$$

From Figure 2, the relative velocity, v_{rn}, is about 0.9411, and substituting into a rearranged equation 3 produces:

$$\frac{l_n}{v_{rn}D_n} = \frac{R_n}{V_{rn}} = \frac{391.125}{0.9411(2.0)} = 207.802$$

Move along the curve on Figure 2 and find the new length-to-diameter ratio divided by the new relative velocity factor which gives the above ratio, or:

$$\frac{R_n}{V_{rn}} = 207.802 = \frac{194.3}{0.9351}$$

The new length-to-diameter ratio is 194.3, and the new relative velocity factor is 0.9351. From this, the new element length becomes:

$$L_n = R_n D_n = 194.3(2.0)$$
$$= 388.63 \text{ inches}$$

Change of Frequency: Assume that a 146 MHz director has a diameter of 3/8 inch and a length of 35.0 inches, and is to be used at 14.2 MHz with a new diameter of 2.0 inches. What is the new length?

First:

$$\frac{l_n}{d_n} = \frac{35.0}{0.375} = 93.333$$

From Figure 2, the relative velocity factor is about 0.9168, and the free space wavelength is:

$$l_o = \frac{35.0}{0.9168} = 38.1763 \text{ inches}$$

or 0.4722 wavelength at 146 MHz.

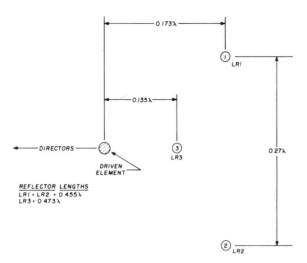

Fig. 3 Trigonal reflector arrangement for use with 4.2 wavelength (or longer) Yagi provides 0.75 dB increase in gain and over 10 dB improvement in front-to-back ratio. Arrangement shows no improvement for shorter Yagis. (Lengths not corrected for boom thickness)

From this, the 0.4722 wavelength at 14.2 MHz is 392.5162 inches (L_o).

Therefore:

$$\frac{L_o}{D_n} = \frac{392.5162}{2.0} = 196.2581 = \frac{R_n}{V_{rn}}$$

Move along the curve on Figure 2 and find that:

$$\frac{R_n}{V_{rn}} = 196.2581 = \frac{184.0}{0.9375}$$

The new director element length, L_n, becomes

$$L_n = R_n D_n = 184.0(2.0) = 368 \text{ inches, or } 30'9''$$

SUMMARY

As the examples show, Figure 2 can be used to solve a number of element scaling problems in a short period of time when a hand calculator is available. Moving from left to right on the graph increases (quite rapidly) the R_n/V_{rn} ratio, and

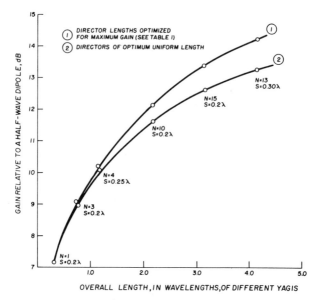

Fig. 4   Gain comparison of different length Yagis, showing relationship between directors optimized in length to yield maximum
gain (1), and directors of optimum uniform length (2). N is number
of directors, S is spacing between directors.

solving for L_n in terms of $R_n D_n$ and $V_{rn} L_o$ (where $L_o = L_n / V_{rn}$)
is a good check (as well as refinement) of the ratio obtained
from the Figure 2 curve.

NBS LONG YAGI DESIGN

The NBS antenna design information has been popularized
by Joe Reisert, Jr., W1JR, and the information necessary to
design these antennas is summarized in this section, together
with design examples. The NBS investigation settled on the use
of one reflector element spaced 0.2 wavelength behind the driven
element, or a trigonal arrangement shown in Figure 3, which
provided an increase in gain of 0.75 dB over a single reflector
when tested on a Yagi 4.2 wavelengths long. It should be
applicable to the other designs and may be useful if high F/B
ratios are desired.

The heart of the Yagi design is the director element. The
NBS study indicated that there are optimum spacings for maximum gain, and as boom length is increased, the optimum director
spacing also increases. In addition, the gain of the antenna can

	Length of Yagi in Wavelengths					
	0.4	0.8	1.20	2.2	3.2	4.2
Length of Reflector, λ	0.482	0.482	0.482	0.482	0.482	0.475
1st	0.442	0.428	0.428	0.432	0.428	0.424
2nd		0.424	0.420	0.415	0.420	0.424
3rd		0.428	0.420	0.407	0.407	0.420
4th			0.428	0.398	0.398	0.407
5th				0.390	0.394	0.403
6th				0.390	0.390	0.398
7th				0.390	0.386	0.394
8th				0.390	0.386	0.390
9th				0.398	0.386	0.390
10th				0.407	0.386	0.390
11th					0.386	0.390
12th					0.386	0.390
13th					0.386	0.390
14th					0.386	
15th					0.386	
Spacing Between Directors, λ	0.20	0.20	0.25	0.20	0.20	0.308
Gain relative to half-wave dipole, dB	7.1	9.2	10.2	12.25	13.4	14.2
Design curve (see fig.5)	(A)	(C)	(C)	(B)	(C)	(D)

Table 1. Optimized length of parasitic elements for Yagi antennas of six different lengths (reflector spaced 0.2 wavelengths behind driven element). Element diameter 0.0085 wavelength.

be further increased if the length of each director is carefully chosen. A comparison between uniform and optimized length directors for gain versus boom length is shown in Figure 4.

A set of optimum director and reflector lengths normalized to 0.0085 wavelength diameter elements is given in Table 1. This information yields optimum performance for the six boom lengths shown. If a different element diameter is desired, the elements can be scaled by using the graph of Figure 5. Element diameters from .001 to .04 wavelength can be scaled, as shown later.

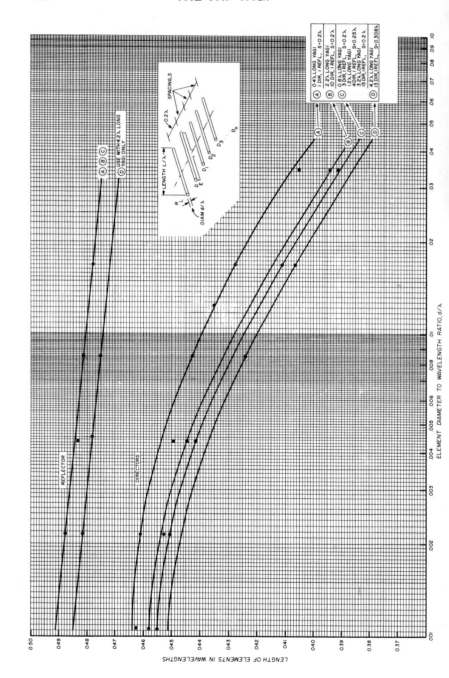

Fig. 5   Yagi antenna design nomograph showing the relationship between element diameter-to-wavelength ratio (x-axis) and element length in wavelengths (y-axis) for different antennas. Procedure for using this chart is presented in the text.

*   *   *

Element data given in the table are based upon elements mounted above a boom, or on an insulating boom (a triangular plexiglass structure was used). Attempts to use a wooden boom failed because changes in moisture made repeatability difficult despite various coatings applied to the wood.

Metal boom Yagis were entirely repeatable if the elements were lengthened to compensate for the boom structure. The effect of passing the element through the center of a metal boom is shown in Figure 6. The correction factor applies for square and round booms alike. If the element is mounted above and insulated from the boom, no correction factor is necessary.

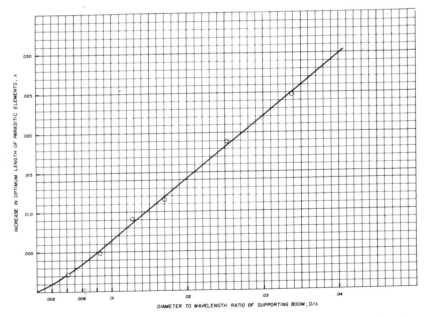

Fig. 6   Correction factor for an element passing through the center of a metal boom. Correction is about 0.7 the boom width or diameter. No correction is needed if element is above the boom.

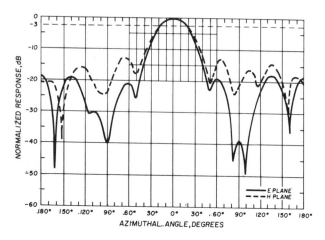

Fig.7 Radiation patterns of a 6 element, 1.2 wavelength long Yagi built with dimensions given in Table 1. Beamwidth of the E plane is 40 degrees; H plane beamwidth is 42 degrees.

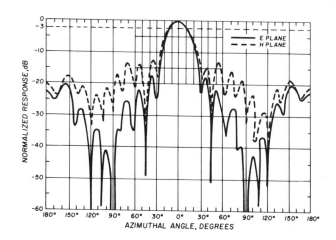

Fig.8 Radiation patters of a 15 element, 4.2 wavelength long Yagi built with dimensions given in Table 1. Beamwidth of the E plane is 26 degrees; H plane beamwidth is 29 degrees. Beamwidth is a function of boom length and number of elements.

Radiation patterns for the 1.2 and 4.2 wavelength Yagis are given in Figures 7 and 8. The patterns are symmetrical, with low side lobes, and exhibit a high front-to-back ratio.

NBS YAGI DESIGNS FOR 50MHz AND 432MHz

The first step in any design is to choose the desired antenna gain, compare it with the designs in Table 1, and see if the stated boom length is within the desired range. Next, the element diameter is chosen to fall within the specified range (.001 to .04 wavelength) on the graph of Figure 5. Finally, the boom or supporting structure is chosen and element length adjustments made. Various feed systems for the beam are discussed later in this handbook.

Example 1. The beam in question is a 6 meter Yagi with 10.2 dB gain, using 0.5 inch (13 mm) diameter elements, mounted on insulating blocks above a 1.5 inch (38 mm) diameter boom. This is the 1.2 wavelength design shown in Table 1.

The formula for wavelength is:

$$L = \frac{11803}{f} \text{ (inches), or } \frac{29980}{f} \text{ (cm)}$$

where L = length
f = frequency in MHz

Design Summary:

Frequency	50.1 MHz
Wavelength	235.6 inches (5.98 meters)
Element diameter (d/wavelength)	0.0021 wavelength
Reflector spacing	47 in. or 120 cm (0.2 wavelength)
Director spacings	59 in. or 150 cm (0.25 wavelength)
Boom diameter	Not important, discussed later
Overall length	283 inches (approximately 24 feet) or 7.2 meters (1.2 wavelengths)

1. Plot the lengths of the parasitic elements for the 1.2 wavelength design from Table 1 on the design nomograph (see Figure 9) for parasitic elements with a diameter/wavelength ratio = 0.0085.

$L_R = 0.482$ wavelength

$L_{D1} = L_{D4} = 0.428$ wavelength

$L_{D2} = L_{D3} = 0.420$ wavelength

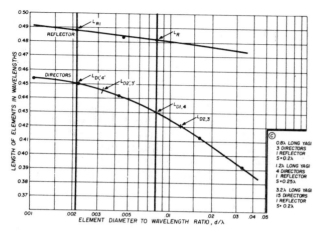

Fig. 9   Use of Yagi design curves (Fig. 5) to determine the parasitic element lengths for a 6 element Yagi for 50.1 MHz. Boom is 1.2 wavelengths long (example 1).

2.   However, the desired element diameter is 0.0021 wavelength so the element lengths must be adjusted.   Draw a vertical line from 0.0021 wavelength on the horizontal axis on the nomograph. This intersects the compensated lengths for the reflector and directors 1 and 4:

$$L_{R'} = 0.488 \text{ wavelength}$$
$$L_{D1'} = L_{D4'} = 0.451 \text{ wavelength}$$

3.   Using a pair of dividers (or a compass) measure the distance between director 1 (D1) and director 2 (D2) determined in Step 1.   Transpose this distance from the point established in Step 2 to the left along the 1.12 wavelength Yagi curve to 0.0021 wavelength to determine the compensated length for directors 2 and 3:

$$L_{D2'} = L_{D3'} = 0.446 \text{ wavelength}$$

When the boom diameter represents a substantial portion of the operating wavelength, however, a correction for the boom diameter is required.

The reflector and director lengths for the 50.1 MHz Yagi are as follows:

Reflector   0.488 wavelength = 115 inches (2.92 m)
Director 1   0.451 wavelength = 106.25 inches (2.70 m)

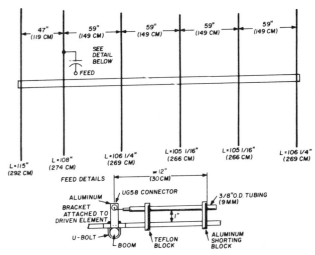

Fig. 10   Layout of a 6 element Yagi for 50.1 MHz on a 1.2 wave-length boom. All elements are 1/2 inch (13 mm) OD aluminum tubing mounted on insulating block attached to a 1-1/2 inch OD (38 mm) boom. Gamma capacitor is 12 inches (30 cm) of RG-8A/U coax with outer jacket and shield removed, then inserted in a 3/8 inch (10 mm) diameter tube.

Director 2	0.446 wavelength =	105.06 inches (2.67 m)
Director 3	0.446 wavelength =	105.06 inches (2.67 m)
Director 4	0.451 wavelength =	106.25 inches (2.70 m)

The approximate length of the driven element can be calculated from:

$$L = \frac{5500}{f} \text{ (inches), or } \frac{13970}{f} \text{ (cm)}$$

where L = length
f = frequency in MHz

Therefore, at 50.1 MHz, the length of the driven element is 109.75 inches or 2.79 meters. For simplicity a gamma match is used and the driven element is attached to the boom with a U-bolt. During the matching adjustments the driven element is shortened to 108 inches (2.74m) for optimum SWR (the length of the driven element is not critical for maximum gain).

The completed 6-meter Yagi is shown in Figure 10. On-the-air receiving tests at W1JR have shown the 3 dB

THE VHF YAGI

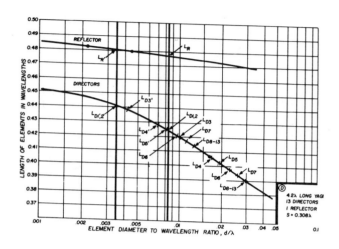

Fig. 11   Use of Yagi design curves (Fig. 5) to determine the parasitic element lengths for a 15 element Yagi for 432 MHz. Boom is 4.2 wavelengths long (example 2).

beamwidth to be between 40-45 degrees, while all sidelobes are at least 15 dB down; the front-to-back ratio is 18 dB.   This agrees closely with the published NBS data.

Example 2.   A 4.2 wavelength Yagi is required for 432 MHz.   The elements are to be mounted through the boom using 3/32 inch (2.4 mm) diameter brass rods.

For the sake of brevity, Steps 1, 2 and 3 will not be repeated.   The design graph for this antenna is shown in Figure 11.   Since the elements are mounted through the metal boom, the lengths must be increased to compensate for the shortening effect of the boom.

Design Summary:

Frequency	432 MHz
Wavelength	27.32 inches (69.40 cm)
Element diameter (d/wavelength)	0.00343 wavelength
Reflector spacing	5-1/2 in or 13.9 cm (0.2 wavelength)
Director spacing	8-7/16 in or 21.4 cm (0.308 wavelength)
Boom diameter	3/4 inch or 1.9 cm (0.0275 wavelength)
Overall length	115 in or 2.915 m (4.2 wavelengths)

$L_{R'}$ = 0.480 wavelength

TABLE 2 - 432 MHz Yagi (4.2 wavelength boom)

Element	Length Correction	Length (In)	Length (cm)
Reflector	0.480+0.02=0.500	13-11/16	34.7
Directors 1 & 2	0.441+0.02=0.461	12-19/32	32.0
Director 3	0.438+0.02=0.458	12-1/2	31.8
Director 4	0.428+0.02=0.448	12-1/4	31.1
Director 5	0.425+0.02=0.445	12-5/32	30.9
Director 6	0.421+0.02=0.441	12-1/32	30.6
Director 7	0.417+0.02=0.437	11-15/16	30.3
Directors 8-13	0.414+0.02=0.434	11-27/32	30.1

$L_{D1'} = L_{D2'} = 0.441$ wavelength

$L_{D3'} = 0.438$ wavelength

$L_{D4'} = 0.428$ wavelength

$L_{D5'} = 0.425$ wavelength

$L_{D6'} = 0.421$ wavelength

$L_{D7'} = 0.417$ wavelength

$L_{D8'}$ through $L_{D13'} = 0.414$ wavelength

To determine the corrected element length, first convert the boom diameter (3/4 inch or 1.9 cm in this case) to wavelength (d/wavelength) or approximately 0.0275 wavelength. Draw a vertical line from 0.0275 wavelength on the boom correction nomograph (see Figure 6) to the curve. Move to left-hand axis and read the correction factor; 0.02 wavelength for this antenna. Add this length correction factor to all elements as shown in Table 2.

Note that all the director lengths are rounded off to the short side. The driven element length is calculated as explained earlier, but a better match is obtained when it is extended to 13-1/2 inches (34.3 cm); a delta match with a 4:1 balun is used. The final design for the 432 MHz Yagi is shown in Figure 12.

THE DL6WU VHF ANTENNA STUDIES

A computer-aided study of Yagi design conducted at the Danish Institute of Technology (Denmark) indicated that maximum vhf Yagi gain could be achieved by suitably tapering the spacing of the director elements. This study has been verified by

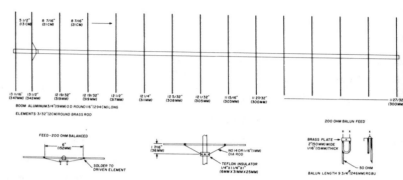

Fig. 12   Fifteen element Yagi for 432 MHz. Element centers are knurled and tapped into undersize holes in the boom. Element spacing of all directors is 8-7/16 inch (21.4 cm). Details of the delta match and 4-to-1 balun are shown at bottom.

measurements made by Gunter Hoch, DL6WU, patterned after the study. The experiments were conducted at 432 MHz and the design shown can be rescaled to the 144 and 220 MHz bands.

This design is summarized in Table 3. Of interest is the fact that a launching director closely spaced to the driven element is used. The remaining directors are spaced at irregular distances from the driven element and the lengths decrease in accord with the distance from the driven element. This design provides nearly one decibel power gain over the NBS design which employs uniform director lengths and spacings. Measurements on an antenna range indicate that the additional gain is obtained by reduction of the amplitude of the side and back lobes of radiation normally present on a Yagi antenna.

Dimensions given in the table are for use with an insulated boom. If the elements pass through the center of a metal boom, they must be lengthened in accord with the information given in Figure 6.

A 23 ELEMENT DL6WU YAGI FOR 432 MHz

A 23 element Yagi designed for 432.0 MHz was built from the design data given. The elements were made of 0.394" (10 mm) diameter aluminum rod using a nonconductive boom. Element dimensions are given in Table 3. Antenna power gain is 16 dB over a dipole. Half-power beamwidth in both planes varies between 22 and 24 degrees across the range of 430 to 440 MHz.

TABLE 3 - DL6WU LONG YAGI FOR 432 MHz

Element	Length In/cm	Spacing In/cm
Reflector	12.99/330	5.12/130
Driven El.	12.79/325	--
Director 1	11.61/295	2.17/ 55
Director 2	11.42/290	4.92/125
Director 3	11.22/285	5.91/150
Director 4	11.02/280	7.68/195
Director 5	10.83/275	7.68/195
Director 6	10.83/275	8.27/210
Director 7	10.63/270	8.66/220
Director 8	10.63/270	9.06/230
Director 9	10.43/265	9.45/240
Director 10	10.43/265	9.84/250
Director 11	10.43/265	10.24/260
Director 12	10.24/260	10.24/260
Director 13	10.24/260	10.63/270
Director 14	10.24/260	11.02/280
Director 15	10.24/260	11.02/280
Director 16	10.16/258	11.02/280
Director 17	10.16/258	11.02/280
Director 18	10.16/258	11.02/280
Director 19	10.04/255	11.02/280
Director 20	10.04/255	11.02/280
Director 21	9.84/250	11.08/280

Element Diam. = 10 mm (0.394 In)

Table 3. Element dimensions and spacings for the DL6WU Yagi design for 432 MHz. Original dimensions are metric, and these figures should be used for greatest accuracy. Antenna power gain is 16 dB over a dipole. Half-power beamwidth in both planes varies between 22 and 24 degrees across the range of 430-440 MHz. (Data courtesy of DL6WU and "VHF Communications" magazine, Germany.)

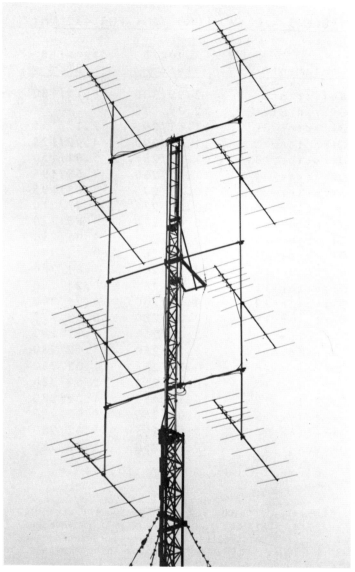

The 72 element stacked array of W3OCV provides high gain and narrow beamwidth on the 2 meter band. The array can be tilted into the horizontal position, pivoting about the midpoint of the vertical mast extension. Arrays similar to this are used for moonbounce work.

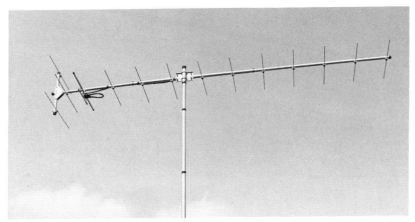

Long Yagi for 432 MHz uses trigonal reflector and is patterned after data given in this chapter. This design is by Cushcraft, PO Box 4680, Manchester, NH 03108.

VHF YAGI FEED SYSTEMS

The feed systems described for hf Yagi beams can be used with vhf antennas with proper scaling. However, because of mechanical problems and the danger of the matching system radiating and spoiling the fine pattern of a long Yagi, the popular vhf matching systems have important differences from their hf counterparts.

The principal feed systems used on high gain vhf and uhf Yagis are the split dipole, the folded dipole, the delta and T-match, and the gamma match (Figure 13).

The split dipole is the simplest feed system but it requires that the driven element be insulated from the boom and the low feedpoint resistance requires a matching device and a balun to match a coaxial line. A hairpin loop or matching stub is commonly used for matching, in conjunction with a low loss, open wire line. A balun and a coaxial line may be substituted for the open wire line. The folded dipole solves some of the problems of the split dipole. The center point of the assembly, opposite the feedpoint, can be grounded to the boom and the impedance stepup of the device provides a more convenient match to available balanced transmission lines. A balun must be used if a coaxial transmission line is connected to the folded dipole.

For a more flexible impedance match, the variable ratio folded dipole can be used (Figure 14). By changing the spacing (S) and/or the diameter ratio d1/d2, this system can provide a

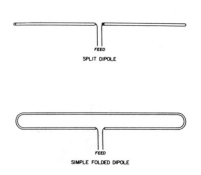

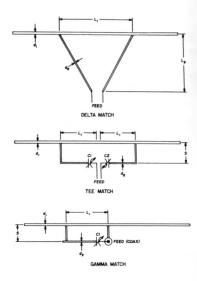

Fig. 13 VHF feed system for use with Yagi beams. Split dipole is fed with balun and coaxial line. Folded dipole provides impedance match to balun or balanced line.

Delta match is a modified folded dipole. Impedance is adjusted by varying lengths L1, L2 and diameter d2. The T-match is adjusted by changing lengths L1, L2, spacing S and capacitors C1, C2. Gamma match is a simplification of the T-match used with coaxial lines.

match to a variety of different transmission line impedance values. At 220 MHz and above, the folded dipole matching system takes a different form in which metal straps are connected between the feedpoint and the ends of the dipole.

The delta match is a modified form of the folded dipole and provides a wide range of match to a balanced feedline or balun. It is easier to adjust than the folded dipole arrangements previously discussed. A variation of this system is the T-match. The feedpoint impedance is adjusted by varying lengths $l1$ and $l2$ or the ratio $d1/d2$. This match is less prone to radiate than is the delta match. Capacitors C1 and C2 are required to tune out the inductive reactance of the matching rods. The principal disadvantage of this system is the requirement for capacitors which are insensitive to power level and weather conditions.

The gamma match, a popular hf device, is a simplification of the T-match and is designed for use with coaxial transmission lines. As with the T-match, the major disadvantages of this device are the use of a capacitor and the need to protect it from the weather.

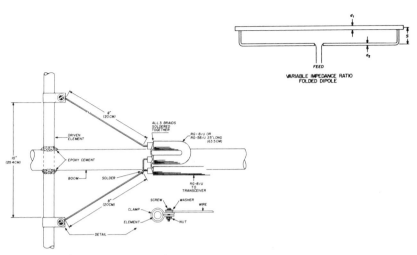

Fig. 14 Popular impedance match for 2 meter beam uses delta feed with a 4-to-1 coaxial balun. Balun may also be used with a folded dipole element (upper right). The ratio of element diameters (d1, d2) and spacing (s) determines the impedance ratio.

VHF FEEDLINES

Transmission line loss is of major importance in the vhf region. Many types of transmission lines are available but only a few are suited for vhf operation. All transmission lines have some degree of loss, or attenuation, which is directly proportional to the length of the line. Loss is commonly expressed in decibels loss per 100 feet and increases with frequency. Attenuation figures for various lines are thus expressed at a particular frequency. For example, a 200 foot (60.9 m) run of line having a 4 dB loss per 100 feet at 450 MHz will have an 8 dB loss at that frequency. Similarly, a 10 foot (3.05 m) length of the same line will have a loss of 0.4 dB.

COAXIAL CABLES FOR VHF

Coaxial cable (coax) consists of a central conductor within a larger cylindrical outer conductor. The central conductor is held in position by an insulating material (dielectric). Coax is generally operated with the outer shield at ground potential and is thus called an "unbalanced" line. A later chapter of this handbook discusses coaxial line in detail.

As far as vhf operation goes, the most popular coaxial lines are RG-58A/U, RG-213/U and RG-223/U. The small RG-58A/U is

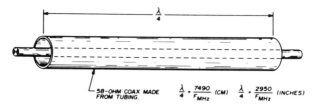

Fig. 15 Quarter-wavelength coaxial transformer used to match a 50 ohm coax line to semi-rigid 70 ohm CATV line. The diameters are not important, but the ratio of the inside diameter of the outer tube to the outside diameter of the inner tube should be 2.6-to-1 for a characteristic impedance of 58 ohms.

useful for very short runs in the station between low power equipments, the RG-213/U is a medium size, general purpose cable, and the RG-223/U is a larger cable suitable for long runs and higher power.

Semi-rigid, foam dielectric, aluminum jacket ("hard line") coaxial cable in the 1/2-inch (13 mm) and 7/8-inch (22 mm) sizes is sometimes used for long runs, as is Heliax, especially the air-filled type.

OTHER FEEDLINES

Interesting vhf cables are available from the CATV business. These installations often use low loss, semi-rigid, foam dielectric 70 and 75 ohm coaxial cables. In some cases the unused ends of reels are sold at low prices by the CATV companies. Connectors are available for these lines. A quarter-wave matching transformer (Figure 15) can be used to transform a 70 ohm line down to 50 ohms impedance.

Twin lead is also an acceptable feedline for use below 250 MHz. Only the low loss, outdoor type should be used. Unfortunately, moisture can adversely affect both SWR and line loss when this material is used outdoors. Open wire line, if properly installed, is also useful at vhf. The line insulators should be spaced about 7 inches (18 cm) apart and line spacing should be small in proportion to wavelength for minimum line radiation. A spacing of 0.75 inch (19 mm) is often used up to 450 MHz. Low loss insulators made of Teflon rod are acceptable.

Regardless of the type of line used, low SWR at the antenna is important, especially when line loss is appreciable. A 3 dB feedline loss will increase to 4 dB if the SWR at the antenna is 3-to-1, and to 6 dB for a 7-to-1 antenna SWR. This condition may be undetected because a lossy line dissipates part of the

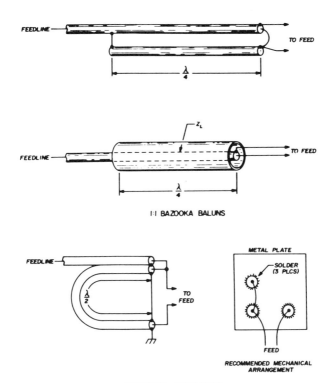

Fig. 16 Simplest VHF balun is the quarter-wave bazooka (top). The coaxial bazooka provides better balance and shielding (center). The 4-to-1 balun (bottom) uses an electrical quarter-wavelength of line. Mechanical termination of lines is shown at right.

reflected power from the antenna so an SWR meter located at the station end of the line will not indicate the true SWR at the antenna.

VHF BALUNS

The majority of vhf operators use coaxial transmission line to their antenna. However, many of the efficient vhf antennas feed are designed for balanced feedlines. If a coaxial line is attached to a balanced feedpoint, there is a good possibility that the transmission line will radiate energy, distorting the antenna radiation pattern and lowering antenna gain. The use of a balun under these conditions is recommended.

Various vhf baluns are shown in Figure 16. The bazooka balun is a 1-to-1 device, the quarter wave section acting as an rf trap to any current on the outside of the shield. Line spacing should be about three times the diameter of the feedline. The coaxial balun does substantially the same job as the bazooka design and provides a better balance in the upper reaches of the vhf spectrum. The 4-to-1 coaxial balun requires an electrical half wavelength coaxial cable and matches a 50 ohm line to a 200 ohm folded dipole. This system is used with many commercially available vhf beams.

FERRITE BEAD BALUNS

A simple vhf balun can be assembled by placing a string of high permeability ferrite beads around the coaxial feedline at the antenna connection. The beads introduce a high impedance in series with the outer surface of the coax braid, and decouple the line from unwanted antenna currents. For 30 to 300 MHz service, twenty-five beads having a permeability of about 950 or more may be used (Amidon FB-43-2401 or equivalent beads will slip-fit over RG-58/U or RG-303/U). The beads are closely grouped about the antenna end of the transmission line and are held in place with heat-shrink tubing or tape. Larger diameter beads are required to slip over RG-8A/U cable.

THE VHF LOG PERIODIC YAGI ANTENNA

Mentioned in an earlier chapter is the log periodic bandpass Yagi antenna. This unique array makes use of a log periodic dipole structure with a bandpass characteristic similar to a Chebyschev-type filter (Figure 14, page 97). A number of parasitic directors are used to enhance the gain of the log periodic structure. This unusual offspring of the conventional Yagi antenna provides good power gain over a large frequency span, and various versions of this design are commercially available for amateur vhf operation.

A 50 MHz LPY BANDPASS YAGI BEAM

Shown in Figure 17 is an effective six meter LPY Yagi designed to cover the first two megahertz of the 50 MHz band. It is composed of five log periodic elements and three parasitic directors. Gain is estimated at 12 dB and front-to-back ratio is better than 20 dB. Receiving response is down about 35 dB at 54 MHz, providing some receiver protection from spill-over from a nearby channel 2 tv transmitter.

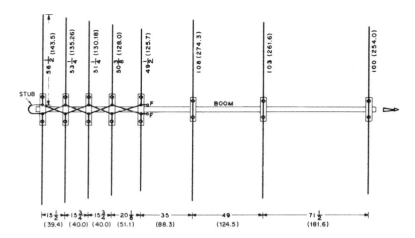

Fig.17 L-P Yagi for 6 meters. Antenna is fed with a balun and coax line at feedpoint F-F. The rear element is shorted with a small stub to provide correct termination and to improve front-to-back ratio.

Feedpoint resistance of the antenna is about 75 ohms. The antenna can be fed with RG-11A/U coaxial line and a one-to-one balun, or a matching device can be placed at the antenna for use with a 50 ohm coax line or 300 ohm balanced line.

General construction for vhf antennas is given later in this handbook. In brief, the LPY Yagi is built on a 19 foot (5.8 m) boom made of 2-inch (5 cm) diameter aluminum tubing. The driven elements are supported at the center on insulating blocks and the parasitic elements are mounted directly to the boom. The driven elements are cross-connected with heavy aluminum wire. The back element is shunted with a six inch (15.2 cm) long loop of wire at the end of the transposed feedline.

A balanced feedpoint (F-F) exists at the front of the log periodic structure and the balun or matching device is placed at this point. The antenna is supported by the vertical mast at the center of gravity and overhead trusses run from the mast to each end of the boom to provide additional rigidity to the array.

AN LPY BANDPASS YAGI FOR 2 METERS

The LPY Yagi technique can be used to advantage over the 144 to 148 MHz range where maximum bandwidth and high gain are desired. The design shown provides uniform gain over the center portion of the band, with the gain dropping only slightly at the band edges (Figure 18).

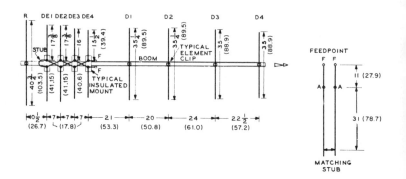

Fig. 18 LPY for 2 meters. Antenna covers 4 MHz with good gain. A half-wave, two-wire matching stub is used, placed at right angles to the elements. Position of shorting bar determines resonant frequency of the driven element. Beam is fed with a coax line and half-wave coaxial balun at A-A. Both shorting bar and feedpoint are adjusted for lowest SWR on the transmission line.

The array consists of four log periodic elements backed up by a parasitic reflector and preceded by two parasitic directors. Overall antenna length is 59 inches (149.8 cm). The beam is fed at feedpoint A-A by a one-to-one coaxial balun and a 50 ohm line.

The elements are supported above and insulated from a 1 inch (2.54 cm) diameter boom. The cross-connected transmission line between the log periodic elements is made of sections of 1/4-inch (6.35 mm) wide aluminum strap, with the last driven element terminated with a strap loop 6 inches (15.24 cm) long. The inner tips of the driven elements are about 1 inch (2.54 cm) apart and the elements are drilled to hold the connecting nut and bolt for the transmission line.

Chapter 6

All About Transmission Lines

The transmission line is a conductor or "radio hose" that guides electrical energy from one point to another. The line is also called a feedline or a feeder. One of the most important applications of a transmission line is to conduct radio energy to and from an antenna.

TYPES OF LINES

Many types of transmission lines have been designed and used over the years but the two types of most interest to radio amateurs are the coaxial line and the two-wire, parallel conductor line (Figure 1). The two-wire line is often used in television reception ("ribbon line" or "twin-lead") and consists of two parallel conductors separated a fixed distance by insulating spacers or by an intervening web of low loss material molded between the wires. This line has an energy field about it and should not be placed near metal objects or the ground because of the possibility of upsetting the operation of the line. Since the line does not match most amateur equipment, its use is restricted mainly to portable, "field day" type antennas.

THE COAXIAL LINE

The coaxial line has advantages which make it very practical for amateur use with beam antennas. The line consists of a wire inside (and coaxial with) a tubular outer conductor (Figure 2). The inner wire is insulated from the outer conductor by a solid and continuous insulating medium such as Teflon or polyethylene. The outer conductor is usually made of metal braid to give the line some degree of flexibility. The chief purpose of the coaxial line is to keep radiation losses at a minimum. In the case of the parallel conductor line, the electric and magnetic

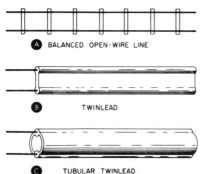

A BALANCED OPEN-WIRE LINE

B TWINLEAD

C TUBULAR TWINLEAD

Fig. 1   Open-wire line (A) as well as TV-type twin lead (B and C) can be used for amateur low power service to feed a balanced antenna from an antenna tuner at the station. The lines are useful to 50 MHz but exhibit increased loss in wet weather.

fields extend out into space for a considerable distance, causing radiation losses on transmission and noise pickup on reception. The coaxial line, however, has no electric or magnetic fields extending outside of the outer conductor if the line is properly operated.   All fields exist in the space between the two conductors, thus the coaxial cable is a perfectly shielded line.   The proximity of objects causes no extra loss or unbalance in the line.   In fact, the coaxial cable may be run along the surface of the earth with no ill effect to the operation of the line.   Examples of such lines are RG-8A/U (52 ohms), RG-213/U (50 ohms) and RG-11/U (75 ohms).

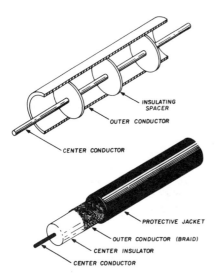

INSULATING SPACER
OUTER CONDUCTOR
CENTER CONDUCTOR

PROTECTIVE JACKET
OUTER CONDUCTOR (BRAID)
CENTER INSULATOR
CENTER CONDUCTOR

Fig. 2   Coaxial cables are recommended for hf/vhf use.   Above is air insulated, rigid line, suitable for high power, vhf service.   Below is the popular flexible solid dielectric cable for medium power hf/vhf service. Center insulation may be teflon, polyethylene or other low-loss material.

Table 1. Important operating characteristics of 50- and 75-ohm coaxial cables used by amateurs. Types with non-contaminating jackets (designated NV) should be selected for long life. Power rating is given for 30 MHz and is somewhat higher on the lower frequencies; this is power into the transmission line, *not* transmitter input power.

Cable Type	Jacket*	Z_0 (Ohms)	Loss in dB/100 Feet (30m)					Power Rating at 30 MHz (watts)
			3.5 MHz	7.0 MHz	14.0 MHz	21 MHz	28 MHz	
RG-8/U	V	52.0	0.29	0.43	0.67	0.81	0.98	1900
RG-8A/U	NV	52.0	0.29	0.43	0.67	0.81	0.98	1900
RG-11/U	V	75.0	0.34	0.55	0.81	1.0	1.2	1375
RG-11A/U	NV	75.0	0.34	0.55	0.81	1.0	1.2	1375
RG-17/U	V	52.0	0.13	0 22	0.35	0.42	0.52	6400
RG-17A/U	NV	52.0	0.13	0.22	0.35	0.42	0.52	6400
RG-58/U	V	53.5	0.54	0.82	1.25	1.6	1.9	575
RG-58A/U	V	52.0	0.69	1.05	1.6	2.1	2.5	500
RG-58B/U	NV	53.5	0.54	0.82	1.25	1.6	1.9	575
RG-58C/U	NV	50.0	0.69	1.05	1.0	2.1	2.5	500
RG-59/U	V	73.0	0.55	0.80	1.15	1.4	1.7	700
RG-59A/U	NV	75.0	0.55	0.80	1.15	1.4	1.7	700
RG-59B/U	NV	75.0	0.55	0.80	1.15	1.4	1.7	700
RG-8 Polyfoam	V	50.0	0.28	0.41	0.60	0.75	0.90	2000
RG-11 Polyfoam	V	75.0	0.32	0.51	0.73	0.93	1.10	1425
RG-58 Polyfoam	V	50.0	0.80	1.18	1.70	2.1	2.5	500
RG-59 Polyfoam	V	75.0	0.40	0.59	0.88	1.1	1.3	750

*V indicates a vinyl jacket; NV indicates a non-contaminating vinyl jacket.

CABLE	Zo	VP	ATTENUATION IN DB/100 FT.				POWER RATING (WATTS)			
			50 MHz	144 MHz	220 MHz	432 MHz	50 MHz	144 MHz	220 MHz	432 MHz
RG-58C/U	52.5	.66	3.0	6.0	8.0	15.0	350	175	125	90
RG-58 (F)	50	.79	2.2	4.1	5.0	7.1	450	230	160	120
RG-59B/U	73	.66	2.3	4.2	5.5	8.0	500	250	180	125
RG-59 (F)	75	.79	2.0	3.4	4.6	6.1	650	320	230	160
RG-8A/U RG-213/U	52	.66	1.5	2.5	3.5	5.0	1500	800	650	400
RG-8(F)	50	.80	1.2	2.2	2.7	3.9	1950	1100	850	520
RG-11A/U	75	.66	1.55	2.8	3.7	5.5	1500	800	650	400
RG-17A/U RG-218/U	52	.66	0.5	1.0	1.3	2.3	4500	2300	1800	1200

Attenuation and power rating for coax lines used in the vhf spectrum. RG-8A/U and RG-213/U are recommended for high power and medium length cable runs. Belden low-attenuation type 9914 has same diameter and less loss than RG-8-type cable family and is recommended for vhf/uhf use. For short cable runs and installation ease the small diameter RG-58C/U is suggested. Foam dielectric cable is indicated by (F). Special small-diameter RG-8/X cable has been used with success up to 150 MHz at powers up to 500 watts.

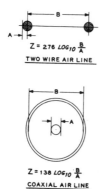

$$Z = 276 \, LOG_{10} \frac{B}{A}$$

TWO WIRE AIR LINE

$$Z = 138 \, LOG_{10} \frac{B}{A}$$

COAXIAL AIR LINE

NOTE: Z OF SOLID DIELECTRIC LINES $= \frac{Z \, OF \, AIR \, LINE}{K}$, WHERE K IS DIELECTRIC CONSTANT OF MATERIAL BETWEEN CONDUCTORS.

Fig. 3 The characteristic impedance of a transmission line is a function of the conductor diameters, the line spacing and the insulating material.

IMPEDANCE OF A TRANSMISSION LINE

A transmission line has an inherent property termed the characteristic impedance of the line. The impedance is expressed in ohms, and is determined by the physical and electrical configuration of the line. The size of the line conductors, the spacing between them, the material used to space the conductors apart, the inductance per foot of each conductor; all these factors determine the characteristic impedance of the transmission line, as illustrated in Figure 3. The impedance of commercially available transmission lines falls between the limits of 35 ohms (RG-83/U coaxial cable) and 300 ohms.

THE NONRESONANT TRANSMISSION LINE

A nonresonant transmission line is one terminated by a resistive load whose ohmic value is equal to the characteristic impedance of the transmission line. All of the energy put into the line is dissipated by the terminating load. The terminating load may be a resistor, or it may be an antenna of some sort whose feedpoint resistance equals the characteristic impedance of the line at the frequency of the exciting source. If line losses are neglected, a nonresonant transmission line has the same value of voltage and current at one point on the line as it does at any other point. A transmission line terminated in this fashion is said to be matched. On a perfectly matched line, the characteristic impedance defines the ratio of voltage to current in the line.

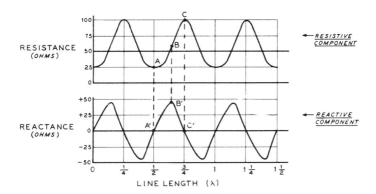

Fig. 4   The input impedance of a mismatched transmission line varies with the degree of mismatch and the length of the line, even though the SWR on the line remains constant. In this example, the feedpoint resistance of the antenna is 25 ohms (at left) and the SWR is 2-to-1. The terminating value is repeated one half wavelength down the line (A-A'). But at B-B' and C-C' the resistive and reactive components are widely different than at the input end of the line. Trimming the line won't change the SWR, but it may make a more satisfactory match for the output circuit of the transmitter.

THE RESONANT TRANSMISSION LINE

A resonant transmission line is one that is terminated by a load that is not equal to the characteristic impedance of the line. When such an impedance discontinuity appears in a transmission line system, part of the power put into the line is reflected back from the termination end of the line towards the input end. This reflected power reacts with the generated power so as to produce points of current and voltage maxima and minima upon the line as shown in Figure 4. The line now has a standing wave upon it. This means that voltage and current measurements made at one point on the line will be entirely different than those made at another point. The reflected power is eventually dissipated by the terminating load on the line (the antenna), but only after it has made one or more trips back and forth along the transmission line.

THE STANDING WAVE RATIO (SWR)

The ratio of the maximum to the minimum value of voltage along a transmission line is called the standing wave ratio (SWR or VSWR). The SWR is a measure of the amount of mismatch between the load terminating the transmission line and the characteristic impedance of the line. The SWR is expressed as a ratio greater than unity (one) by the following expression:

$$\text{Standing Wave Ratio (SWR)} = Z_o/Z_t \text{ or } Z_t/Z_o$$

where Z_o is the characteristic impedance of the transmission line in ohms, and Z_t is the impedance of the terminating load. The choice of formula used depends on whether the terminating load is numerically larger or smaller than the characteristic impedance of the line. A transmission line properly terminated by a resistive load equal in value to the surge impedance of the line will have a SWR of 1-to-1 (sometimes written 1/1 or 1:1).

A line does not have to be of any particular length to have a standing wave condition. The only requirement for the production of a standing wave is that reflection occurs at some point along the line. The usual reason for a reflection is improper line termination.

It may be seen in Figure 4 that a 50 ohm transmission line terminated by a 25 ohm load produces a 2/1 SWR. If a series of measurements are made along this line, it will be found that the resistive component at any point to ground varies between the limits of 25 and 100 ohms. In addition, reactance (both positive and negative) is measured in varying amounts at certain positions along the line. If, by chance, the transmission line is one-half wavelength long (points A-A'), a resistive load of 25 ohms is presented to the measuring device. At this point it is difficult for the observer to determine if an SWR exists upon the line unless he has a directional coupler or SWR meter that indicates the presence of the reflected wave.

If the observer shifts his measuring device to point B-B', however, he measures an impedance composed of 62 ohms resistance and 48 ohms inductive reactance. If the transmission line happens to be just this length, he may experience difficulty in obtaining proper transmitter loading. By lengthening the transmission line to three-quarter wavelength (points C-C'), the observer can eliminate the unwanted reactance, but he will have a resistive termination of 100 ohms. At no point on the line, trim it as he might, will he find a point that presents a 50 ohm resistive load to his transmitter. He can make the best of a bad bargain by cutting his transmission line to some multiple of one-half wavelength to eliminate any reactive component at the transmitter end of the line, and accept the fact that he does not have a "flat" line. Whether the transmitter can effectively couple power into the 25 ohm load would be the next problem that he will face.

REACTIVE TERMINATION OF A TRANSMISSION LINE

Even though a transmission line might be terminated in a load whose ohmic resistance is equal to the characteristic impedance of the line, there is a special case when a SWR greater than one-to-one will occur. This is when the terminating load has reactance at the frequency of operation of the line. If the load happens to be an antenna, this is another way of saying that the antenna is not resonant at the frequency of operation. The <u>resonant</u> <u>frequency</u> of an antenna system is that frequency at which the antenna presents a nonreactive load to the transmission line. If a transmitter is operating on a frequency of 14.005 MHz, and is supplying power through a 50 ohm transmission line to an antenna that presents a nonreactive 50 ohm load to the transmission line at 14.340 MHz, there will be an appreciable SWR on the transmission line. To reduce the SWR to 1/1, it is necessary that the transmitter either be tuned to 14.340 MHz or that the antenna be retuned to present a nonreactive load at the transmitting frequency of 14.005 MHz.

For proper operation of a nonresonant transmission line, two important requirements must be met by the antenna system:

1. The antenna must be resonant at the frequency of operation of the transmitter.

2. The antenna must present a feedpoint resistance to the transmission line that is equal to the characteristic impedance of the line.

When these two requirements are satisfied, the SWR on the transmission line will be one-to-one (unity), the line is in a nonresonant condition and maximum power is transferred to the antenna.

IMPORTANCE OF A NONRESONANT LINE

Why the fuss over the importance of a nonresonant line? If a resonant line will do the job, why go to all the trouble of adjusting the antenna system so as to obtain a low value of SWR on the transmission line? Resonant lines, in fact, are used to feed power to many types of simple antenna systems. Before World War II produced low loss coaxial transmission lines, and before the advent of television produced the TV-type balanced 300 ohm line, open wire 600 ohm resonant lines were used by most amateurs to couple power from the transmitter to the antenna. The 600 ohm lines are museum pieces today.

Most transmitters and beam antennas are designed to work in conjunction with a coaxial feedline. An antenna tuner at the station is not necessary provided the transmission line and antenna are properly matched and operation is not over too wide a frequency range. However, many amateurs with coaxial feedline still use some form of tuner to reduce harmonic radiation (TVI) and to permit efficient transmitter operation over a wide range of frequencies. The matching circuit at the antenna covers a relatively narrow frequency range and SWR values of 2- or 3-to-1 may develop on the feedline under wide frequency excursions from the antenna design frequency. This prevents proper operation of the equipment, particularly if it is solid state. Well-designed solid state equipment incorporates protection circuits for the final stage transistors that reduce power output automatically as the SWR on the transmission line increases in value. Maximum transmitter power output thus depends upon a low value of SWR as "seen" by the transmitter.

LINE LOSS AND RESONANCE

Most coaxial lines can handle a considerable value of SWR before line heating occurs. In low power service, the SWR can be. allowed to rise as high as the transmitting equipment can handle without problems. However, when high power is passed through a line having a high SWR on it "hot spots" occur along it at points of maximum current. Coaxial line loss increases with frequency and also with SWR so it is prudent to limit SWR to 2-to-1 or less under most circumstances. High values of SWR at low frequencies are generally less "lossy" than lower SWR values at the very high frequencies.

It must be remembered that Yagi beam antennas are resonant at only one frequency in a given band and present a mismatch to the line at other frequencies. The transmission line then, strictly speaking, is a nonresonant line only at the resonant frequency of the antenna. And when the antenna is nonresonant, the line is resonant! The terms "resonant line" and "nonresonant line" may be useful in studying feedlines, but today's amateur speaks in terms of the standing wave ratio on the line. He's expressing the same concept in different words.

TRANSMISSION LINE RULES

Without belaboring the point, and without going into the theory of transmission lines or a study of standing waves on the line, the following simple rules outline the situation which makes an antenna and feed system <u>work</u>:

1. The antenna array must be resonant at some frequency within the operating band of interest.

2. The resonant antenna should present (directly or through a matching device at the antenna) a feedpoint resistance roughly equal in ohms to the characteristic impedance of the transmission line.

TODAY'S POPULAR COAXIAL LINE

Table 1 lists some of the many varieties of coaxial line manufactured in the United States and Japan. For amateur service, the 50 ohm line is widely used. In Europe (and in U.S. cable television service) 75 ohm transmission line is standardized. The widespread popularity of CB radio has brought many cable manufacturers on the scene, and some of the less-expensive cable is not suited for amateur service. Many cheap makes of coaxial line economize by reducing the amount of copper in the braid, providing as low as 60 percent coverage of the inner conductor. Good, high quality line provides over 90 percent coverage. A skimpy braid reduces the isolation between the real world and the radio energy flowing along the inner conductor. Power loss and increased television interference from line radiation are prices the user of cheap coaxial line must pay. Buy the best line you can from a reputable manufacturer.

COAXIAL CABLE CONTAMINATION

The radio frequency power loss for new, unused flexible polyethylene dielectric coaxial line is listed in Figure 2 for some of the more popular types. The rf loss is modest at 100 MHz for reasonable lengths of line and can be considered to be insignificant at frequencies below 30 MHz. A one hundred foot length of new RG-8A/U coaxial cable operating with a matched load at 30 MHz, for example, has an rf attenuation of only one decibel. At 21 MHz, the loss is only 0.8 dB and at 14 MHz the loss has dropped to approximately 0.65 dB. As the SWR on the cable rises, however, the rf losses also rise by virtue of the standing wave of current existing on the line. Even so, the degree of rf cable loss in the high frequency spectrum for coax line is moderate until the SWR approaches values of 3/1 or so (Figure 5).

Power lost in a coaxial line is the sum of resistance loss, dielectric loss and radiation loss. Of these three factors, radiation loss for good, high quality coax is negligible at frequencies below several hundred megahertz and dielectric loss is quite small below a hundred megahertz or so. The resistance loss, on the other hand, makes up approximately 80 percent of the rf power loss of the cable at the lower frequencies. Most of this loss is concentrated in the center conductor of the cable as loss in the outer braid is very small for new cable.

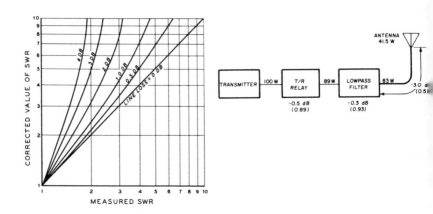

Fig. 5 Rf loss in coax line rises with high SWR (left). Circuit losses add up, as shown at right. In this vhf example, 100 watt transmitter output shrinks to 41.5 watts at the antenna due to total circuit loss of 3.8 dB. The reduction factor for each loss is shown in parenthesis.

Older varieties of coaxial line such as RG-8/U and RG-11/U have a flexible black jacket of polyvinylchloride to protect the cable from moisture, abrasion and sunlight. To make the vinyl jacket flexible a plastic additive is mixed with the vinyl during the manufacturing process. Upon exposure of the cable to heat and sunlight over a period of time the additive undergoes a chemical change and migrates through the flexible copper braid and into the polyethylene inner dielectric. As a result of this migration, the rf resistance of the braid rises and it becomes discolored and corroded. At the same time, the dielectric loss of the inner insulation rises sharply. After prolonged exposure, the outer jacket becomes brittle and looses its flexibility. Cracks in the jacket permit moisture and dirt to enter the cable further lowering its efficiency. The practical life of cables having contaminating black vinyl jackets is from three to seven years, after which time the rf attenuation of the cable may reach an unusually high figure. Old, weathered RG-8/U coaxial line may exhibit a loss figure as high as four decibels per hundred feet of line at 30 MHz. Care must therefore be exercised when purchasing and using "surplus" or "CB-type" coaxial cable, as these varieties have finite life and should be discarded when they approach the end of the period of usability.

Recent improvements in coaxial cable have led to the development of non-contaminating jackets and cable types such as RG-8A/U, RG-11A/U, RG-58A/U and RG-59A/U which make use of a special plasticizer in the jacket that permits life expec-

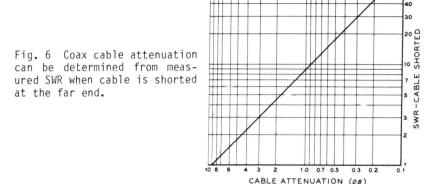

Fig. 6 Coax cable attenuation can be determined from measured SWR when cable is shorted at the far end.

tancies of fifteen to twenty years. RG-213/U cable is similar to RG-8A/U and should be used when a low cost, non-contaminating coaxial line is desired.

Not all black-jacket cables are subject to contamination as various coaxial lines have a special carbon black polyethylene jacket with a life expectancy in excess of twenty years and which is impervious to moisture. It is impossible to catalog all types and varieties of coaxial line in this handbook, and the prospective purchaser is advised to arm himself with a cable catalog or specification sheet before purchasing his transmission line. Above all, he should be wary of cheap cable as it might very well be on the surplus market by virtue of its extremely high rf loss. Coaxial line whose outer copper braid is discolored or corroded, or whose inner dielectric exhibits a greenish tint, should be avoided.

MEASUREMENT OF LINE LOSS

The efficiency of your coaxial line may be determined by measuring the line loss at the operating frequency of the transmitter. When the line is terminated in a short circuit, the reflected power will be equal to the transmitted power and the SWR will be infinite if the line has no loss. Line loss will reduce the reflected power and the SWR, and the relationship between the two is shown in Figure 6.

In order to measure the line loss, the antenna termination is removed from the far end of the line and the outer shield is firmly shorted to the center conductor. A small amount of power is applied to the line through an SWR bridge and the SWR is measured at the operating frequency of the antenna. If, for example, the SWR turns out to be 9/1, the line loss is one decibel. A line with a loss of 3 decibels will show an SWR of

UG STANDARD

COUPLING RING

**83-168 OR 83-185
REDUCING ADAPTER
(WHEN REQUIRED)**

PLUG SUB-ASSEMBLY

PLUGS 83-1SP, 83-5SP, 83-21SP, 83-59, 83-67, 83-822

Cut end of cable even and strip jacket, braid, and dielectric to dimensions shown in table. All cuts are to be sharp and square. Do not nick braid, dielectric or center conductor. Tin exposed center conductor and braid, avoiding excessive heat.

Stripping dims. inches (mm)	a ±1/64(0.4)	b ±1/64(0.4)	c ±1/64(0.4)
83-1SP, 83-5SP	1¼(31.8)	⅝(15.9)	1/16(1.6)
83-21SP	1(25.4)	11/16(17.5)	⅛(3.2)
83-59, 83-67	27/32(21.4)	¼(6.4)	9/64(3.6)
83-822	1⅛(28.6)	⅝(15.9)	1/16(1.6)

STRAIGHT PLUGS (except 83-5SP). Slide coupling ring on cable. Screw the plug sub-assembly on cable. Solder assembly to braid through solder holes, making a good bond between braid and shell. Solder conductor to contact. Do not use excessive heat. For final assembly, move coupling ring forward and screw in place on plug sub-assembly.

83-5SP PUSH-ON PLUG. Screw the plug sub-assembly on cable and solder to braid as described above. Screw coupling ring in place over plug sub-assembly until threads bottom.

ANGLE PLUGS. Screw plug body assembly on cable. Solder assembly to braid as above. Solder conductor to contact through hole in back of connector. Screw cap into place.

PLUGS 83-1SP, 83-59, 83-67, 83-222, 83-750 USING 83-168 OR 83-185 REDUCING ADAPTER

Cut·end of cable even. Remove vinyl jacket to dimension **a** in table below.' Slide coupling ring and adapter on cable.

Stripping dims. inches (mm)	a ±1/64(0.4)	b ±1/64(0.4)
83-1SP, 83-822, 83-750	¾(19.1)	⅝(15.9)
83-59, 83-67	½(12.7)	5/16(7.9)

Fan braid slightly and fold back as shown.

Position adapter flush with cable jacket. Press braid down over body of adapter and trim to ⅜″(9.5). Bare conductor to dimension **b**. Tin exposed center conductor.

Screw plug sub-assembly on adapter. Solder braid to shell through solder holes. Use enough heat to create bond of braid to shell. Solder conductor to contact.

For final assembly, screw coupling ring on plug sub-assembly.

Fig.7   AMPHENOL instructions for assembly of UHF-type (PL-259) plug for RG-8A/U cable and assembly to RG-58-family of cable with a reducing adapter. Drawing courtesy Amphenol.

about 3/1 when terminated in a short circuit. The accuracy of this test depends upon the accuracy of the SWR bridge and many of the cheaper imported models are notoriously inaccurate at high values of SWR. More on this interesting subject later in this handbook.

COAXIAL PLUGS AND ACCESSORIES

A bewildering mix of coaxial plugs, adapters, receptacles and fittings exists today. Which are the proper ones to use? Most amateur equipment is outfitted with the so-called "UHF connector" series which combines an SO-239 receptacle with a PL-259 plug. Developed during World War II, these inexpensive couplings are adequate up through the 2 meter band and are recommended for general amateur hf operation. They are designed for 0.405 inch (1.03 cm) diameter cable, such as the RG-8 series. The fittings may be used with smaller cable such as RG-58A/U, 0.195 inch (0.5 cm) diameter, by the addition of an insert, UG-175/U. This information is shown in Figure 7.

None of the UHF couplings is waterproof. When used outdoors, they should be protected from the weather, otherwise water will be drawn into the coaxial line by capillary action and line loss will skyrocket. Exposed cable connections and terminations should be completely wrapped with vinyl electrical tape and then given an overcoat of flexible sealant such as RTV. Care must be used in selecting the brand of sealant as some contain acetic acid which corrodes metal and affects the wrapping tape and outer jacket of the coaxial line. Read the label on the tube of sealant before you buy it. Most "bathtub caulks" contain acetic acid.

THE W6SAI ASSEMBLY TECHNIQUE

The popular and widely available UHF-type plug (PL-259) can be placed on an RG-213/U or RG-8A/U type coax cable without too much trouble if the proper technique is used. The following assembly sequence is recommended:

The first step in preparing the coaxial cable for the plug is to slide the coupling ring of the plug onto the cable with the ring threads toward the open end of the cable. Next, take a utility knife (Stanley 99A Shop Knife, for example) and circumscribe a cut in the outer black jacket of the line. Make the cut at right angles to the cable and about 1-1/2 inches (3.8 cm) back from the end of the cable. Try not to nick the braid. The small cylinder of jacket material you have cut may be slit carefully with the knife and removed.

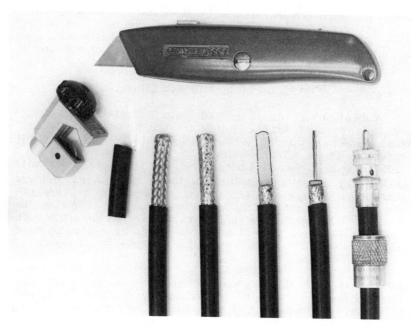

Fig. 8 Coax plug onto line -- the easy way. Midget tubing cutter (left) and utility knife (top) are used. At left is a sample coax line with the outer jacket removed by the knife. Next, the outer, braided conductor of the line is tinned. Third view shows the outer braid cut to length by the tubing cutter. Fourth view shows inner insulation of the line cut to length and inner conductor tinned. Right view shows coax plug and ferrule on the line, with plug in position for soldering to shield thru four holes in plug shell. Gun or iron with high wattage and small tip is recommended.

You have now exposed over an inch of the outer copper braid of the cable. Without disturbing the braid, which should be lying flat against the inner insulation, take a small soldering gun or iron and quickly and smoothly tin the exposed braid, making it a solid entity. Don't overheat the braid, or the inner insulation may melt and "squirt" out between the basketweave strands of the braid. (Cheap coax with a loosely woven braid will do this every time!) Clean the left-over flux from the braid with a rag moistened with paint thinner or alcohol (Figure 8).

The next step is to trim the soldered braid to the correct length. Use a small tubing cutter for this job. The General Hardware Midget Tubing Cutter is recommended. Cut the braid so that one-half inch (1.3 cm) is left on the cable end. Mark a line this distance from the black vinyl jacket and place the tubing cutter over the braid, letting the cutting wheel fall on the mark. Tighten the cutter slightly and slowly revolve it about the cable. After one turn, tighten the wheel again, and continue to revolve the cutter. Four or five turns and the cutter will neatly slice the soldered braid. The unwanted slug of braid may then be snipped off with a pair of wire cutters.

The next step is to trim the center insulation. Cut it cleanly with the utility knife so that a collar 1/16-inch (1.59 mm) wide extends beyond the soldered braid. Don't nick the center conductor. Once the insulation is cut, you can pull the slug off the end of the cable by grasping it with your fingers and gently pulling it, rotating it at the same time so that it follows the twist of the inner conductor wires. When the slug is off, tin the center conductor.

Now the cable end is ready for the PL-259 plug. Push it carefully on the cable end, rotating it with the fingers so that the internal threads of the plug screw onto the outer vinyl jacket of the cable. Make sure the inner conductor is centered into the plug pin. As the plug body is screwed onto the cable, you will see the tinned braid appear through the four solder holes in the shell. Continue twisting the plug onto the cable until the braid is completely visible through all holes (Figure 9A).

The plug is now fixed on the cable by soldering the braid through the four solder holes. Use a soldering gun with a small tip and proceed with care, using small diameter solder. Hold the plug in a bench vise during this operation. Take care that solder does not run over the outer threads of the body. The last step is to solder the center conductor to the plug pin. After the assembly cools down, slide the coupling ring down and screw onto the plug.

THE PL-259 PLUG WITH SMALL COAXIAL CABLE

The PL-259 may be used with small diameter cable (RG-58A/U, for example) by adding a reduction adapter (type UG-175/U). A slightly different assembly technique is used for this cable (Figure 9B).

The end of the cable is passed through the coupling ring and the adapter, with the threads of the ring and the narrow end of the adapter facing the end of the cable. Using the utility knife, cut 3/4-inch (19 mm) of the vinyl jacket off the cable. Fan the braid out slightly and carefully fold it back over the adapter. Next, trim the braid with a small scissors to about 3/8-inch (9.5 mm) long, so that it fits about the barrel of the adapter. Following this, take the utility knife and remove

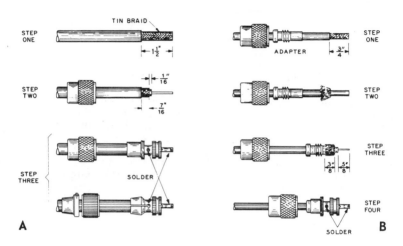

Fig. 9   Assembly technique for use with PL-259 series coaxial plugs (A).   Braid, inner insulation and inner conductor are trimmed to length before plug is soldered into position.   (B) PL-259 series plug and adapter permit use with small-diameter cable such as RG-58/U.

5/8-inch (15.9 mm) of the insulation from the center conductor. Don't nick the conductor. Finally, tin the conductor.

Now, carefully screw the plug body onto the adapter. The center conductor of the cable should pass easily through the center pin of the plug, and the strands of the braid should appear through the side holes of the shell.   Using a small soldering gun, solder the braid through the holes.   Lastly, solder the center conductor to the plug pin and slide the coupling ring down over the plug.

THE "N" FAMILY OF CONNECTORS

The N-type family of coaxial fittings is designed for use up to 450 MHz and the connectors are considered waterproof under normal conditions.   They have supplanted the old UHF-type connectors on all military and high grade commercial equipment. The N-type coaxial plug is designated UG-21/U.   A smaller family of similar connectors is the BNC group of fittings for small cable such as RG-58A/U and RG-59A/U.   These plugs feature a bayonet-type lock for quick disconnect and are also considered waterproof. A variety of connectors for each family exists and a summary of coaxial fittings is contained in the general catalog of connectors issued by Amphenol North America, 33 East Franklin Street, Danburry, CT 06810.

HOW TO ASSEMBLE THE N-TYPE PLUGS

The following assembly sequence is recommended for the N-type plugs:

The first step is to remove 9/16-inch (14.3 mm) of the outer vinyl jacket with a utility knife, as described earlier. The copper braid is then carefully combed out using a large pin or small pointed instrument and folded back upon the cable. Next, cut the inner dielectric with a sharp knife or razor blade, removing 7/32-inch (5.6 mm) of material. The center conductor is tinned (Figure 10).

Carefully smooth out the copper outer braid and taper it over the tinned conductor in such a manner that the nut, washer and gasket can be slipped over the vinyl jacket of the line. Pass the clamp over the braid with the internal shoulder of the clamp fitted flush against the end of the vinyl jacket. Smooth the copper braid back over the clamp and trim the ends flush with a small, sharp scissors. Solder the center contact to the center conductor with a small iron or gun. Avoid excess heat and solder. If necessary, trim away excess solder with a small file and clean the butt-end of the dielectric. Make sure the center contact is flush against the dielectric.

Finally, slide the plug body into place so that the center contact enters the hole in the center insulator. Slide completed assembly into the body by pushing the retaining nut. When the nut is in place, tighten with small wrenches. When completed, the center pin conductor can be felt by passing the ball of the thumb across the end of the plug.

AVOID CHEAP COAX CABLE!

A lot of cable is available for CB radio at cut-rate prices. Avoid this inexpensive cable as it is not suitable for amateur service. Off-brand types (such as "RG-8 type") are cheaply made, with a smaller center conductor and fewer wires in the outer braid. Such a cable exhibits higher losses and handles less power than the better made cables. It also makes plug assembly a more difficult job as the outer braided conductor is hard to tin because the inner insulation can be easily melted and "squirts" through the many interstices in the braid. In addition, the outer vinyl jacket is often made of inferior material that will craze or crack in hot weather.

The cost of good coaxial cable is but a small portion of the money spent in an amateur station and it is foolish to jeopardize station operation by saving a few cents on cheap coax line. Buy the best and you won't regret it!

N
ASSEMBLY INSTRUCTIONS

STANDARD CLAMP

| NUT | WASHER SPREAD | GASKET | CLAMP | FEMALE CONTACT | JACK BODY | MALE CONTACT | PLUG BODY |

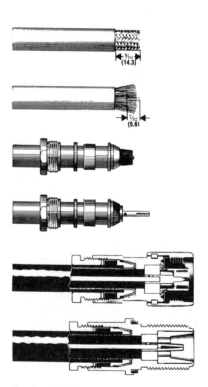

Remove ⁹⁄₁₆″(14.3mm) of vinyl jacket. When using double shielded cable, remove ⅝″(15.9mm).

Comb out copper braid as shown. Cut off dielectric ⁷⁄₃₂″(5.6) from end. Tin center conductor.

Taper braid as shown. Slide nut, washer and gasket over vinyl jacket. Slide clamp over braid with internal shoulder of clamp flush against end of vinyl jacket. When assembling connectors with gland, be sure knife edge is toward end of cable and groove in gasket is toward the gland.

Smooth braid back over clamp and trim. Soft solder contact to center conductor. Avoid use of excessive heat and solder. See that end of dielectric is clean. Contact must be flush against dielectric. Outside of contact must be free of solder.

Slide body into place carefully so that contact enters hole in insulator. Face of dielectric must be flush against insulator. Slide completed assembly into body by pushing nut. When nut is in place, tighten with wrenches. In connectors with gland, knife-edge should cut gasket in half by tightening sufficiently.

NOTE: For armored cable slide cap over armor first. Push armor and cap back out of way and proceed with assembly as directed above using armor clamp in place of standard clamp nut. When assembly is complete straighten bulge in armor and trim so it can be clamped between nut and cap.

Amphenol instructions for type-N waterproof coaxial plug. Shown here is the UG-21/U-type plug (Amphenol 82-96) used with RG-8/U family of cable. Matching cable jack is UG-238/U (82-63). The straight adapter between two plugs is UG-29B/U (82-101).

BNC ASSEMBLY INSTRUCTIONS

STANDARD CLAMP

NUT   WASHER   GASKET   CLAMP   BUSHING   FEMALE CONTACT   JACK BODY   MALE CONTACT   PLUG BODY

✦ THIS PART IS USED ONLY WITH RG-62, 71 OR 210 CABLE

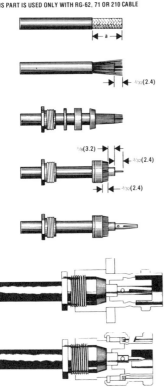

Cut jacket to correct dimension. Select part number or cable from table below:

Part number or RG-/U cable	Dimensions inches(mm)
P/N 31-1, -2, -18, -20 -23, 14525. RG-55, 71, 142	5/16(7.9)
P/N 31-12, -21, -11. RG-59, 62, 210	19/64(7.5)
RG-58, 140, 141	9/32(7.1)

Fray shield and strip inner dielectric 3/32″(2.4). Tin center conductor.

Taper braid and slide nut, washer, gasket and clamp over braid. Clamp is inserted so that its inner shoulder fits squarely against end of cable jacket.

With clamp in place, comb out braid, fold back smooth as shown and trim 3/32″(2.4) from end.

Slip contact in place, butt against dielectric and solder. Remove excess solder from outside of contact. Be sure cable dielectric is not heated excessively and swollen so as to prevent dielectric from entering into connector body.

Push assembly into body as far as it will go. Slide nut into body and screw in place with wrench until tight. For this operation, hold cable and shell rigid and rotate nut.

AMPHENOL assembly information for BNC-type fitting. This popular twist-on plug is used for RG-55/U, RG-58/U and RG-59/U cables. Amphenol plug number is 31-002 and matching receptacle is 31-201. (Drawing courtesy Amphenol.)

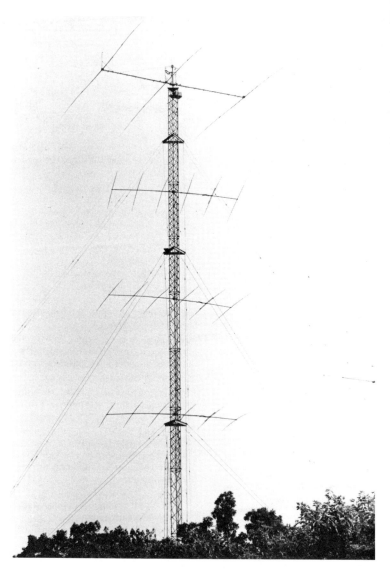

The imposing 20 meter stacked array of K2GL is topped by a three-element 80 meter beam. Four six-element beams are used on 14 MHz. Bottom beam is at tree-top level and cannot be seen in this view. Rugged, guyed tower has survived the East Coast's worst weather.

Chapter 7

Matching the Antenna to the Line

A transmission line terminated in other than its characteristic impedance transforms a value of impedance back to the input end of the line that is a function of the load mismatch and the length of the line. This transformer action is desirable in some matching devices, but is generally undesirable in transmission lines as it can cause loading problems and erratic operation of the transmitting equipment.

Since few beam antennas present a 50 ohm feedpoint impedance to the transmission line, some form of matching device is usually placed between the antenna and transmission line to reduce the SWR on the line to a reasonable value. Then, too, most beam antennas are symmetrical devices; that is, they present a two-terminal load at the feedpoint that is electrically balanced to ground. Even so, it is possible to connect an unbalanced, coaxial line to a balanced antenna element in the hf region and get away with it.

THE SPLIT DIPOLE

The cheapest way to feed a beam antenna is to split the driven element at the center and connect it directly to a coaxial line (Figure 1A). If the feedpoint resistance of the driven element is moderate (25 to 35 ohms is a common range) the SWR on the transmission line will be moderate (2-to-1 or less at antenna resonance).

The drawback to this inexpensive system is that nothing prevents rf line current from travelling down the outside of the outer shield of the line from the antenna back toward the transmitter. The result is that the coaxial line shield is not at

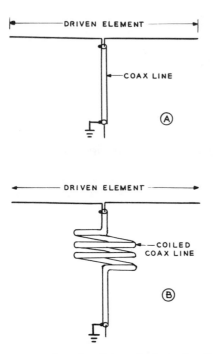

Fig.1 Shield of coaxial line may be grounded at transmitter end but upper end assumes potential of driven element feedpoint (A). Outer shield acts as an antenna, radiating a portion of the power that otherwise would go to the antenna. Line radiation can affect the gain and front-to-back ratio of a beam antenna. Unwanted effects can be minimized by coiling coaxial line into an rf choke (B). Choke coil is placed near the antenna feedpoint.

ground potential and that the line acts somewhat as an antenna, radiating a portion of the power that would otherwise go to the driven element. Line radiation can cause television interference, rob the beam of some of its signal gain, affect the radiation pattern of the array and invalidate SWR measurements.

These unwanted effects can be minimized by coiling the coaxial line up into a simple choke, or inductor, immediately below the antenna (Figure 1B). This prevents, or greatly reduces, current flowing on the outside of the line while not affecting the current flowing inside the line. Four or five turns of the line about a foot in diameter (30 cm), taped together, will do the job. If the transmitting equipment can accept a rather high value of SWR across an amateur band, or if a matching device is used at the transmitter, this is a simple way to feed a beam antenna. It may not be the best feed system, but it is quick and easy -- and it works!

THE SPLIT DIPOLE AND THE LINEAR BALUN

The balun is an electrical device that converts a balanced system to an unbalanced one, or vice versa. A balun is placed between a balanced antenna and an unbalanced line to effect the

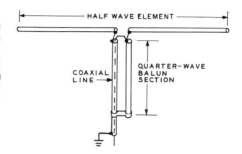

Fig.2 Quarter-wave balun reduces line radiation when coax feeds balanced element. Balun tube is shorted to coax shield at bottom end and connected to center conductor of line at the antenna end.

necessary conversion. Baluns take many forms, and one of the less-expensive ones is shown in Figure 2. This is a quarter-wavelength conductor placed adjacent and parallel to the feedline at the antenna end. For best balance a small air space is left between the two lines. The linear balun cancels the field of the currents that otherwise flow along the transmission line and provides a balanced feedpoint for the antenna system. Balun connections are shown in the drawing. No impedance matching takes place in this simple device.

THE BALUN TRANSFORMER

The linear balun is a narrow-band device useful only over a single amateur band. It is useless when a multi-band beam is employed. A broadband balun, such as shown in Figure 3, can

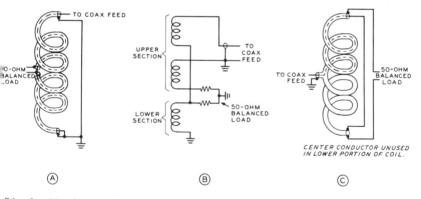

Fig.3 Simple one-to-one broadband balun is made up of coiled co-axial line (A). Equivalent transformer circuit of balun is shown at (B). Connections of balun can be reversed with balanced load attached to outer winding connections (C).

Fig.4 A ferrite core balun transformer
is used to convert a balanced feedpoint
to an unbalanced (coaxial) transmission
line. This inexpensive design consists
of three windings of No. 14 enameled
wire wound on 3-1/4" long ferrite core.
(See text for details) Balun should be
mounted at the antenna terminals in a
waterproof container.

be operated over several amateur bands and is easier to handle
than the linear device. This balun costs little as it is made of a
single length of coaxial cable. RG-8A/U cable is used for power
levels up to the maximum amateur limit and RG-58C/U cable for
input powers up to 250 watts PEP.

The designs shown cover the frequency range of 14
through 30 MHz and provide a 1-to-1 (unity) transformation
ratio. They provide good balance for an antenna feedpoint
resistance as low as about 20 ohms. Either design may be built
with 75 ohm cable, if desired, but the minimum antenna feedpoint
resistance required for good balance is higher than if the device
uses the 50 ohm coax.

The balun transformer is air wound, or wound on a length
of plastic tubing, the turns held in position by drilling small
holes in the tubing at the ends of the winding and lacing the
cable to the coil form. If the coaxial connections are protected
from moisture, the assembly is waterproof.

THE FERRITE CORE BALUN TRANSFORMER

Even smaller and lighter than the coax balun is the 1-to-1
ferrite core balun, shown in Figure 4. This device consists of a
three-wire transmission line wound on a ferrite rod, or toroid.
Operational bandwidth is very wide, typically ranging up to 3 to
30 MHz. Versions of this design are commercially available built
into a center insulator for a wire antenna, or in a waterproof
inclosure to be mounted on a beam antenna next to the split

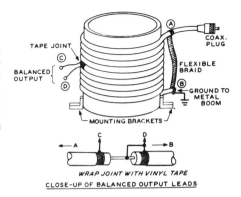

Fig.5 Simple coaxial balun can be made of coil of RG-213/U or RG-8A/U. Balun provides good balance over a 4-to-1 frequency range. Center joint (C-D) is wrapped with vinyl tape to prevent water from entering the line.

dipole. The ferrite core balun is power and SWR limited at the low frequency end of its operating range. Most amateur-style baluns of this type are rated for 1 kW PEP power input with an operating SWR of less than 2-to-1.

Since the balun is a transmission line wound up into a coil, it exhibits the impedance transforming characteristics of the line when it is terminated in a mismatched load. This means that the balun may increase the measured SWR on the transmission line over that value measured when the balun is removed from the antenna. This tends to make the whole antenna system more frequency-conscious than normal, with the SWR rising rapidly when the antenna is operated near the ends of the frequency range.

A bandwidth test can be run on a 1-to-1 balun by attaching it to a 50 ohm dummy load and observing the SWR at the input of the balun as power is fed to it across the desired operating range. A high SWR reading at any frequency in the operating range denotes poor balun performance. The balun works best when terminated in the proper load. However, many amateurs feed a Yagi antenna (typically, a feedpoint resistance of about 20 ohms) with a balun designed for 50 ohms with good results.

BUILDING BROADBAND BALUNS

TWO COAXIAL BALUNS

Described in this section are two simple and inexpensive baluns that match an unbalanced 50 ohm coaxial line to a balanced termination over the range of 7 to 30 MHz. The devices are small enough to be mounted directly on the boom of the antenna at the driven element.

A coaxial balun is illustrated in Figure 5 and consists of nine turns of RG-213/U coaxial cable, wound into a coil having an inside diameter of 6-3/4 inches (17 cm). The balun may be thought of as an autotransformer tuned to resonance near 14 MHz by the distributed capacitance of the cable in the top portion of the coil. The selectivity of the resonant circuit is quite high but when loaded with a low impedance balanced load the response is broadened out to encompass a passband of over 23 MHz. The unbalanced 50 ohm coaxial transmission line is coupled to the top half of the balun coil and the balanced antenna load is placed across the taps at the center of the coil. Each portion of the balun coil "feeds" one side of the balanced load and the bottom coil section is coupled to the top section with near-unity coupling. An equivalent circuit of this broadband balun is shown in Figure 3B.

Construction details of the cable assembly are shown in Figure 5. A length of 50 ohm coaxial cable 16 feet 6 inches (5.03 m) long is wound into a nine turn coil, leaving an inch or so at the ends for connections. Before winding the coil, mark the midpoint of the cable with a piece of tape. Manipulate and flex the coil so that the ends of the cable fall opposite the center mark. If necessary, trim 1 inch (2.54 cm) or so equally from the ends so that they fall within a half-inch of the correct points. Now, once the approximate configuration of the coil has been ascertained, unwind it and prepare the ends and center point for the terminations. The inner conductor is shorted to the outer shield at the ground end and a length of heavy wire connects this point to the outer shield of the coil at the input end of the balun.

The center termination is now prepared. Using a sharp knife, slit the outer dielectric of the cable for 1 inch (2.54 cm) each side of the center mark. Next, run the knife around the circumference at each end of the slit and remove a 2 inch (5 cm) length of the vinyl jacket, being careful not to damage the fragile copper wires of the outer braid. Cut the braid in two at the center mark, pushing the ends back to expose the center dielectric of the cable. A short slug of the dielectric is cut away to expose the center conductor of the cable and a length of heavy wire is soldered to the conductor. The outer braid of the lower portion of the balun cable is now slid back into place and soldered to the center conductor adjacent to the wire.

The last step is to trim back the outer braid of the upper section of the balun so it cannot short to the center conductor, and solder a length of wire to the braid. Use a hot iron and make the joints quickly so that the center dielectric of the cable is not overheated. When the joint is completed it should be wrapped securely with vinyl electrical tape to prevent moisture from entering. Finally, the coaxial cable is wound back on the form, the ground lead is cut short and soldered to the input shield and the whole assembly taped with vinyl tape at several points. The coil form may be an 8 inch (20 cm) length of Polyvinyl Chloride (PVC) or polypropylene material available from a plumbing supply house. Alternatively, the coil may be "air wound" and taped. Using this simple construction technique, several coaxial baluns have been built having an SWR of less than 1.1-to-1 over the range of 7 to 30 MHz when terminated with a noninductive 50 ohm load.

The balun can be taped or bolted to the boom of the beam antenna with the balanced termination wires directly feeding the center of the driven element, as discussed in the chapter covering multiband beam antennas. The balun may also be used with equal success to feed a single-band beam antenna having a split element. A similar balun for matching 75 ohm coaxial transmission line to a balanced load may be made up of RG-11A/U coaxial cable, following the dimensions and procedure outlined above. These baluns will handle a power level in excess of one kilowatt.

Various similar baluns may be made from other types of coaxial cable. Light duty baluns capable of power levels up to 250 watts are wound from lengths of RG-58A/U (50 ohm) or RG-59A/U (75 ohm) coaxial line. The coil size will have to be changed to compensate for the different outside diameter of the cable. The procedure is to adjust the length of cable and size of the coil to allow it to self-resonate at 14 MHz. The shorting connection, load and transmission line must all be removed when resonating the coil with a dip meter.

A modification of this balun is shown in Figure 3C where the unbalanced input is applied at the center of the coil and the balanced output appears across the ends of the coil. The inner conductor of one-half the coil is unused, the ends being trimmed back to prevent accidental shorts.

A second compact air-core balun that covers 14 to 30 MHz is shown in Figure 6. It is designed to be used with multiband beams to the kilowatt power level. The balun is wound on a section of plastic (PVC) water pipe with an outside diameter of 1.25 inches (3.2 cm) and a length of 4 inches (10.2 cm). The winding length of the coils is 3 inches (7.6 cm). The trifilar winding is composed of two coils wound with No. 10 enameled wire and one coil (labelled 2A-2B in the drawing) wound with No. 16 enameled wire. The windings are attached to 4-40 hardware as shown in the photograph. The trifilar winding is made up of 27 turns; that is, 9 turns composed of three wires each. The three wires are attached to the bolts at one end of the form and are wound on the form simultaneously. Keep the wires under tension so that the winding is tight. Make sure the

Fig. 6 Inexpensive air core balun covers 14 to 30 MHz. Power capability of balun is in excess of one kilowatt when operating into low value of SWR. Nine turn trifilar winding is composed of two windings of No. 10 and one winding of No. 16 enameled wire. Balun is wound on plastic form having an outside diameter of 1.25 inches (3.2 cm).

insulation is scraped off the ends of the wires before they are wrapped around the bolts. When finished, spray the winding with a quick, thin coat of plastic Krylon spray. The external jumpers which connect the ends of the center winding to the outside windings are now installed. This completes the balun except for a waterproof housing.

The common junction at terminal 3B is taken as the input ground point and is attached to the shield of the coaxial line. The center conductor of the line is attached to terminal 1B. Terminals 1A and 3A are attached to the feedpoint of the driven element of the Yagi antenna. Terminals 2A and 2B have no connections other than the jumpers. Winding technique for the balun is shown in Figure 7. The balun may be modified to cover the 7 to 25 MHz range by increasing the trifilar winding to twelve turns.

THE FERRITE CORE BALUN

A compact and easily built ferrite core balun is shown in Figure 4 . The core material is #61 (Q-1), having a permeability of 125. Core diameter is 0.5 inch (12.7 mm). Ferrite cores are manufactured by Indiana General Corp., in Keasby NJ, and by Ferroxcube Corp., Saugerties, NY, and others.

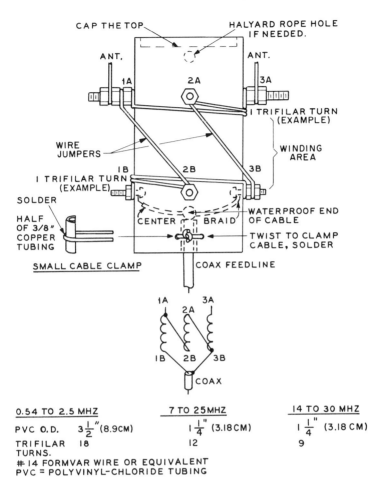

Fig.7 Air-core balun design which covers 0.54 to 2.5 MHz, 7 to 25 MHz and 14 to 30 MHz. Balun has trifilar winding of #14 insulated wire on PVC (plastic) form. Winding information is shown in lower drawing. The 7 to 25 MHz design can be modified to cover 80-40 meters by increasing winding to 18 trifilar turns. Balun should be enclosed in waterproof shroud to protect it from the weather and top end of coax line is sealed with waterproofing compound. Note that braid of coax attaches to terminal 3B.

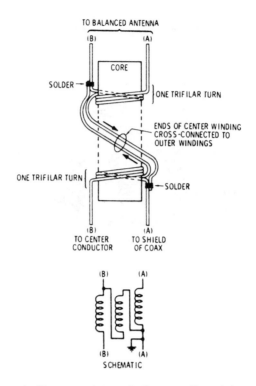

Fig.8 Trifilar winding consists of three coils with center winding cross-connected at the ends. Each winding consists of six turns of No.14 Formvar insulated wire. Coax shield connects at (A). Balun core is 3-1/4" (8.25 cm) long by 1/2" (1.27 cm) diameter.

The ferrite rod is nicked with a file around the circumference at the desired length and broken with a sharp blow of the hand. The windings are made of three lengths of No. 14 enamel copper wire, each piece about three feet long. Place one end of the wires in a vise and smooth out the sections until they lie parallel. Grasp the free ends in your hand and wind them side-by-side on the rod as if they were one wire. Wind the wires under tension and they will remain in position. When finished, straighten the leads away from the core. The balun requires that the center winding is cross-connected to the opposite ends of the two outer windings. Either end may be taken as input or output, but the common connection between the inner and outer winding at the end chosen as the input must be taken as a ground point and attached to the outer shield of the coaxial line.

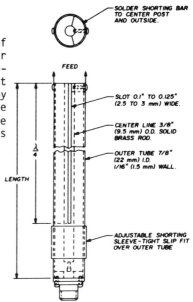

Fig. 9 Four-to-one balun for vhf range is made of brass tubing. Outer tube is slotted on two sides to provide balanced antenna feedpoint at the top. Balun length is varied by an adjustable shorting sleeve. The inner conductor is shorted to the outer tube at the top by a brass block (top drawing).

When the windings are completed, a drop or two of coil dope, <u>Krylon</u> or nail polish is placed on the winding ends to anchor them in position. Do not coat the windings themselves as this tends to upset the balance of the transformer. The balun should be placed in a weatherproof container, such as a plastic bottle, to protect it from the ravages of wind, rain and sunlight.

IMPEDANCE MATCHING DEVICES

Rare indeed is the antenna that provides a direct match to a 50 ohm coaxial transmission line. The use of a balun provides a balance between the antenna and the line, but most simple baluns do not provide an impedance transformation. Four-to-one ratio baluns are available but there are very few antennas that have a feedpoint impedance of either 200 ohms or 12.5 ohms. What is required, then, is an impedance matching device that provides a transition between the feedpoint resistance of the antenna and the characteristic impedance of the transmission line. Various matching devices that do the job are described in the next sections of this chapter.

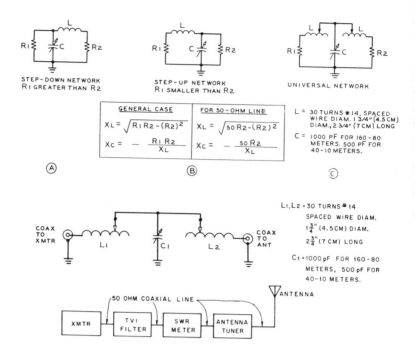

Fig. 10 The L-network can be used to provide a step-up or step-down transformation (A,B). Two networks back-to-back provide a convenient method of reducing the SWR on a transmission line (C). A practical universal network is seen below, made up of two rotary inductors and a variable capacitor. The universal network is placed after the SWR meter and before the coaxial line to the antenna. Such a device is commonly termed an "antenna tuner", although it does not "tune" the antenna. Assembly should be placed within a shielded enclosure.

AN L-SECTION MATCHING NETWORK

The electrical characteristics of a matching device can be combined in a circuit in the form of an inductor and capacitor combination that forms a simple <u>L-network</u> (Figure 10). Such a unit is compact and when built in a waterproof container can be conveniently mounted at the antenna terminals. Various impedance transformations can be achieved, and the unit arranged either single-ended (for an unbalanced system with coaxial feed) or balanced (for two-wire transmission line). The

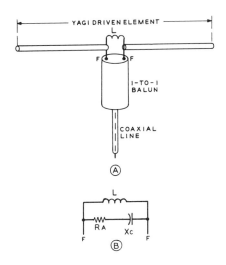

Fig. 11 Split driven element of a Yagi beam can be adjusted to form a portion of an L-network (A). Inductance across feedpoint completes the network (B). Feedpoint impedance is made capacitive by slightly shortening the element past its normal resonant length. The network L/C ratio determines the transformation ratio when the feedpoint resistance of the antenna is known.

L-network, however, does not provide balance between coaxial line and a balanced antenna termination. Even so, this device is the basis for some of the more flexible networks described in the next sections of this chapter.

THE INDUCTOMATCH

The split driven element of a beam antenna can be adjusted to form a portion of an L-network whose input impedance over a small frequency range is close to 50 or 75 ohms. A network of this type is shown in Figure 11. The feedpoint resistance of most parasitic arrays falls in the 10 to 40 ohm range and it is possible for the driven element to be made a part of an equivalent parallel resonant circuit in which the feedpoint resistance appears in series with the reactive branch of the circuit. The input impedance of such a circuit varies nearly inversely with respect to the radiation resistance of the antenna, thus the low feedpoint resistance of the parasitic beam antenna is transformed

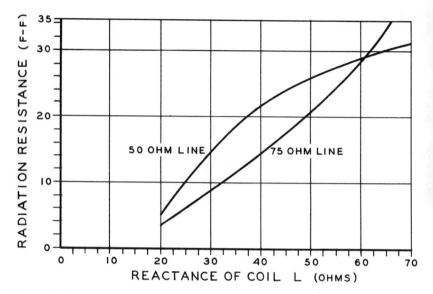

Fig. 12 When the feedpoint resistance of the driven element is known, the reactance of the shunt coil can be determined from this graph. For example, if the feedpoint resistance is 20 ohms and it is desired to feed the antenna with a 50 ohm line, the coil reactance (L) is about 37 ohms. A coil reactance of 49 ohms is required for a 75 ohm line.

to a larger value which matches the impedance of the chosen transmission line.

The feedpoint resistance of a parasitic beam can be made to appear as a capacitive reactance at the terminals of the antenna element by slightly shortening the element past its normal resonant length. The inductive portion of the tuned network consists of a small coil or "hairpin" placed across the driven element terminals as shown in Figure 11 B, and the transmission line or balun is connected across the terminals of the inductor. The L/C ratio determines the transformation ratio of the network when the LC product is parallel-resonant at the design frequency of the antenna.

In order to make convenient use of the inductomatch the feedpoint resistance of the antenna should be known, otherwise it may be necessary to try various combinations of parallel inductance and driven element length before a satisfactory value of resonant frequency SWR on the feedline is obtained. Methods of determining the feedpoint resistance of the antenna are discussed in later chapters of this handbook.

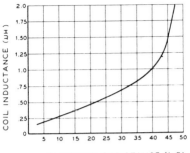

14 MHz

RADIATION RESISTANCE (A-B)
OF DRIVEN ELEMENT

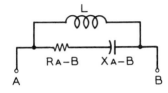

General Case
For R = 22 Ohms

f (MHz)	L (uH)
3.80	1.87
7.15	0.99
10.12	0.70
14.17	0.50
18.11	0.39
21.22	0.34
24.94	0.29
28.60	0.25
50.10	0.14

For other values
of R, multiply L
by ratio R'/R,
where R' is the
desired new value

Fig. 13 Feedpoint (radiation) resistance of driven element determines value of coil inductance (L) from top graph. Chart at left shows inductance value for amateur bands for the general case when feedpoint resistance is approximately 22 ohms. The inductance value and element length can be varied for good match.

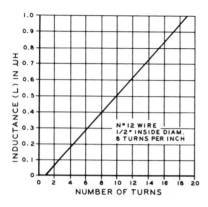

Fig. 14 The inductance of a coil made of No. 12 wire, 1/2-inch (1.25 cm) inside diameter, wound 8 turns per inch (2.54 cm).

USING THE INDUCTOMATCH

Once the feedpoint resistance of the driven element is determined, the correct value of parallel inductance required to match the element to the transmission line or balun is found from the graphs of Figures 12 and 13. The size of inductor (or hairpin) required to give various values of inductance is shown in Figures 14 and 15. The driven element of the beam is split and insulated from the boom and the inductor placed across the center terminals of the element. The feed system is also connected at this point.

The next step is to place the beam antenna in the final position atop the mast (or upon a tall ladder to clear it of nearby metallic objects and the ground) and to insert a SWR meter in the transmission line to the array. The overall length of the driven element is now varied a bit at a time, making sure that the two halves of the element are kept equal in length. Adjust-

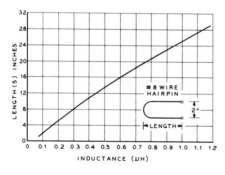

Fig. 15 The inductance of a "hairpin" made of No. 8 wire, spaced 2 inches (5 cm) between the legs.

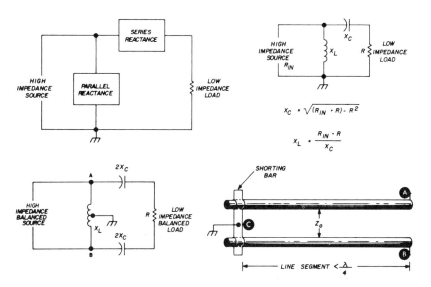

Fig. 16 General case for L-network matching a low impedance load is shown at upper left with circuit elements and formulas given at upper right. The network is converted to a balanced state as shown at lower left, with ground placed at center point of the inductor. Series capacitors in each leg having twice the reactance replace the single capacitor in the unbalanced network. A practical balun is shown at lower right.

ments are carried out to lower the SWR on the transmission line to a value near unity at the design frequency of the antenna. When the SWR has reached a reasonably low value, the beam should be placed in its final operating position (if not already there) and the spacing between turns of the coil or length of the hairpin inductor adjusted slightly to drop the SWR to near-unity at the design frequency of the array.

THE ADJUSTABLE BETA MATCH

This single-band linear balun provides an adjustable impedance match plus an accurate transformation from an unbalanced to a balanced mode for antenna feedpoint resistance values ranging from 10 to 50 ohms. Basic operation follows that outlined for the inductomatch described earlier. The linear balun is the parallel reactance portion of a balanced L-network (Figure 16) and the series reactance is attained by shortening the driven element beyond the point of self-resonance.

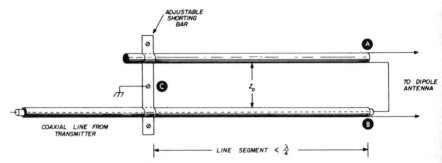

Fig.17   Broadband matching balun is constructed by passing a co-axial line down one leg. Points A and B are balanced to ground. The inner conductor of the line is cross-connected to opposite balun leg. The impedance transformation is adjusted by varying length of balun and driven element of array.

The L-network is converted to a balun as shown in Figure 17. Points A and B of the balun are balanced to ground and present the correct impedance transformation to match the shortened dipole. The unbalanced coaxial line is brought into the balun through one of the balun tubes, with the center conductor of the coax line crossing over at the antenna end of the balun to contact the opposite balun tube. By adjusting the shorting bar on the balun and the length of the driven element of the beam this device provides excellent balance and transformer action. Balance is achieved by permitting the outer shield of the coax line to assume the potential of the balun tube as it passes from the grounded end (C) to the terminal end (B). Cross-connecting the center conductor to the opposite balun leg insures the desired 180 degree phase reversal is maintained.

Once the transformation ratio and the values of series and parallel reactance have been determined, the balun is designed from transmission line formulas. A shorted, two conductor transmission line exhibits inductive reactance at the terminals if it is less than a quarter wavelength long and this makes it possible to substitute the line for the inductor in the L-network. The relationship between the balun constants and the dipole is given in Figures 18 and 19. A plot of the ratio XL/Z_o in terms of line length for 20 meters is provided in Figure 20.

A PRACTICAL BETA MATCH BALUN FOR 20 METERS

A balun built along these principles is shown in Figures 21 and 22. The balun tubes are made of 3/8-inch (0.95 cm) diame-

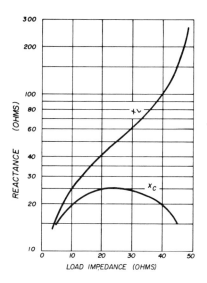

Fig. 18 Inductive (XL) and capacitive (XC) values for antenna load impedance when a 50 ohm transmission line is used. For example, if the feedpoint resistance is 25 ohms, the inductive shunt element (XL) is 50 ohms. The chart may be used with the network of fig. 16.

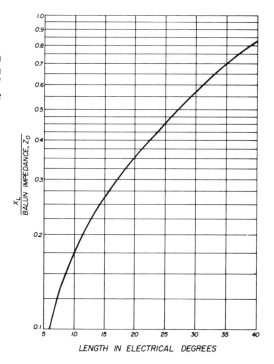

Fig. 19 Balun length in electrical degrees as a function of the ratio of load impedance to the balun impedance (XL/Zo).

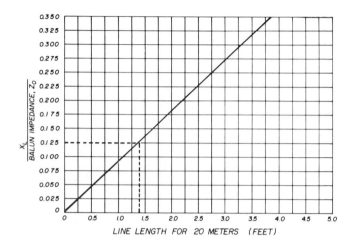

Fig. 20 Balun conversion chart for 20 meters. Balun length in feet may be determined if feedpoint resistance of driven element is known. The ratio of these two items is found on the y-axis, and the balun length is read on the x-axis. The chart may be used for other bands (multiply length by 2 for 40 meters, divide by 1.5 for 15 meters, divide by 2 for 10 meters, etc.)

ter copper tubing. The feedline, RG-8A/U cable, will just pass through the tubing when the braid and vinyl jacket are removed from the line. Using a center-to-center spacing of 3 inches (7.6 cm), the balun tubes form a balanced line having a characteristic impedance of about 325 ohms.

Assume the transmission line impedance is 50 ohms and the antenna feedpoint resistance at resonance is 20 ohms. Using Figure 18, the value of Xc is determined to be -24.5 ohms and the value of X_L is 41.5 ohms. Turning to Figure 19, the ratio of X_L to balun impedance is 41.5/325 = 0.127, as read on the Y-axis. The balun line length, as read on the X-axis, is about 7.5 electrical degrees. To get the answer directly in feet, Figure 20 is used for the 20 meter band. In this example, for a ratio of 0.127 (read on the y-axis), the balun length is about 1.4 feet, or 16 inches (40.6 cm).

The series reactance, Xc, is -24.5 ohms. This reactance takes the form of a shorter-than-resonance driven element. The amount of shortening required is a function of the length-to-diameter ratio of the element and the feedpoint resistance at resonance. It may be computed but it is easier to determine experimentally. For a three element 20 meter beam, shortening

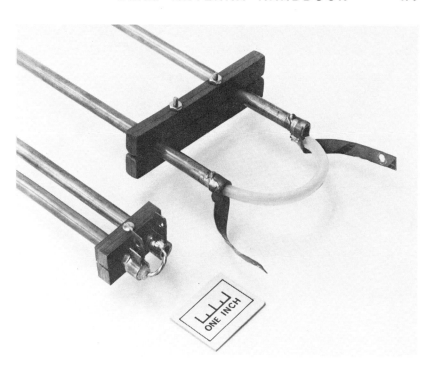

Fig. 21   Vhf (left) and hf (right) balun construction. Balun tubes are held in position by phenolic blocks.   Inner conductor of coax line crosses over and is soldered to opposite tube at open end. Short copper straps provide easy connection to driven element.

the driven element about 3 to 6 inches each side (7 to 15 cm) is nearly correct.

The beta match is preset and attached to the beam with the balun elements running parallel to the boom at a distance of about 6 inches (15 cm).   Balun length and driven element length are then adjusted to drop the measured SWR to a 1-to-1 ratio near the center of the band.   Setting the balun length to the dimension given in Figure 20 for a given value of feedpoint resistance and preshortening the element a few inches will insure that the starting point is not too far out of line.

A VHF BALUN

A vhf balun of this type can be made.   It is the same length as the hf version but has a center-to-center spacing of only 1.25 inches (3.17 cm).   The extra balun length is helpful

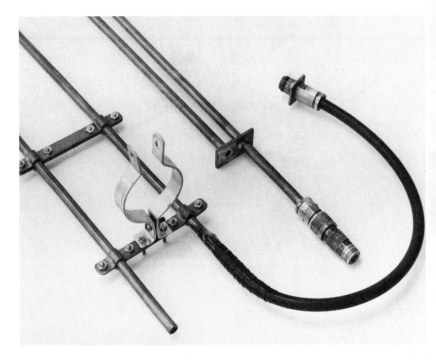

Fig. 22 Adjustable shorting bar is shown on hf balun. Vhf balun has similar bar (not visible). Coax line passes out of hf balun whereas vhf balun has coaxial fitting soldered to the tube. Coax braid is soldered to end of tube with inner conductor passing through the tube.

during adjustments as it permits the operator to remove himself from the immediate field of the antenna. Once the proper adjustments are determined, an electrical half-wavelength is cut from the balun to make it more compatible with the size of the antenna.

THE SHUNT FED DELTA MATCH

A simple matching system, popular with vhf antennas fed with a balun or balanced line, is the delta match (Figure 23). The two wire transmission line is fanned out to tap the driven element at impedance points which provide a good match to the system. Because of the size, the delta match is not commonly used on hf antennas but it provides a simple, low-loss system for antennas above 50 MHz. The tap points and length of the delta wires are adjusted for minimum SWR on the transmission line.

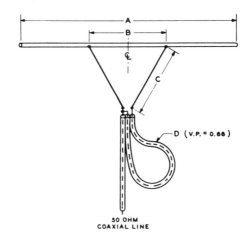

BAND	A		B		C		D	
MHZ	IN	CM	IN	CM	IN	CM	IN	CM
50	111.0	281.9	22.0	55.9	15.0	38.1	79.0	200.7
144	38.0	96.5	6.5	16.5	4.0	10.2	27.0	68.6
220	25.4	64.6	4.2	10.7	2.7	6.9	18.0	45.7
432	12.9	32.8	3.0	7.6	1.5	3.8	9.1	23.1

Fig. 23 Delta match dimensions for the vhf bands. The delta is adjusted to provide a 200 ohm termination for use with a 50 ohm coaxial line and a four-to-one coaxial balun. Delta spacing (B) is adjusted for lowest SWR on the transmission line.

THE GAMMA MATCH

A simplified version of the delta match system can be used with benefit in both the hf and vhf regions (Figure 24). The gamma match couples a coaxial line directly to either a balanced or unbalanced driven element. The gamma match consists of a small diameter rod or wire placed parallel to the driven element and connected to it at one end with a shorting bar. A series-

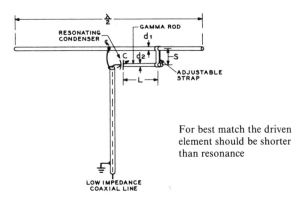

For best match the driven
element should be shorter
than resonance

Fig.24 Gamma match is used to match an unbalanced coaxial line to
a balanced dipole element. The device consists of a short gamma
rod parallel to the element and a series-resonating capacitor. In
general, the diameter of the gamma rod should be small compared to
the diameter of the element. Length of the gamma rod, spacing of
the rod and diameter ratios of rod and element determine the
transformation ratio. The two parameters to be adjusted are the
transformation ratio and the cancellation of the gamma rod inductance. In general d2 is about one-quarter d1, S varies from 3
inches at 50 MHz to 10 inches at 7 MHz. Capacitor C is approximately six times the operating wavelength in meters. Length L is
about 0.04 to 0.05 wavelength. For example, a 20 meter gamma
system will have a capacitance of about 120 pF, a rod length of
approximately 45 inches and spacing S is six inches.

connected variable capacitor and the length of the rod are
adjusted to provide a good match to the transmission line at the
design frequency of the antenna. The outer shield of the
transmission line must be grounded to the center point of the
driven element.

ADJUSTING THE GAMMA MATCH SYSTEM

The variables in the gamma match system are series capacitance, rod length, and rod spacing from the driven element.
These elements are interrelated and the adjustment tend to be
interlocking. The dimensions given in this handbook provide a
starting point which eliminates much of the "cut-and-try" process. In general, rod length runs from 0.04 to 0.05 wavelength, rod diameter about one-quarter to one-half that of the
driven element, and center-to-center spacing between rod and
driven element about 0.007 wavelength. The capacitance value is
approximately 7 pF per meter of wavelength.

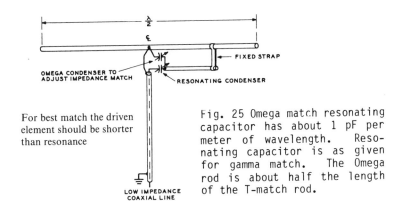

For best match the driven element should be shorter than resonance

Fig. 25 Omega match resonating capacitor has about 1 pF per meter of wavelength. Resonating capacitor is as given for gamma match. The Omega rod is about half the length of the T-match rod.

Adjustment of the gamma system is done with the aid of an SWR meter in the transmission line to the array. The series capacitor is adjusted for minimum measured SWR at the resonant frequency of the antenna. If the minimum value is too high, the position of the shorting bar is varied and the measurement repeated. If the SWR still cannot be reduced to an acceptable value, the spacing between the gamma rod and the driven element should be increased.

THE OMEGA MATCH

The omega match (Figure 25) is a refined version of the gamma match. In this device, the matching rod is made shorter than the normal gamma rod. The impedance ratio adjustment, instead of being made by changing the length of the rod, is made by varying the capacity to ground (the center of the element) at the terminating end of the rod. This is a point of high impedance in the circuit and a small variable capacitor connected between the rod and ground permits an impedance variation at the input terminal of the omega match of about two-to-one. On a large array, an adjustment of this type is more easily made than one that entails moving the shorting bar at the far end of the matching rod.

THE COAXIAL GAMMA MATCH

A coaxial version of the gamma match includes the gamma resonating capacitor in a portion of the gamma rod. The rod is constructed of concentric sections of aluminum tubing as shown in Figure 26. A length of polystyrene tubing ·is used as the dielectric of the coaxial rod-capacitor. With the dimensions shown in the illustration, the capacitor has a value of approxi-

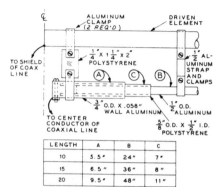

Fig. 26 Construction of a coaxial gamma match. The dielectric material is polystyrene.

LENGTH	A	B	C
10	5.5"	24"	7"
15	6.5"	36"	8"
20	9.5"	48"	11"

For best match the driven element should be shorter than resonance

mately 15 pF per inch engaged. The capacitance is adjusted by loosening the inner clamp and varying the position of the outer aluminum tube. The gamma rod setting is determined by the placement of the outer clamp. When the gamma system has been properly adjusted the tubes are waterproofed at the ends by wrapping the joints with vinyl electrical tape or covering with heat-shrink tubing.

THE TRI-GAMMA MATCH

Three gamma matching devices may be connected in parallel to feed a tri-band beam as shown in Figure 27. Adjustment of each gamma is virtually independent of the other two and the whole configuration is conveniently fed with a single coaxial transmission line. The 20 meter gamma is adjusted for lowest transmission line SWR, then the 15 meter gamma adjustment follows. Ten meter adjustment is done last. The tri-gamma

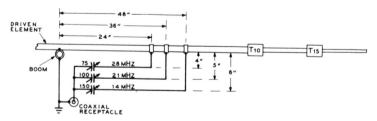

NOTE: MAKE GAMMAS OF #8 ALUMINUM WIRE.

Fig. 27 Three gamma match systems connected in parallel can be used to feed a triband Yagi element. Two gamma matches may be used for dual-band-beam. Capacitors should be protected against the weather.

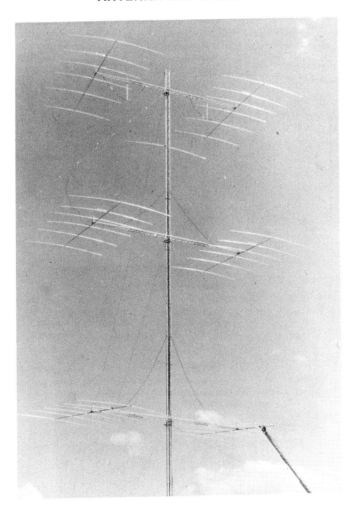

Moveable crane helps Simo Lehto, OH8OS, assemble his giant 36-element rotary array for 20 meters. Installation consists of 6-element Yagis, placed two over two on rotating tower. DX Amateurs can attest to the powerful signal produced by this giant antenna located in northern Finland.

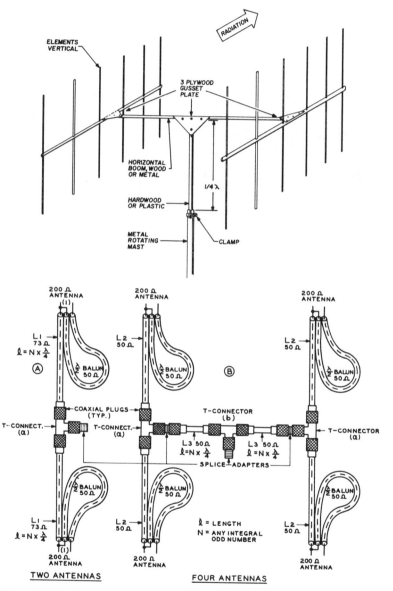

Fig. 29 (Top) Assembly of vhf Yagis to be fed in phase with a matching harness. Folded dipole or delta match system provides 200 ohm feedpoint at each antenna. Harnesses for two and four antennas are shown below.

device is fed with a single coaxial line of 50 to 75 ohms impedance. As with any multiband matching system, care must be
taken with the tri-gamma match to suppress transmitter harmonics since the antenna system will radiate harmonics of the lower
frequency bands with ease.

HARNESS FEED FOR AN ARRAY OF BEAMS

Two or more beam antennas may be combined, or stacked,
to provide an array having high power gain and narrow beam
width. This is commonly done with small vhf beams, but more
and more stacked arrays are showing up on the high frequency
bands (Figure 28). Stacking antennas to obtain additional power
gain or directivity requires that each antenna in the array be
fed an equal amount of power in the proper phase. In most
cases a coaxial feedline "harness" interconnects the individual
antennas. The harness provides a symmetrical feed system
which matches the arrays to a single feed line. There are many
ways to accomplish this, and the system described is only one of
them. However, it is a simple arrangement and works well
without critical adjustments.

As shown in Figure 29, each driven element is equipped
with a matching device that provides a 50 ohm feedpoint. The
feedpoint value is stepped up to 112 ohms by virtue of a 75
ohm, quarter-wavelength coaxial transformer. At the junction,
the two 112 ohm terminals are placed in parallel to provide a
nominal impedance of about 56 ohms; a good match for the 50
ohm transmission line. Adjustments to the system are made by
monitoring the SWR in the main transmission line. For hf antennas, the stacking distance is usually equal to the boom length of
a single array, provided the minimum stacking distance is at
least one-half wavelength.

MATCHING THE COAXIAL LINE TO THE TRANSMITTER

Yagi antennas are single frequency devices that have been
adapted for operation over the relatively narrow amateur bands.
They are usually matched to the transmission line by a frequency-
sensitive network, examples of which have been shown earlier in
this chapter.

At antenna resonance, the Yagi can be adjusted to provide
a good match to the line, but as the frequency of operation is
removed from the design frequency the antenna and matching
device together present an increasingly poor match to the transmission line. The result is increased SWR on the line caused by
the off-frequency operation of the antenna and the matching
device. This is a natural process and happens to any sharply
tuned antenna system.

At any frequency removed from the design frequency the SWR on the transmission line remains constant along the line but the impedance presented to the transmitter at the end of the line varies with the line length. Amateurs have found that by trimming the length of their transmission line it may be possible to achieve an acceptable transmitter match, regardless of the actual SWR value on the line.

In the case of the Yagi beam, the rate of rise of SWR as the antenna is operated off-resonance is determined by the frequency selectivity of the antenna. If the selectivity is high, the SWR will rise rapidly off resonance; if the selectivity is low, the rise in SWR will be small.

Antenna selectivity is determined principally by the length of the director elements and the spacing of the first director from the driven element. By making the director slightly shorter than normal, the operational bandwidth determined by the maximum value of SWR will increase. That is to say, there will be a greater spread between the higher and lower frequencies at which the SWR approaches the limit set by the transmitting equipment. Making this change will not appreciably affect either antenna gain or front-to-back ratio.

In most high frequency designs shown in this handbook, decreasing director length by about two percent will increase the bandwidth at the 2-to-1 SWR level by about 15 percent.

Most tube-type transmitting equipments are quite forgiving as far as reactive antenna loading is concerned, some units being able to accept an SWR on the line as high as 4-to-1. Other equipments, particularly those with a broadband, solid state output stage, are quite sensitive with regard to the SWR on the line, regardless of line length. Many such transmitters incorporate a fail-safe circuit that decreases transmitter power as the SWR value of the antenna load rises. This means that as operation removed from the design frequency of the antenna takes place, the transmitter output drops as the SWR value rises.

It is easy to remedy this vexing problem by placing a simple matching network between the transmission line and the transmitter. Such a device is called a transmatch. This unit permits the transmitter to work into a low value of SWR regardless of the actual SWR on the transmission line. In this way full transmitter output power is achieved regardless of the SWR created by operation of the antenna away from its design frequency. In addition to the transformation properties of the transmatch, when properly adjusted it can provide attenuation of transmitter harmonics which is beneficial with regard to TVI problems.

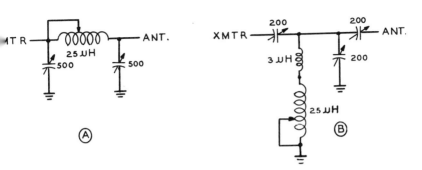

Fig. 30 Two versions of the transmatch. Design (A) is a pi-network made up of a variable inductor and two capacitors. Version (B) has more components but provides better harmonic suppression. Series-connected capacitors must be insulated from ground.

TRANSMATCH CIRCUITRY

The transmatch can take a number of forms (Figure 30). One of the simplest is the pi-network. In practice, the two capacitors are variable and the inductor is either a roller coil or a tapped inductance.

A second version of the transmatch, designed by Doug DeMaw, W1FB, provides improved harmonic reduction and ease of adjustment. Either of the circuits shown, together with an SWR meter placed between the network and the transmitter, can provide an excellent match to the transmitter even with SWR values on the transmission line as high as 5-to-1.

SUMMARY

Various matching systems are available that can reconcile the relatively low feedpoint resistance of a Yagi beam antenna with the standardized 50 or 75 ohm output termination requirement of modern transmitting equipment. In most instances the matching system is placed directly at the antenna.

Yagi beam antennas normally present a balanced-to-ground, two terminal feedpoint to be matched to an unbalanced line. Operational problems caused by connecting the coaxial line directly to such a mismatch can be alleviated by winding the line into a choke coil below the antenna, or by the use of a balance-to-unbalance (balun) device. In addition, in many cases the balun device can also provide impedance transformation so that the antenna presents a good match to the transmission system at its design frequency. When operated off the design freequency, most beam antennas present a reactive load to the feedline, thus increasing the SWR on the line.

The mechanical requirements of the matching system are as important as the electrical. The device must be rugged enough to withstand the weather and be waterproof so that moisture and rust cannot damage the device or the coaxial line attached to it, or destroy their electrical effectiveness.

Since both the antenna and its matching circuit are frequency sensitive it may be necessary to place an additional matching circuit such as a transmatch at the station end of the line, especially if the transmitting equipment has a solid state output stage.

Chapter 8

How to Build and Install Beam Antennas

The strongest, lightest and easiest Yagi beam to build and install is the all-metal design. This employs a metal boom with the antenna elements fastened directly to the boom without the use of insulating clamps. This assembly is possible because no rf potential exists between the center of a half-wave element and the boom, since both are considered to be at ground potential. The all-metal array constructed of the proper materials is remarkably sturdy and weather resistant. In contrast, the insulating materials often used in composite structures (wood, lucite, sheet plastic, ceramics, etc.) may be damaged by heavy wind stresses on the array, or deteriorate due to ultraviolet radiation from the sun which breaks down many insulators.

CHOICE OF MATERIALS

The first choices of material for boom and elements are aluminum and steel. Elements and supporting boom are generally made of aluminum and clamps, brackets and accessories are made of steel--preferably stainless steel.

Beam antenna elements are easily constructed from aluminum tubing of the proper alloy. A summary of the various tubing alloys is given in Figure 1. The higher strength alloys are a mixture of aluminum and copper, or aluminum and zinc and the softer ones are almost pure aluminum. From an electrical standpoint, all of the alloys are satisfactory for antenna elements. From a mechanical standpoint, only the high strength alloys should be used in a beam antenna. It is interesting to note that the deflection of tubing under load is independent of the alloy. Equal length tubes of soft or hard aluminum alloy will deflect the same amount, emphasizing that element sag is a function of tubing diameter and wall thickness rather than of tubing strength.

DESIGNATION	USE	STRENGTH	CORROSION RESISTANCE
7075	Aircraft	Best	Least
2024	Aircraft	--	--
6061	Commercial	--	--
6063	Architectural	--	--
5052	Gas lines	--	--
2014	Irrigation	--	--
3003	Electrical EMT	--	--
1100	--	Least	Best

Fig. 1 Aluminum tubing alloys. Commercial alloy 6061 or aircraft alloy 2024 are the best to employ for beam antenna construction.

The resistance of aluminum tubing to corrosion is an inverse relationship to the strength of the material, as the softer alloys are less susceptible to corrosion than the harder alloys. In general, the commercial alloy 6061 is the best to employ for beam antenna elements. It is strong, relatively inexpensive and readily obtainable. The alloy 2024 may be obtainable as surplus material and is also acceptable for antenna elements. The difference in strength between the two alloys is minor. Sources of aluminum tubing are often listed in the Yellow Pages of the telephone director in large metropolitan areas.

ALUMINUM ELEMENTS

The elements of vhf antennas are commonly made of small diameter aluminum tubing. The whole element is a single section of tubing and no splice or joint is required. The elements for arrays lower in frequency than 50 MHz, on the other hand, must be made of several sections of tubing, since commercial tubing is only available in twelve foot (3.65 m) lengths. Telescoping lengths of tubing are therefore used to make up a full-size hf element. For the 14 through 29.7 MHz range, the element is usually composed of a center section and two outer tips. Longer, lower frequency elements are made up of multiple sections of tubing.

For ease of shipment, many Yagi antenna kits supply elements made up of six or more short sections of tubing. In some cases the sections are swaged at one end so that element diameter is reduced rather quickly near the end sections. If the proper selection of tubing diameters and wall thicknesses is

ELEMENT CONSTRUCTION

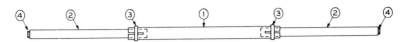

1 – USE 1" X 0.035" WALL FOR CENTER SECTION

2 – USE 7/8" X 0.035" WALL FOR END SECTIONS

3 – LOCK JOINTS WITH TUBING CLAMP OR RADIATOR HOSE CLAMP

4 – TIPS PLUGGED WITH CORK OR WOOD BLOCKS

5 – COAT ELEMENT WITH ALUMINUM PAINT

ig. 2 Constriction details for telescoping antenna elements. hinner wall tubing may be used for end sections to decrease eight. Wall thickness determines degree of sag of the element.

hosen, the element sections can telescope easily into each other or quick assembly. Representative elements are shown in Figure 2.

ELEMENT ASSEMBLY

Shown in Table 1 is a list of standard sizes of aluminum tubing available from most large metal suppliers and distributors n the United States and Canada. All tubing comes in twelve foot (3.65 m) lengths and various wall thicknesses. Any diameter tubing will telescope into the next larger size if the larger size has a .058" (1.47 mm) wall thickness. The inner section (to save weight) can have a wall thickness of .049" (1.2 mm) or .035" (0.9 mm) with some sacrifice in rigidity.

In order to fix telescoping tubes in position, a narrow slot about a foot long is cut in the end of the outer tube with a hacksaw. The slot should go through both walls, on a line with the center axis of the tube. All burrs must be carefully removed from both inside and outside walls of the tube. The tube tips are then sanded and cleaned to lessen the possibility of seizure after the tubes are telescoped. The slot should be wide enough so that when pressure is put upon the walls of the outer tubing, the inner tube will be held firmly in place.

Before the tubes are telescoped, a precaution must be taken to eliminate corrosion and oxidation at the tubing joint. Only a small amount of corrosion between the tubes will hamper disassembly at a later date. A special anti-oxidizing compound composed of grease and minute zinc particles is employed as a joint

ANTENNA CONSTRUCTION

TABLE 1 - ALUMINUM TUBING - STANDARD SIZES

Recommended for antenna construction

Outer Diam.		Wall	Inner Diam	
inch	decimal	inch	inch	lb/ft
3	(3.000)	0.125	2.700	1.33
2-1/2	(2.500)	0.125	2.250	1.10
2-1/2	(2.500)	0.083	2.334	0.74
2-1/2	(2.500)	0.083	2.084	0.66
2-1/2	(2.500)	0.065	2.120	0.52
2	(2.000)	0.083	1.834	0.59
2	(2.000)	0.065	1.870	0.45
1-7/8	(1.875)	0.058 *	1.759	0.39
1-3/4	(1.750)	0.083	1.584	0.51
1-3/4	(1.750)	0.058 *	1.634	0.36
1-5/8	(1.625)	0.058 *	1.509	0.34
1-5/8	(1.625)	0.035	1.555	0.21
1-1/2	(1.500)	0.083	1.334	0.43
1-1/2	(1.500)	0.065	1.370	0.34
1-1/2	(1.500)	0.058 *	1.384	0.31
1-1/2	(1.500)	0.049	1.402	0.26
1-1/2	(1.500)	0.035	1.430	0.18
1-3/8	(1.375)	0.058 *	1.259	0.28
1-3/8	(1.375)	0.035	1.305	0.17
1-1/4	(1.250)	0.058 *	1.134	0.26
1-1/4	(1.250)	0.049	1.152	0.21
1-1/8	(1.125)	0.058 *	1.009	0.23
1-1/8	(1.125)	0.035	1.055	0.14
1	(1.000)	0.058 *	0.884	0.20
1	(1.000)	0.049	0.902	0.17
1	(1.000)	0.035	0.930	0.12
7/8	(0.875)	0.058 *	0.759	0.18
7/8	(0.875)	0.049	0.777	0.15
3/4	(0.750)	0.058 *	0.634	0.15
3/4	(0.750)	0.049	0.652	0.13
5/8	(0.625)	0.058 *	0.509	0.12
5/8	(0.625)	0.049	0.527	0.11
1/2	(0.500)	0.058 *	0.384	0.10
1/2	(0.500)	0.035	0.430	0.06
7/16	(0.438)	0.035	0.367	0.05
3/8	(0.375)	0.058 *	0.259	0.07
5/16	(0.313)	0.058 *	0.196	0.06
1/4	(0.250)	0.058 *	0.134	0.04

* telescopes into next larger size having 0.058 wall.

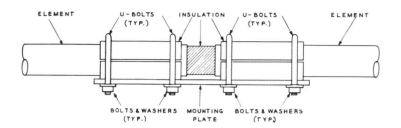

=ig. 3 Split driven element is attached to a mounting plate by
J-bolts insulated with lengths of plastic electrical pipe. The
ɔipe is slit and placed around the element as shown above.

lubricant. This compound is commonly used in industrial power
installations having aluminum wires or conduit and can be bought
at a large, commercial electrical supply house. Some of the
trade names for this compound are "Penetrox", "Cual-aid", and
"Ox-guard". The compound is smeared lightly over the mating
sections of tubing, and when the tubes are telescoped this
compound forms an air-tight seal, preventing corrosion. The
compound is a good electrical conductor and insures a trouble-
free joint.

Once the element has been assembled and adjusted to
length, the joint is locked in position. Stainless steel hose
clamps are recommended for this job as they will not distort the
tubing, nor will they work loose. Clamps that press a screw
into the element are not recommended, nor are sheet metal
screws, as these are hard to remove and distort the tubes so
that separation at a future date is difficult. If the element tip
sections are made of a tubing size too small to form a telescopic
fit with the next larger section, the joint may be shimmed with
thin strips of aluminum or aluminum foil. All shim stock should
be given a coating of anti-oxidant grease to prevent corrosion.

Element length tolerance in an hf Yagi should be held to ±
0.003 wavelength, or less. This corresponds to a measurement
accuracy of ± 2.5" (6.35 cm) at 7 MHz, ± 1.25" (3.18 cm) at 14
MHz, ± 0.62" (1.57 cm) at 28 MHz and ± 0.25" (0.63 cm) at 50
MHz.

THE SPLIT DRIVEN ELEMENT

Some feed systems require a split driven element. If this
is the case, the two element halves are driven onto a round
center insulator made of red structural fiberglass, linen bakelite

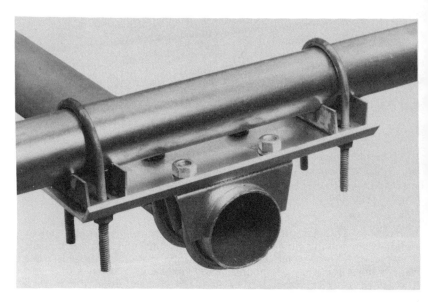

Fig. 4 Representative element-to-boom assembly. Plated muffler clamps can be used to attach mounting plate to the boom and TV assembly clamps hold the elements to the mounting plate. Assembly is given coat of aluminum paint to protect it from the weather.

or PVC. The center insulator can be turned on a lathe until it forms a tight slip-fit into the sections of tubing. If a Micarta rod can be obtained, it is the best material to use. The element sections are permanently fastened to the center insulator by epoxy cement or can be slotted and held in position with hose clamps.

The split driven element can be attached to a mounting plate in the manner shown in Figure 3. Lengths of PVC electrical pipe are slit and placed around the element, insulating it from the U-bolts. This provides good insulation while permitting a rigid mount to the plate. The use of ceramic standoff insulators is not recommended as they may fracture under wind stress.

THE ELEMENT-TO-BOOM CLAMP

The hardware required to attach the antenna elements to the boom is often a vexing problem. In all cases (except for the split driven element) insulators are not required. The simplest solution is often the best. The element is fastened to the mounting plate by means of U-bolts and the plate is attached to

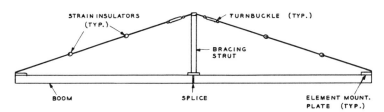

Fig. 5 Long boom for multielement Yagi array is built up from sections of tubing spliced together and supported by a top bracing strut. The guy wires are broken with strain insulators to prevent unwanted boom resonance. Turnbuckles keep boom under slight upwards tension.

the boom by a second set of U-bolts (Figure 4). Replacement muffler clamps make good mounting hardware, provided they are given a heavy coat of anti-rust paint before they are used. These clamps mount the element to any flat surface not more than 1/4-inch (6.35 mm) thick. A good anti-rust paint is Zinc Chromate which may be obtained in an aerosol dispenser at large hardware stores. The element mounting plate can be cut from a scrap of 1/4-inch aluminum or steel. A sheet metal shop can do the job. Have the long edges "rolled up" for 1/2-inch (12.7 mm) to add strength to the plate.

PREVENT CORROSION!

Many plates, clamps and other antenna accessories are available at auto supply and tv stores. Often hardware items may be purchased directly from antenna manufacturers. In any event, thought should be given to the mechanical design of your beam so that it may be easily assembled and disassembled.

Rust and corrosion are the enemies of the beam antenna. All nuts, bolts, washers and screws used in the assembly should be stainless steel, if possible. If not available, a substitute is cadmium plated hardware. The latter, however, will rust after a few years in the air. Do not use "stove bolts" or any bolts lacking a corrosion-proof finish. Use hexagonal-headed bolts and elastic stop nuts instead of screw-head bolts and washers. Standard A-N type bolts have matched heads and stop nuts, permitting the use of two similar end wrenches for quick assembly. The slot-headed screws are not recommended since it is easy for a screwdriver to slip out of the bolt head, possibly inflicting a bad wound on the unlucky assembler. The standard 1/4-28 A-N hardware is recommended for antenna construction.

METHODS FOR JOINING MAST AND SUPPORT SECTIONS

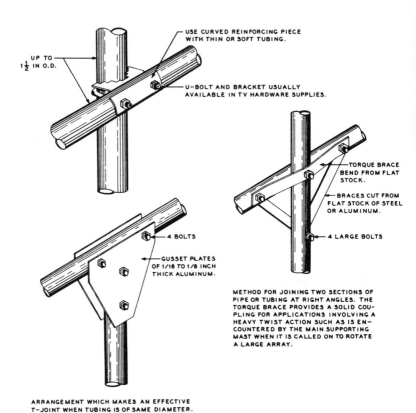

USE CURVED REINFORCING PIECE
WITH THIN OR SOFT TUBING.

UP TO
1½ IN O.D.

U–BOLT AND BRACKET USUALLY
AVAILABLE IN TV HARDWARE SUPPLIES.

TORQUE BRACE
BEND FROM FLAT
STOCK.

BRACES CUT FROM
FLAT STOCK OF STEEL
OR ALUMINUM.

4 BOLTS

4 LARGE BOLTS

GUSSET PLATES
OF 1/16 TO 1/8 INCH
THICK ALUMINUM.

METHOD FOR JOINING TWO SECTIONS OF
PIPE OR TUBING AT RIGHT ANGLES. THE
TORQUE BRACE PROVIDES A SOLID COU-
PLING FOR APPLICATIONS INVOLVING A
HEAVY TWIST ACTION SUCH AS IS EN-
COUNTERED BY THE MAIN SUPPORTING
MAST WHEN IT IS CALLED ON TO ROTATE
A LARGE ARRAY.

ARRANGEMENT WHICH MAKES AN EFFECTIVE
T–JOINT WHEN TUBING IS OF SAME DIAMETER.

Fig. 6 Representative methods of mounting vhf antenna boom to the
mast. Lower left arrangement is recommended for large arrays as
one boom-retaining bolt may be removed and the array tipped into a
vertical position for assembly or adjustment.

THE BOOM

Aluminum tubing normally comes in 12 foot (3.65 m) sections, but lengths up to 20 feet (6 m) can often be obtained as
irrigation pipe from some farm supply distributors. Long booms
for multielement hf Yagi arrays are usually built up from short
sections of tubing, spliced together and supported by a top
bracing strut, mounted on the mast above the boom (Figure 5).

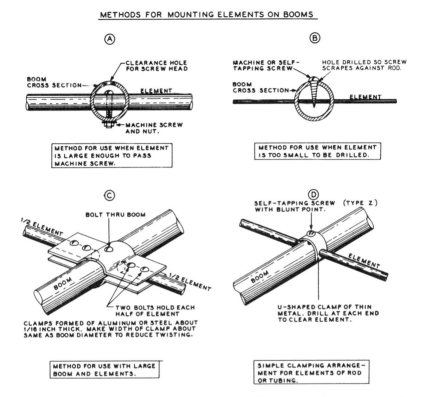

Fig.7   Element to boom mounts. Large diameter elements may be mounted as shown in (A) and (C). Small diameter elements can be passed through hcles in the boom and affixed with self-tapping screw (B) and (D). Some manufactured arrays mount elements above the boom by means of a special clamp. Thru-boom mounting requires change in electrical length of element.

Wire guys are run from the bracing strut to each end of the boom. Each wire is broken up at one or two points with strain insulators and has a turnbuckle as shown in the illustration. The turnbuckles place the boom under a slight tension which helps to keep it from weaving about in a heavy wind. Boom sections can be joined by slipping adjacent sections onto a short length of tubing which provides a close fit to the inside or outside wall diameter of the boom sections. The sections are firmly bolted to the splicing section by means of heavy, stainless steel hardware.

VHF ANTENNAS

Much of the assembly information given for hf antennas applies equally well to vhf antennas, but because of their smaller size certain different techniques are used for antennas operating in this portion of the radio spectrum.

The mark of any good beam antenna is that it will stay up, even in wind and storm. The secret of success is the construction technique used. The mechanical assembly of multielement arrays where dimensional precision is important calls for rugged components that are corrosion-proof and do not change position in the wind. Figure 6 shows three methods of joining the antenna boom to the support structure. The double gusset plates are recommended for a large array or a windy location.

The vhf antenna elements are made of smaller diameter material than the boom and present a problem in mounting. Figure 7 shows four methods of mounting elements to a metal boom. In addition to these methods, the element may be mounted above the boom on an insulating block. In the illustration, methods B and D are especially useful for mounting "thin" parasitic elements to a "fat" boom. By making use of the assemblies shown, vhf arrays of any practical size may be built with the assurance that they will not collapse in a heavy wind or crumple under the weight of ice and snow.

THE VHF STACKING FRAMEWORK

It is important that a suitably rugged framework be constructed to support an array of antennas and the interconnecting cables. Figure 8 shows a framework that will support four long Yagi antennas. The graph of Figure 9 shows the required stacking distance between the antennas which determines the dimensions, tubing diameters, etc. of the framework.

Very often in the design and construction of a large metal framework, too little consideration is given to the lateral force which a heavy wind exerts on the structure. This force is a function of the frontal area facing the wind, and its distance from the supporting mast. The downward pull of gravity is a relatively small force compared to that of a strong wind, so the lateral bracing of the framework deserves at least as much attention as the vertical bracing. A good rule of thumb to follow is to design the outer members of the assembly with adequate strength, and then increase the size of successive members as the design progresses inward toward the main supporting mast. Needless to say, the main mast should be the largest and strongest member of the configuration.

STACKING FRAMEWORK

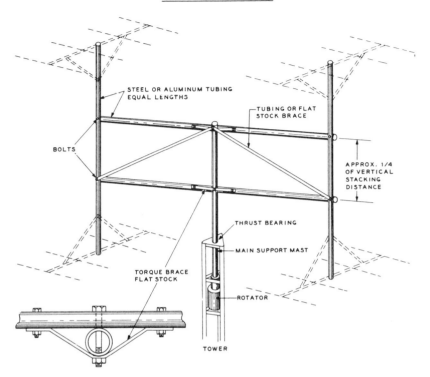

RECOMMENDED TUBING DIAMETER WALL THICKNESS .065" (0.17 CM)			
TUBING LENGTH	VERTICAL MEMBERS	HORIZONTAL MEMBERS	MAIN MAST
6 FT. (1.83 M)	0.75" (1.9 CM)	1.00" (2.54 CM)	1.25" (3.18 CM)
10 FT. (3.05 M)	1.00" (2.54 CM)	1.25" (3.18 CM)	1.50" (3.81 CM)
16 FT. (4.88 M)	1.50" (3.81 CM)	2.00" (5.08 CM)	2.50" (6.35 CM)
20 FT. (6.10 M)	2.00" (5.08 CM)	2.50" (6.35 CM)	3.00" (7.62 CM)

Fig.8 Vhf stacking framework for four long Yagis. Cross bracing is very important to counteract wind forces. Lateral stresses on the framework are a function of frontal area facing wind and distance of antennas from the support mast. Stacking distance must be carefully chosen to maximize antenna gain and front-to-back ratio.

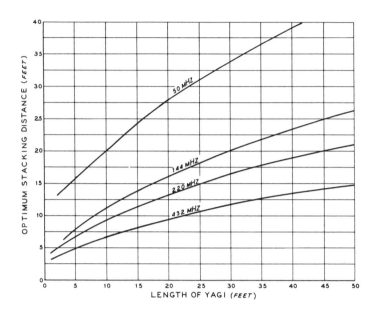

Fig.9 Stacking distance between Yagis is a function of frequency and aperture. As antenna gain and size increase, stacking distance increases. Vertical stacking, boom-to-boom, is represented here. Distance must be adjusted experimentally to decrease side lobes.

THE ELECTRICAL EFFECT OF MOUNTING HARDWARE

In the hf range the electrical effect of mounting the elements to a metal boom may be safely ignored because the size of the mounting hardware is only a small fraction of the operating wavelength of the antenna. In the vhf region, however, the method of mounting the elements to the boom may alter the electrical characteristics of the array.

One simple mounting method is to pass the element directly through the boom. The boom acts as a shorted turn at the point of maximum current in the element, and experiments have shown that the element length should be increased by about 0.7 times the diameter (or width) of the boom when a round or square boom is used. An alternative clamping system is to bolt the element to a flat, rectangular metal plate which, in turn, is bolted to the boom. U-bolts are generally used in this assembly. When the element, plate and boom are in direct contact, the element length should be increased by about 0.08 times the plate length. If there is a slight separation between the element and the plate, such as caused by using a saddle or cradle on the U-bolt, this correction need not apply as the detuning effect is extremely small. If the element is supported above the boom by a mounting block, no correction in element length is required.

VHF DIMENSION TOLERANCES

As the frequency of operation increases, the element lengths of a Yagi beam become more critical. A change in length of a 40 meter Yagi element of two inches, for example, will not affect antenna operation. A change in length of a 432 MHz Yagi element of 1/4-inch may cause serious deterioration of antenna performance. Experience has proven that an element tolerance of 0.003 wavelength, or less, in length should be maintained in the vhf region. This tolerance calls for a measurement accuracy of ± 1/8 inch (3.18 mm) for the 144 MHz band, ± 0.08" (2 mm) for the 220 MHz band, ± 0.04" (1.08 mm) for the 420 MHz band, and ± 0.02" (0.4 mm) for the 900 MHz region. To maintain these tolerances, it is best to set up a jig to cut the elements slightly long and then square off the tips accurately to the desired length with a file.

Antenna range tests show that gain and pattern width degrade quite rapidly on the high frequency side of the design frequency, but much more slowly on the low side. Therefore, if the element is rounded off to a standard dimension, it is better to cut the director elements slightly shorter--not longer. Reflector length, on the other hand, should be rounded off on the long side. Finally, it should be remembered that the feed system can affect the driven element length of a vhf Yagi. It is usually necessary to increase driven element length slightly to compensate for the reactive effect of the feed system. The length of the driven element is not a critical factor in antenna performance as long as the driven element is always physically shorter than the reflector.

ELEMENT VIBRATION

Under certain antenna headings and with particular wind velocities, the beam elements can start a sympathetic vibration that will shake the array and the tower. Rotating the beam a few degrees will usually stop the vibration. A sure cure is to place a length of light rope or clothesline inside the element, running from tip to tip. The rope can be epoxied to the element ends or clamped in some manner so that it does not slide out of the element. Very large arrays can pass into a slow vibration under certain wind conditions and it may be necessary to add additional boom-to-element stays, or additional stays from the ends of the boom to the center support mast, to stop this an-

noyance. Vibration is difficult to predict in advance, but placement of ropes in the elements is recommended in any case since
it is easy to do and eliminates the need for taking the array
down after the first windstorm to install the vibration damp-
eners.

BUILD OR BUY YOUR BEAM ANTENNA?

A quick look through the pages of any amateur radio magazine reveals numerous antennas of all types for sale as kits. An
inquiry into the price of aluminum tubing at a metal supply
house shows that when bought in small quantities, the cost of
aluminum tubing is nearly equal to the cost of a pre-cut beam
kit. Gone are the days when surplus aluminum tubing could be
obtained at the junkyard for a few cents a foot. Thus, it is
economical to buy a good beam kit and assemble it, saving the
time and effort required to collect odd lengths of tubing to make
your own Yagi. Regardless of the make of the kit, the dimensions should be checked against those given in this handbook.

Many amateurs have designed and built exotic and complex
Yagi arrays and enjoyed their labors. In fact, antenna design
and construction is one of the last fields left to the average
amateur who is not blessed with an advanced degree in electronics. If you have the desire, time and mechanical know-how to
build your own beam, go to it! You'll have a lot of fun. Join
the legion of amateurs who have built their own "sky hook."

ANTENNA ROTATORS

Antenna wind loading is an important factor in the choice of
an antenna rotator. Most amateurs underestimate the force of
the wind and the damage it can do to an antenna installation and
the rotor mechanism. Wind loading is a function of the area of
the antenna exposed to the wind and the larger the antenna, the
greater the wind loading. Light duty tv rotators may be used
for small vhf antennas, or possibly a 6 or 10 meter three element
beam in areas of the country having light wind conditions.
However, most of these devices lack braking capability and a
high wind will turn the antenna and the rotor motor via the gear
train. In a heavy storm, when the antenna whips back and
forth, the rotator may be permanently damaged by the wind
forces. A more expensive rotator includes a brake which locks
the antenna in position when power is not applied to the motor.
The less-costly units have a simple disc brake which may slip.
The large rotators will handle a triband beam or a large monoban-
der, up through the 20 meter band, under strong wind conditions.

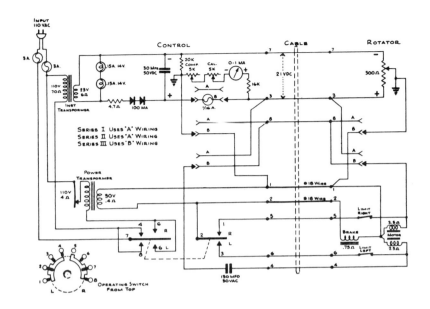

Fig.10 Schematic of representative rotor. Control box is at left, connected to rotor via an eight-wire cable. Terminals 1 & 2 carry the heavy motor current. Direction is sensed by 360° potentiometer in the rotor unit. Variable resistors in control unit allow meter calibration.

Special heavy-duty rotators are available for large beams, or where stacked beams are used. These units are recommended for general amateur use since they pay for themselves over the years in reliable service. Some of the more expensive designs have a computer controlled system which automatically select-and-return to a heading, or search an arc of the horizon for weak signals. The schematic of a typical heavy duty rotator is shown in Figure 10.

Wherever possible the rotator should be mounted inside the tower and a few feet below the top. The mast section from the rotator to the beam absorbs much of the torsion shock developed by high winds and will help to reduce the lateral forces on the rotator casting. All the rotator does, then, is support the weight of the antenna and turn it. Mechanical joints between the antenna mast and the rotator should be pinned with a heavy machine screw and nut to prevent the antenna from twisting

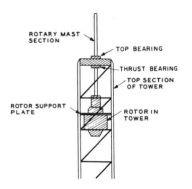

Fig.11 The weight of a large array mast can damage a rotor unless a thrust bearing is used to take the weight, leaving the rotor only the task of turning the antenna.

about in a heavy wind. Slippage between the antenna and the directional indicating system in the rotator can cause a large error to be built up over the months as the wind buffets the antenna.

A THRUST BEARING FOR HEAVY ARRAYS

The weight of a large array and mast can run well over 100 pounds (45 kg). Excessive downward thrust on the rotor can damage the gearing system or cause the rotor to stall when lateral wind loads add to the strain on the mechanism. If the rotor is placed 5 feet (1.5 m) or more below the top plate within the tower, a thrust bearing can then be placed at the top of the tower to take the weight of the array, leaving the rotor only the task of turning the antenna (Figure 11).

CABLES TO THE ROTATOR AND ANTENNA

The rotator control cable and coaxial cable to the antenna should be supported and not allowed to droop of their own weight over long distances. In most cases, the installer tapes the cables to a tower leg using a wrapping of vinyl tape or steel plumber's tape. Abrupt turns and curves in the cables should be avoided. Coaxial cable, in particular, should not be bent on a radius of less than one foot.

In the case of the crank-up tower, the cables cannot be lashed to a tower leg, as the legs telescope inside each other as the tower is lowered. Some amateurs tie cables off at the top of the antenna and then again at the bottom. Others install horizontal metal loops at the top of each tower section through which the cables may slip as the tower descends.

Chapter 9

Antenna Test Instruments

The operator who wants top-notch performance from his beam antenna requires a few simple instruments to determine the operating parameters of his array. An important measurement is the standing wave ratio (SWR) on the transmission line, as this figure is an overall indication of the operation of the complete installation. The SWR is measured by comparing the ratio of direct to reflected power in the transmission line by means of an SWR meter (sometimes called a directional coupler).

The SWR may also be determined indirectly by measuring the feedpoint resistance of the antenna and comparing it with the characteristic impedance of the feedline. This measurement is made with a modified form of the SWR meter called the antennascope. Both instruments require an external source of rf energy to operate. The power source may be the station exciter or a dip oscillator depending upon the sensitivity of the instruments. The source should be free of harmonic content, and tunable across the operating range of the antenna under test.

A third useful item is the rf noise bridge which combines a wideband rf noise generator and a bridge circuit. Bridge balance provides an accurate reading of the feedpoint resistance of the antenna.

THE SWR METER

What does the SWR meter measure? And what does the measurement signify? To understand SWR it is helpful to compare a radio wave traveling through space with a water wave made by throwing a stone into a quiet pond. The waves travel outward from the stone in expanding, concentric circles until

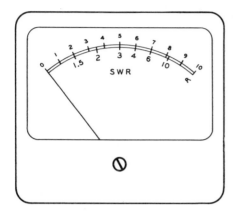

Fig.1 Typical SWR meter face. The top scale is for reference and the lower one is calibrated in SWR. Lowest SWR is at left of scale. The SWR meter monitors forward and reverse waves and indicates ratio of the energy in the waves. Zero reading indicates no wave reflection.

they meet an obstacle, at which point they are reflected back towards the source. The forward traveling waves (incident waves) and the reflected waves interact with each other and form interesting patterns of interference on the surface of the water.

If, instead of a stone, you have a motor driven device that agitates the water to make a continuing series of waves, you will find that by speeding up or slowing down the motor, the incident waves and reflected waves reinforce each other, creating a new set of waves that seemingly remain motionless while the incident and reflected waves are moving back and forth. This wave phenomenon is called a stationary wave or standing wave. An electric wave of this type can be set up in an antenna system if the antenna presents a mismatch that creates reflected waves traveling back down the feedline toward the transmitter.

The presence of standing waves in an antenna system was known as far back as the first radio experiments of Heinrich Hertz, who measured them by means of reflections from large metal sheets. But it was not until the general use of radar in World War II that a simple, accurate and reliable instrument was developed that would accurately and quickly measure standing waves in a transmission line.

SWR METER OPERATION

The SWR meter monitors the voltages in the incident and reflected waves and provides a reading which expresses the ratio of energy in the two waves. The SWR is read directly from a meter scale with unity (zero) reading indicating no wave reflec-

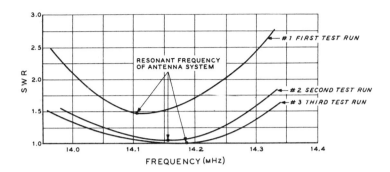

Fig.2 The SWR plot of a typical antenna. Graph is made by taking SWR measurements at various frequencies across the band. The first test run indicates that antenna system resonance seems to be near 14.11 MHz with a minimum SWR indication of about 1.5-to-1. The slope of the SWR curve is even and rises smoothly from the lowest point to higher readings at the band edges.

Adjustments are made to the antenna matching system at the design point of 14.17 MHz and a second test run is made. The SWR curve has dropped to a low value of about 1.1-to-1 at 14.16 MHz and rises smoothly to about 1.5-to-1 at the band edges.

In attempt to achieve a "perfect" SWR at the design frequency, the matching system is adjusted once more, with the results shown in the third curve. The SWR is dropped to near-zero at 14.18 MHz and reduced below 1.3-to-1 at the low frequency end of the band. Judging from the results, the third antenna adjustment was not necessary. Time should not be wasted trying to achieve the absolute minimum value of SWR.

Note that accurate SWR readings are achieved only when a good SWR meter is used, and only under the proper test conditions, as explained in this chapter.

*   *   *

tion and infinity (full scale) reading indicating a state of maximum wave reflection (Figure 1). With a perfect antenna match, the reflected wave on the transmission line is zero and the SWR is termed to be one or one-to-one. As the match between the antenna and the line becomes worse, the reflected wave increases in amplitude and the SWR reading increases, indicating the degree of mismatch between the antenna and the line.

The advantage of the SWR meter is that it may be left in the line as adjustments are made to the antenna to reduce the indicated value of SWR. Generally speaking, the reverse SWR reading should be brought to as low a value as possible. If the reverse reading is unusually high, it indicates there is a bad degree of mismatch between the antenna and the transmission line. No adjustment at the station end of the line can help this problem, and trimming the transmission line length won't help either, contrary to popular belief.

The problem is further complicated by the fact that there are some cheap and inaccurate SWR meters on the market. Some time ago, the authors of this handbook had the opportunity to connect three SWR meters in series in one transmission line and compare the readings of the three instruments. Needless to say, none of the readings agreed, and the variation between readings changed with the power level of the transmitter! This is confusing, but in the long run the absolute value of SWR is not too important. Some amateurs make a fetish of low SWR readings, and even an inexpensive SWR meter can get an antenna system "in the ballpark" if the operator knows what he is doing.

WHAT THE SWR METER TELLS YOU

Since the impedance of most popular coaxial lines used in the United States is 50 ohms, most amateur antennas are designed with a feedpoint resistance close to 50 ohms at the design frequency.

The SWR plot of a typical amateur antenna is shown in Figure 2. This may be a Yagi beam, a Quad, or just a dipole, since most antennas show a similar SWR curve. At the design frequency of the antenna the SWR is the lowest, while above and below the design frequency the SWR curve rises to a much higher level. The shape and slope of the curve change from antenna to antenna, but this drawing shows a representative case. The design frequency is at, or near, the center of the amateur band. If the lowest SWR is near one end, or even outside the end of the band, it signifies that adjustments must be made to the antenna to get the design frequency back to where it should be.

Amateurs often adjust their antennas so that the lowest SWR point occurs near their favorite operating frequency, allowing the SWR to rise to a higher level at the ends of the band. In either case, the goal is to reduce the SWR at the design point to a reasonable value. The lower the value at this point, the lower will be the SWR curve across the entire band. A reasonable level of SWR at the design point is below 1.5-to-1. If the SWR can be decreased to near unity, so much the better, but time should not be wasted trying to achieve the absolute minimum

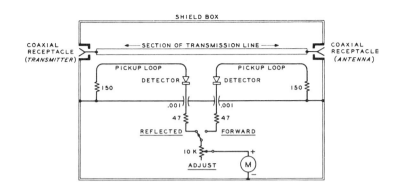

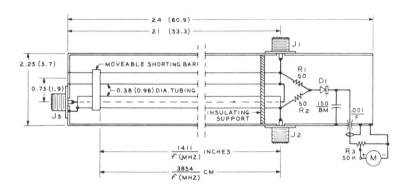

Fig.3 (Top) Representative SWR meter is made of two directional couplers reverse-connected in the line. Each coupler senses energy flowing in one direction and rejects energy flowing in the reverse direction. A single indicating meter is switched between the couplers. A scale of the meter may be calibrated in terms of the standing wave ratio.

(Bottom) VHF SWR coupler for 130 to 1300 MHz is made up of a tuned quarter-wavelength line in shielded box. Line serves as a balun for energy introduced through J3. If resistors R1 and R2 are equal and nonreactive, and the loads connected to J1 and J2 are equal, the bridge is balanced and no current flows in the diode circuit. To use the bridge a standard VHF dummy load resistor is connected to J1 or J2 and the antenna under test connected to the other receptacle. D1: 1N914. M: 0-100 uA. R1,R2: 50 ohm, 1% carbon resistors, TI-MC-65D or equivalent.

value of SWR. At the edge of the band, a 2.5-to-1 value of SWR is within reason and some antennas do better than this.

INSIDE THE SWR METER

The SWR meter, or directional coupler, provides erroneous readings if it is not used properly and the limitations of this device should be understood if meaningful results are to be obtained. The directional coupler is a device which samples energy flowing in one direction in a transmission line but is insensitive to energy flowing in the reverse direction. Most modern SWR meters are made up of two directional couplers and a detector built into one case and reverse-connected in the line. A single meter is switched between the couplers and the detector meter is calibrated directly in terms of SWR (Figure 3).

The electrical balance of a coupler is such that energy induced from the reverse-traveling wave is rejected, resulting in a directivity factor in the coupler. The device is sensitive to only one of the traveling waves which produces standing waves by interference and reflection. In order to obtain accurate readings, both couplers must be identical, and each coupler should be insensitive to energy passing through it in the unwanted direction. This is a big order! If the coupler is sensitive to the unwanted energy, the accuracy of the coupler is seriously affected.

WHAT DETERMINES A GOOD COUPLER?

A good laboratory-type directional coupler has a directivity of better than 25 dB, indicating that the coupler provides about 17 times the sensitivity to the desired energy than to the energy flowing in the opposite direction. SWR meters made up of two such couplers provide an indicated value of SWR differing from the true value as shown in Figure 4. As an example, a true SWR value of 1.5-to-1 on a transmission line can provide an indicated value on the SWR meter which can vary between 1.23-to-1 and 1.8-to-1 if the coupler has 25 dB discrimination. And most inexpensive imported SWR meters are not this accurate. More on this interesting subject later in the chapter. Added to the directivity limitation, most inexpensive SWR meters have additional built-in error because of the nonlinearity of the diode used to provide voltage for the indicating meter. At low power levels where the SWR reading is of the greatest importance, diode linearity is poorest. Finally, all SWR meters are sensitive to second harmonic voltage that may exist in the output of the transmitter. Since the antenna is probably mismatched at the harmonic frequency, it is possible for high SWR to exist at the harmonic. Pickup of this current will adversely affect the reverse reading of the SWR meter. Unfortunately, the unwanted

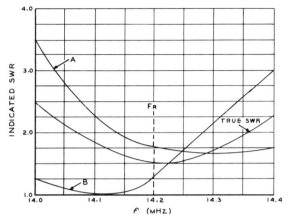

Fig.4 Three SWR curves run by three different SWR meters on the same antenna illustrate the importance of good directivity in the instrument. The true SWR is shown, along with curves run by inferior instruments (A and B). Instrument A provides a curve that is accurate enough to make preliminary adjustments to the antenna but instrument B is so inaccurate that it would be impossible to make meaningful antenna adjustments with it.

transmitter harmonic, small as it may be, may approach in magnitude the amplitude of the reflected fundamental wave when the SWR on the transmission line is low.

For best results, then, the highest quality SWR meter should be used. Some directional couplers made in the United States have plug-in detector heads which can be changed for various power levels and various frequency ranges, and reversed for SWR readings. An instrument of this type is recommended for accurate antenna measurements.

PITFALLS IN MAKING SWR MEASUREMENTS

The best SWR meter in the world can produce erroneous readings if it is not used properly. It is up to the user to make sure the meter reads what he is looking for and not a jumble of misinformation resulting from unwanted coupling between the transmission line and the antenna.

The outer shield of a coaxial line can be inductively coupled to the field of the antenna if it runs parallel, or nearly so, to the antenna elements and is elevated above ground level, as shown in Figure 5. Antenna currents induced on the outer shield of the line influence the SWR reading of the currents

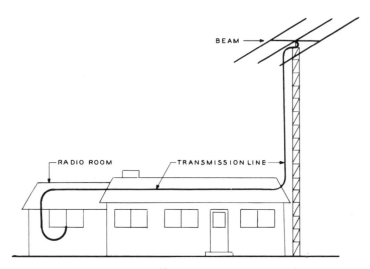

Fig.5   Running your coax line above ground in the vicinity of the antenna invites trouble in the form of unwanted coupling between the line and the antenna. The line, in effect, becomes a part of the radiating system. Measured SWR is determined by combination of antenna load and radiation or pickup from the line outer shield.

within the line, as the outer shield is no longer at ground potential even though the SWR meter and transmitter are supposed to be near ground potential.   The outside of the coaxial line has become part of the antenna system due to the undesired coupling, and thus is part of the antenna load.   The SWR inside the line is now determined by the combined load of the antenna and radiation from the outside of the coax line.   This is one reason why changing the length of the transmission line often changes the SWR reading on the line.   The portion of the load caused by unwanted line coupling to the antenna is being changed.

HOW TO REDUCE UNWANTED LINE CURRENTS

To achieve accurate SWR readings on an antenna system, it is necessary to detune and decouple the transmission line from the field of the antenna.   Ideally, the line should drop down to ground level directly beneath the center of the antenna and then travel underground from that point to the transmitter which itself should be shielded from the antenna.   Such an installation doesn't occur very often in real life!

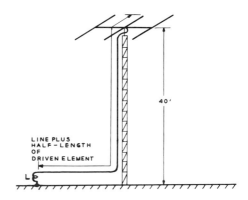

Fig.6 Line-plus-antenna can be checked for un-wanted resonance by coupling dip-oscillator to shield of line via a 2-turn coil which is connected between line and ground.

LINE PLUS
HALF-LENGTH OF
DRIVEN ELEMENT

40'

The first step is to make sure that the length of the trans-mission line and driven element (as measured from one tip of the element to the SWR meter) is not resonant in the amateur band that the antenna operates on. This can be accomplished by shorting the antenna terminals together at the SWR meter point and inductively coupling them to a dip oscillator via a short lead. The dip oscillator is tuned to determine if resonance occurs in the band of operation. If resonance is found, the line length should be altered until the point of resonance is moved outside of the amateur band (Figure 6). The length for a nonresonant line condition cannot be predicted in advance be-cause of bends in the line and the proximity of nearby objects.

The second step is to make sure that the transmission line does not run parallel to the antenna elements. This is a big order with a rotary beam antenna. The solution is to keep the transmission line close to the ground, or to bury the line be-neath the ground in a section of garden hose for moisture pro-tection. The worst thing is to run the line a long distance above ground from the antenna to the station (along the roof top, for example). This places the coax line up in the air and close to the active antenna.

But what does the operator do when he cannot trim his line to length, and whose line must run along the roof in the vicinity of the antenna? How can he make meaningful SWR measurements under these conditions?

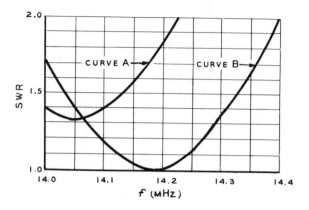

Fig.7 Unwanted transmission line currents caused by coupling between outer shield of line and antenna can result in misleading
SWR measurements (curve A). A quick check of system performance
can be made by simply adding a few feet of line between the SWR
meter and the antenna and rerunning the SWR curve. The difference
between curves A and B indicates that unwanted coupling between
antenna and coax line exists in this installation.

DECOUPLING THE TRANSMISSION LINE

For example, assume a triband beam for 20-15-10 meters
atop a 40 foot (12 m) high tower. The coax feedline runs down
the tower to the 10 foot (3 m) level, along the roof horizontally
for about 20 feet (6 m), and then down to ground level at the
station. How can the operator be sure that the SWR checks
made on this system are valid? The easiest and quickest check
is to add about 5 feet (1.5 m) of coaxial line between the SWR
meter and the antenna and rerun the SWR curve. If the shape
or amplitude of the curve changes, it is probable that unwanted
coupling exists between line and antenna as shown in Figure 7.
(Note: Such a test is valid only if you have a good SWR
meter.)

If interaction between line and antenna exists, one helpful
and easy thing to do is to coil the line into a simple rf choke at
the point the line leaves the tower. Four or five turns about a
foot (0.3 m) in diameter, held together with electrical tape,
helps to decouple the line at the antenna end. At the station
end of the line, a second similar choke coil may help solve the
problem. The coil can be made by splicing an extra length of
line into the system with adapters. Once the chokes are in the
line, a new SWR curve should be run. Don't expect the final
curve to be perfect, a degree of line coupling may still exist,

Fig.8 Three SWR meters placed
in series in your coax line
may show different readings!
Are the SWR meters inaccurate
or is your test setup faulty?
A quick SWR meter check will
tell, explained in the text.

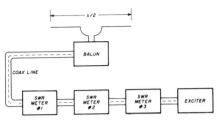

particularly if the transmitter and amplifier are in the strong
field of the antenna.

HOW RELIABLE IS YOUR SWR METER? - A QUICK CHECK

There is a simple and inexpensive test you can run that
determines the accuracy of any SWR meter. Consider the situation in Figure 8. Three SWR meters are placed at random spots
along a coax line to an antenna. At any given value of SWR the
three instruments should provide identical readings. This
probably never happens in real life. Which meter reading is
correct? Move the meters along the line. Does the SWR reading
of any meter change? All meters should read the same at any
point in the line. If the SWR meters are accurate and no line
coupling exists, all readings will be the same! This concept is
the basis for a check of any SWR meter. The test procedure is
shown in Figure 9. Instead of moving a meter along a line, a
deliberate SWR mismatch is created and measured through various line lengths. As before, if the SWR meter is perfect, it will
read the same degree of mismatch at any point along the line.

In order to make the test meaningful, a dummy load is used
at one end of the test line, and a harmonic filter is required
between the signal generator (your transceiver or exciter) and
the test setup. The mismatched load is made up of a 50 ohm
dummy load plus a quarter-wave section of 75 ohm coax line.
The line section serves as a step-up transformer, providing an
output load of 112.5 ohms. If this load is measured through a
50-ohm SWR meter at the test frequency, the indicated SWR
should be the ratio of the load to the instrument impedance, or:

$$\frac{112.5}{50} = 2.25\text{-to-}1$$

This test is conducted as shown in the illustration. The
mismatch load is measured directly, and then remeasured through
various extra lengths of 50 ohm line. If the SWR meter is
perfect (and none of them is), the SWR reading will remain

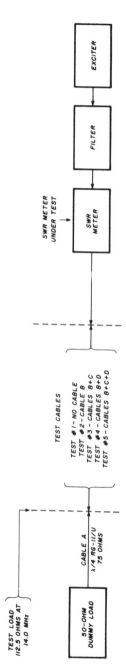

Fig.9 This is how you check your SWR meter. A mismatched load of 112.5 ohms is measured through various lengths of coaxial line. If the SWR meter is absolutely accurate, indicated SWR will be 2.25-to-1, as explained in the text. Five tests are run and indicated SWR tabulated as shown in Fig.11. A graph can then be plotted showing indicated SWR as a function of coax line length (Fig.12).

The indicated SWR excursions can now be used to determine the directivity factor of the SWR meter with the aid of Fig.13. The measured (indicated) SWR excursion points are located on the Y-axis and the true value of SWR (2.25-to-1 in this case) is found on the X-axis. The slanting curves indicate the directivity of the SWR meter. A directivity of about 40 dB is considered good, but even that degree of excellence allows an error of about five percent in the reading.

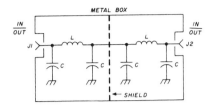

Fig.10 Harmonic filter for 14 MHz. Each capacitor C is 220 pF 500 DCWV silver mica. Each inductor L is 0.55 uH, 7 turns #16 wire, 3/4-in.(19 mm) diam, 7/8-in.(22 mm) long.

constant at 2.25 for each observation point. The amount of variation in the indicated SWR from the true value determines the excellence of the SWR meter.

PREPARING FOR THE TEST

For this example, the test is run at 14.0 MHz. The 75 ohm "mismatch" line section is made from an 11'7" (3.54 m) section of either RG-59B/U or RG-11/U. This length takes into account the velocity factor of the line. Suitable connectors are placed on each end of the line and line length is measured from tip to tip of the center conductor.

Next, three sections of 50 ohm line are made up. Two are one-eighth wavelength long (5'9½" or 1.77 m) and the third is one-quarter wavelength length long (11'7" or 3.54 m). Again, suitable plugs are placed on the lines and length is measured from tip to tip of the center conductor. An accuracy of plus or minus one-half inch (1.3 cm) is satisfactory. Suggested cable types are RG-8A/U, RG-213/U, RG-58A/U or RG-58C/U. Do not use the old cable designation of RG-8/U or "RG-8 type" cable. Such cable usually runs close to 52 ohms impedance. When the cables are completed, label the 75 ohm cable A, the two short 50 ohm cables B and C, and the long 50 ohm cable D. You can make up paper labels and tape them directly over the jacket of the lines with transparent tape.

The last step is to make up the second harmonic filter. A suitable filter is shown in Figure 10. It is made up of air-wound coils and mica capacitors and built in a small metal box. A shield is placed between the filter sections, as shown, and suitable coaxial receptacles are placed on the ends of the box. This filter is rated for 20 meter operation at a power level of about 150 watts.

RUNNING THE TEST

Test #1 consists of measuring the SWR directly at the end of cable A. A suitable chart is made up and all readings are

TEST NUMBER	CABLES	LENGTH (λ)	INDICATED SWR
1	0	0	3.35
2	B	1/8	2.00
3	B+C	1/4	1.50
4	B+D	3/8	2.75
5	B+C+D	1/2	3.35

Fig.11   Representative SWR readings with "Brand X" SWR meter as run in Fig.3. The actual value of SWR in each case is 2.25-to-1. Results plotted in Fig.12 (below).

recorded on it.   Later, a graph can be drawn from the chart data (Figure 11).

For test #2, cable B is added between the SWR meter and cable A and an SWR reading is taken and logged.   Test #3 consists of using cables B and C in series.   Test #4 consists of cables B and D in series.   Test #5 consists of using cables B, C and D in series.   What has been done, in effect, is to add one-eight wavelength sections of coax line between the "mismatch" line section and the SWR meter.   This is electrically equivalent to moving the SWR meter along the line, as shown in Figure 9.   (Note: This test procedure was developed by Willy Sayer, WA6BAN.)

RESULTS OF THE TEST

A representative test on two SWR meters is charted in Figure 12.   One instrument is a <u>Bird 43</u> coupler and the other device is a cheap, imported SWR meter.   The variations of the

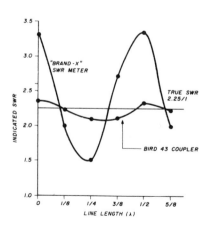

Fig.12   Using data in Fig.5 plus test run on a Bird 43 coupler produces these curves.   Indicated SWR is plotted against cable length.

Fig.13 Directivity of SWR meter or directional coupler is determined from measured SWR excursions. The maximum excursions are noted on the Y-axis and the true value of SWR is found on the X-axis. Intersection of these values on the directivity (D) curves indicates directivity of the instrument.

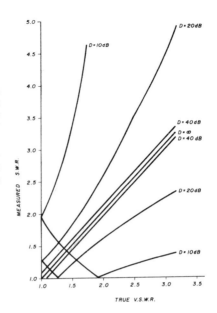

indicated reading from the true SWR values are obvious and startling!

This graph explains one of the reasons that the indicated SWR can vary with placement of the instrument in the line. It also gives the lie to the popular but incorrect belief that changing line length changes the SWR on the line! Changing line length changes the indicated SWR reading to a degree depending upon the accuracy of the SWR meter, but the actual SWR on the line remains the same. (It is true that actual SWR will decrease with line length due to line attenuation, but this is another matter and may be ignored in the hf spectrum. Most amateur handbooks provide tables of line attenuation for those interested in pursuing that subject further.)

INTERPRETING THE RESULTS

The graph shows that even an excellent SWR coupler such as the Bird provides a reading that varies with line length to a small degree. The inexpensive "Brand-X" SWR meter, however, is not to be trusted. The indicated reading varies between a low value of 1.5-to-1 to a high value of 3.35-to-1 for a true SWR value of 2.25-to-1. The observer can get almost any reading he wishes by merely moving the instrument back and forth along the line! The test results are based upon a single frequency measurement (14.0 MHz) and the variation in SWR reading changes with frequency, growing worse as the frequency of operation is increased. This is why most cheap SWR meters provide unreliable readings at 10 meters and higher. The Bird-type coupler, on the other hand, has frequency-rated, plug-in detectors which provide good accuracy in the vhf and uhf regions.

The indicated SWR excursions illustrated by these tests can be used to determine the directivity factor of the SWR meter (directional coupler) with the aid of Figure 13. (This drawing is reproduced with thanks from the November, 1959, issue of QST. It is from an article entitled, "Possible Errors in V.S.W.R. Measurement" by Louis D. Breetz, W3KDZ/W8QLP.)

The instrument directivity is found by locating the maximum excursions of SWR on the graph you have made and finding them on the Y-axis (vertical) of Figure 13. For example, the Bird coupler has an SWR excursion of 2.35-to-1 to 2.1-to-1. Find the true value of SWR (2.25-to-1) on the X-axis (horizontal) and proceed upwards until you cross the points you have located on the Y-axis. This indicates a directivity of almost 40 dB, which is excellent. On the other hand, the indicated maximum SWR excursions of the "Brand-X" SWR meter are 3.35-to-1 and 1.5-to-1. Locating these points on Figure 13 indicates a directivity of about 15 dB, which is very poor.

As can be seen from an inspection of the graph and Figure 13, a directivity of about 40 dB is required to give a meaningful SWR reading and even that degree of excellence allows an error of about 5 percent. Note, too, that the indicated SWR curve plotted for both instruments is not symmetrical about the true SWR value, further complicating interpretation of data.

SAVE YOUR SWR MEASUREMENTS

It is recommended that an SWR test run be made on a new beam and the data carefully filed away for future comparison. If doubt exists about antenna operation in the future, it is helpful to compare a newly-run SWR curve with the original one. Many operators run an SWR check every month or so, especially during stormy weather periods when the antenna might be damaged by sleet, hail or high winds.

THE ANTENNASCOPE

Various types of SWR measuring devices have been developed since World War II and one of the most versatile designs is shown in Figure 14. This is a modernization of the venerable Wheatstone Bridge developed in 1843.

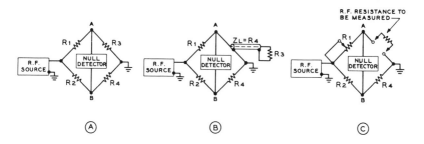

Fig.14 The resistor-bridge SWR measuring device is an adaptation of the Wheatstone bridge (A). When the arm ratio is balanced, no voltage is present at the null detector. One arm of the bridge may be removed & replaced with the feedpoint resistance of an antenna (B). If another arm of the bridge is made variable, measurements may be taken over a wide range of antenna feedpoint values (C).

This rf version of the bridge employees noninductive resistors in each arm and uses an rf oscillator as the signal source. The principle of operation is exactly the same as the earlier bridge designs. When the arm ratio R1/R2 equals R3/R4, the bridge is balanced and no output voltage is present at the null detector. As one arm of the bridge (or the ratio of two arms) changes from the balance value, the bridge becomes unbalanced and the voltage detected across points A-B increases in proportion to the unbalance.

The arm resistor R3 may be removed and the feedpoint resistance of an antenna substituted in its place. If the adjacent bridge arm is made variable, the bridge will be balanced when the variable arm equals the resonant feedpoint resistance of the antenna. The variable arm permits measurements to be taken over a wide range of antenna feedpoint values and the exact feedpoint resistance is read from the variable resistor setting when the bridge is adjusted to balance. This updated antenna bridge is an antennascope and was perfected by Bill Scherer, Jr., ex-W2AEF. The version shown in this chapter is an adaptation of that design as modified by J. Sevick, W2FMI.

BUILDING THE ANTENNASCOPE

The antennascope requires a low power rf source to drive it. A practical source is a dip oscillator. The older, tube-model dip oscillator has sufficient power to drive the bridge and detector directly, but the newer, solid state dip oscillators provide less than 50 mW power output. A dc amplifier added to

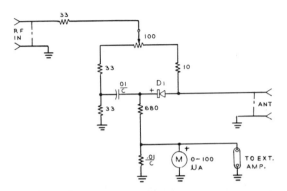

Fig.15 Bridge circuit of Fig.14C is adapted as an Antennascope. The instrument is driven by a dip oscillator via a 2-turn loop placed at "rf in" jack. Antenna under test is attached to "ant" terminals. Resistors are 5% accuracy composition units.

the antennascope provides a usable meter reading. The circuit of the antennascope is shown in Figure 15 and the meter amplifier in Figure 16.

The antennascope has three connectors: one for the rf drive source, one for the indicating meter, and one for the antenna under test. The instrument is built in a small aluminum box just large enough to hold the components and provide room for a dial (Figure 17). The bridge design is modified slightly in that the variable arm subtracts resistance from one leg and adds it to the other, spreading out the low end of the resistance scale for increased accuracy. The small components are supported by their leads and no extra wiring is required in this compact assembly (Figure 18).

After the antennascope is assembled it is calibrated with the use of one-half watt composition resistors of known value. The antennascope is coupled to the rf drive source and various resistors (4.7, 10, 18, 27, 47, 56, 68, 82 and 100 ohms) are placed across the terminals of the output receptacle. Resistor leads are clipped short to reduce extraneous inductance. The variable bridge resistor is adjusted for a meter null for each test resistor and the dial setting is logged. Intermediate points may be obtained by interpolation. Calibration points are now marked

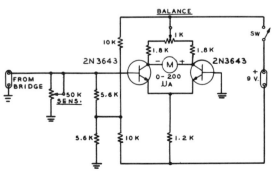

Fig.16 Meter amplifier for Antennascope when low power signal source is used. Meter is balanced for zero by 1K potentiometer.

ig.17 Much-modified Antennascope is
onverted into design of Fig.15.
onnector for external oscillator is
t the bottom of the assembly and
ntenna terminals are at the top.
he 100-ohm composition resistor
ial is calibrated directly in ohms
y means of an external ohmmeter.

on a paper scale for the complete rotation of the dial.   Cali-
oration will hold from 2 MHz to 30 MHz if the instrument is
constructed as shown.

USING THE ANTENNASCOPE

The antennascope is used in conjunction with a dip oscillator.   The amplifier circuit of Figure 16 may be added externally
to the device if the oscillator power is insufficient for a good
null reading.   The antennascope is attached to the feedpoint
terminals of the antenna under test and drive power is applied
to obtain a near-full scale reading on the null meter.   The
frequency of the dip oscillator and the antennascope resistance
dial are varied until a meter null is found.   The frequency of
the driving source (as monitored on a nearby receiver) corresponds to the resonant frequency of the antenna element and the
feedpoint resistance of the element is read directly in ohms on
the calibrated dial of the antennascope.

Note that the case of the antennascope is common to one
side of the input and output circuits.   If the antenna terminals
are balanced to ground, it may be necessary to place a one-to-
one balun between the instrument and the antenna.   In this
case, the antennascope reading takes into account the electrical
characteristics of the balun as well as the antenna.   If the use
of a balun is not desired, the antennascope and driving source
must be insulated from the antenna structure.   This is easily
done by placing both devices on a short wood plank and resting
the plank on the boom of the antenna.

Fig.18 Internal view of antenna-scope. Components are clustered around control at top. Coax line is extended from the bottom receptacle up to 33-ohm resistor mounted near potentiometer terminals.

The antennascope can be used for measurements when coupled to the antenna through an electrical half-wavelength transmission line. Measurements are not quite as accurate as when directly made at the antenna terminals, but the convenience of placing the antennascope at a more convenient spot at, or near, ground level may outweigh the possible loss of accuracy. Various handbooks describe the method of trimming a section of coax line to an electrical half-wavelength with the aid of a dip oscillator. The line is attached to the antenna terminals and brought down to the antennascope. Measurements are now conducted and, as long as the interconnecting line is an electrical half-wavelength long at the test frequency, it is "transparent" to the antennascope which only "sees" the antenna load.

THE RF NOISE BRIDGE

The rf noise bridge includes five major elements, three of which are internal to the instrument. The heart of the instrument is the bridge section itself (Figure 19). This is excited by a broad spectrum noise source (often a zener diode). The unknown impedance and a reference impedance form separate legs of the bridge section. The reference impedance is varied until it equals the unknown impedance. When this occurs, the bridge is balanced and the output, as monitored on a high frequency receiver, goes to a minimum.

The schematic of a useful noise bridge is shown in Figure 20. Output from the noise diode is amplified and applied to a balanced transformer. The antenna under test and a detector (the station receiver) are connected as shown. An adjustable

Fig.19 Rf noise bridge consists of a wideband noise source and an rf bridge. Unknown impedance is balanced against a reference impedance, as in the case of the Antennascope. The station receiver is used as a null detector.

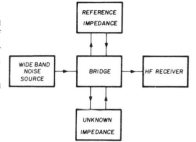

reference load (potentiometer) is varied to determine the nominal feedpoint resistance of the antenna under test. The receiver is adjusted to complete the null, and the resonant frequency of the antenna element is read from the receiver.

This simple noise bridge measures only the resistive component of the antenna load which is found at antenna resonance. A more sophisticated design measures both the resistive and reactive load components. Construction and use of a suitable noise bridge are shown in the Radio Handbook, 22d ed., Howard W. Sams Co., 4300 West 62nd Street, Indianapolis, IN 46268, and in The ARRL Antenna Book, ARRL, Newington, CT 06111.

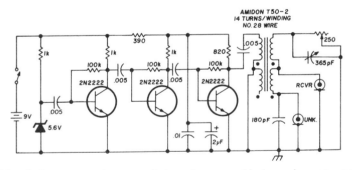

Fig.20 Noise generator consists of zener diode noise source and three stages of wideband amplification. Balanced ferrite transformer couples generator to bridge at right. Unit is placed near the receiver and coupled to the antenna through a coax line which is a multiple of electrical half-wavelengths long and "transparent" to the measurements.

Difficulty in erecting your big Yagi array? Wilse Morgan, KL7CQ, solved this tough problem with the aid of a tethered hot-air balloon! The 6-element, 20 meter monoband beam was gently lowered to the top of an 80-foot tower using this novel technique.

photo by Rod Maney, KL7SA

Chapter 10

HF Antenna System Evaluation

It doesn't make any ultimate difference whether you assemble your beam from a purchased kit, or build your array from materials that you bought, because the same electronic rules apply to either antenna. If you buy a beam kit you should compare the important dimensions against those given in this handbook for a similar beam. If the measurements are compatible, the beam should perform in the manner intended. If the dimensions differ by an appreciable amount, it is a good idea to determine whether the differences are important or not. You will have to "second guess" why the manufacturer chose the dimensions he did. On one hand, some small antenna manufacturers are merely "aluminum salesmen" selling a kit of questionable design. On the other hand, the manufacturer may have departed from standard dimensions for a reason. If, for example, the reflector dimension seems long or the director dimension short, this deviation may have been made intentionally to achieve greater bandwidth and lower SWR on the feedline at the expense of power gain.

In any event, the Yagi beam "wants to work" and designs having unorthodox dimensions often work surprisingly well. Top performance, however, especially with regard to front-to-back ratio, is achieved if the dimensions given in this handbook are employed.

HOW WELL DOES YOUR BEAM WORK?

Whether your beam is homemade or a commercial product, the primary interest is the result achieved. Can you hear the distant station other local amateurs are working? Can you compete in a DX contest with stations equal to yours? Do you seem to get bad interference from stations received off the back of the array? Suspicions such as these may make you wonder if your beam antenna is working properly. It is possible to gain a subjective feeling of how well your antenna is performing by on-the-air tests with similar antenna installations, but this pseudo-scientific approach cannot provide specific information. It only tells the operator if his antenna is functioning or not. If he cannot hear weak signals that others copy, or if his reports are consistently less than those of his peers, it <u>may</u> be an indication that something is amiss.

A SIMPLE RECEIVING TEST

Can you hear the distant station as well as other operators in your area? If you suspect something is wrong, listen to the receiver background noise as you disconnect the antenna and substitute a 50-ohm composition resistor in its place. If the noise level drops, it means the noise pickup of the antenna is higher than the inherent noise level of your receiver, which is good. Run this test with the receiver agc turned off. If there is no change in noise level, it may mean antenna problems or it may mean your receiver front-end is out of alignment.

SWING YOUR BEAM ON A LOCAL SIGNAL

When the band is dead, have a station located several miles away send you a continuous signal. Swing your beam on the signal and watch your S-meter. There should be good signal nulls off both sides of your array and you should be able to discern some front-to-back ratio. This ratio varies tremendously from one antenna installation to the next and depends upon linearity of the S-meter in the receiver and the gain setting of the if strip, signal reflection from nearby buildings and power lines, and other obscure factors. But checks against several local signals should indicate if your antenna exhibits a satis-factory degree of front-to-back ratio.

SWR EVALUATION OF YOUR BEAM

You can tell a lot about overall antenna performance by running a simple test with an SWR meter in the coax line to the antenna. Before this test is run, the chapter concerning SWR meter accuracy should be read.

As already stated, the SWR meter, in addition to telling you basic characteristics of your antenna, also provides a long-term method of checking your antenna performance. Once SWR meas-urements are made, they should be filed away and rechecked after a period of time to see if the antenna is working properly. The SWR curve may vary a bit with the weather, the amount of humidity in the atmosphere, and with the time of year as the amount of moisture in the soil in the vicinity of the antenna changes. Even so, the SWR measurements provide a quick and reliable means of checking antenna performance over the months and years. For convenience, the SWR meter is located near the operating position. Matching coax plugs are placed on the cables going to the instrument so that proper electrical and mechanical connections are made. All connections should be made in a neat, workmanlike manner.

RUNNING AN SWR CURVE

To properly evaluate any antenna, SWR measurements are taken across the operating range. In most cases, measurements made every 50 KHz across the band will suffice. After a frequency run across the band and logging the SWR reading at each 50 kHz point, the SWR readings are plotted against frequency on a sheet of graph paper. The point of lowest SWR on the curve is the resonant frequency of the antenna system. Generally speaking, the slope of the SWR curve is greatest on the high frequency side of antenna resonance, as the operating frequency of the array approaches the self-resonant frequency of the director element.

If the measurements are carefully made, a smooth SWR curve will be the result. Abrupt jumps in the curve may indicate an inaccurate measurement or the influence of some unwanted object affecting proper antenna operation. A good example of this problem is to have the beam pointed toward a nearby power line or tv antenna, or to have another amateur band antenna in the immediate vicinity. Unusual SWR readings can come about because of unwanted coupling between the antenna under test and a nearby object. If antenna dimensions are correct and a good match is achieved between antenna and transmission line, the SWR will approach unity (one-to-one) at the design frequency of the array. If the minimum SWR value is higher than desired, further adjustments to the driven element are needed, or a transmatch may be used at the station to lower the SWR value that the transmitter "sees". If the SWR reading jumps about, look for a loose connection in the antenna system.

Even when a one-to-one SWR ratio is achieved at antenna resonance, certain lengths of transmission line may present loading problems for a solid state transmitter when the antenna is operated at a frequency removed from resonance. Some amateurs prune the length of the coax line until they achieve good loading. It is simple enough to make up short line segments and splice them into the main transmission line until good loading is achieved. A permanent solution to this problem is to use a transmatch at the station.

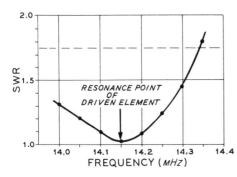

SWR	FREQUENCY
1.32	14.00
1.20	14.05
1.10	14.10
1.01	14.15
1.08	14.20
1.25	14.25
1.45	14.30
1.80	14.35

Fig.1 Representative SWR run is plotted in terms of indicated SWR versus frequency (right). Values are then transferred to graph and smooth curve is drawn between readings. Minimum point of curve is frequency of antenna system resonance, 14.15 MHz in this example.

A REPRESENTATIVE SWR RUN

A plot of frequency versus SWR across the band for your antenna is a revealing measurement. This is how you do it: The SWR is measured at 50 kHz intervals across the band and the results tabulated as shown in Figure 1. (The remarks earlier in this handbook concerning SWR meter accuracy should be noted.) Once the run has been made and the information tabulated, a graph is made up such as the one shown in the illustration. Note that the SWR curve is reasonably smooth, reaching a minimum point at antenna system resonance. This minimum point should be near the center frequency of the band in use. This curve is representative of most types of antennas from ground planes to dipoles to multi-element beams. The observer cannot tell the type of antenna measured by merely examining the SWR curve. But he can tell if the antenna is properly adjusted or not.

The top graph of Figure 2 shows the SWR plot of a three element Yagi designed for a center frequency of 21.15 MHz. The maximum value of SWR tolerated by the particular solid state transmitter used is 1.75-to-1, as indicated by the horizontal, dashed line. Obviously something is wrong, as the beam exhibits a prohibitively high value of SWR across the entire band except for the small span between 21.42 and 21.45 MHz.

In this example, running the SWR examination up to 22 MHz pays a big dividend as it shows that antenna system resonance is near 21.75 MHz. After this test was completed, the antenna was lowered to the ground and all dimensions rechecked. It was found that the driven element length was incorrect, and had

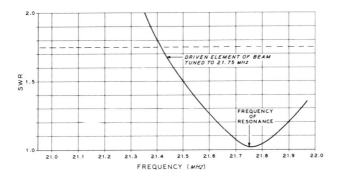

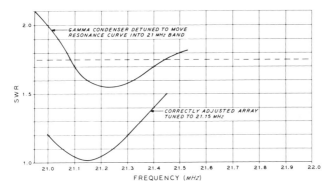

Fig.2 (Top)   Driven element of beam is misadjusted to 21.7 MHz (element too short). False resonance is achieved by using matching device to "pull" frequency of driven element (lower drawing, top curve). Lower curve shows proper driven element adjustment.

been since the original assembly. The error was corrected, the beam placed in position, and a second SWR plot run. This result is the top SWR curve in the bottom drawing of Figure 2. Now, antenna system resonance seems to be close to 21.2 MHz but the SWR curve is excessively high across the entire band. Under these conditions, the transmitter will not deliver full output. The final step was to adjust the driven element matching system. The results are shown in the lower curve of this illustration. Antenna system resonance is 21.15 MHz and the highest value of SWR is only 1.5-to-1 at 21.45 MHz, well within the capability of the transmitter.

This experiment took only a few hours and was a success because the operator was familiar with his equipment, he had run tests like this before, and (viewing the antenna from the ground with binoculars) he had guessed where the problem was. The SWR measurements were then used as a "before and after" verification of the correction applied to the problem. In some cases, however, a more comprehensive checkout procedure is required. This evaluation is described in the following sections.

SIX IMPORTANT QUESTIONS ABOUT BEAM PERFORMANCE

The answers to the following six questions provide a good basis for evaluation of the performance of your antenna.

1. Is your antenna situated in the most advantageous location consistent with the local topography? An antenna mounted eight feet (2.5 m) above a tin roof, or surrounded by utility wires and tall structures, bears a handicap and cannot be expected to compete with a similar array mounted high and in the clear. A change in antenna height of only a few feet to avoid local obstructions often works wonders with the signal.

2. Are the parasitic elements of the array self-resonant outside the desired operating range of the array? A quick check against the lengths given in this handbook will answer this question. Determination of the resonant frequency of each element can be accomplished with a dip oscillator, if required.

3. Is the driven element of the array resonant within the band of antenna operation? Check the length against the information given in this handbook. If in doubt, dip the driven element to determine the resonant frequency.

4. Does the driven element of the array present directly (or through a matching device) the correct feedpoint resistance to match the feedline? The test instrument chapter of this handbook tells how this observation can be made and what to do to correct the problem.

5. Does the SWR on the transmission line reach near-unity (one-to-one) within the operational range of the array? A frequency run with an SWR meter will answer this question.

6. Does the antenna system present a compatible load to the transmitter? Erratic loading or damage to the output stage of the transmitter is a sure sign that the antenna system is out of adjustment.

If the answer is "yes" to these questions, there is really nothing more the operator need know about his installation. The ability to achieve good contacts has shifted from the antenna to the operator's skill and his transmitter. If the answer is "no" to one or more of these questions, further investigation is called for. The following evaluation program is suggested.

ANTENNA EVALUATION WITH A SPLIT DRIVEN ELEMENT

The antenna may either be mounted in its ultimate position, or placed temporarily atop a 12 foot (3.6 m) high pole or ladder in the center of a clear area. If it is possible to reach the center of the array when it is atop the tower or other support structure, the test may be run from that position. The higher the beam is above ground, the more accurate will be the results of the test. The beam should be rotated so that the tips of the reflector point toward any nearby utility wires, or structures. The terminals of the driven element are temporarily shorted with a small one turn loop of wire. A dip oscillator is loosely coupled to the loop and tuned back and forth across the resonant frequency of the antenna. The resonant dip should be monitored on a nearby calibrated receiver. The average frequency noted by several measurements can be taken as the resonant frequency of the driven element.

The careful observer will note slight deflections of the dip oscillator when the instrument is tuned to the resonant frequencies of the parasitic elements, even thought the instrument is coupled to the driven element. These indications should occur outside the frequency range of beam operation. If not, the lengths of the parasitic elements are adjusted until this requirement is satisfied. In such circumstances, the reflector is lengthened and the director shortened.

MATCHING NETWORK CHECKOUT

The split driven element may be matched to the transmission line with a balun and a network, such as the hairpin match described previously. This arrangement can be checked either at the antenna feed terminals or through an electrical half-wavelength of coaxial line, which places the investigator at, or near, ground level.

In order to run this test, a dip oscillator and an antenna-scope (described in the previous chapter) are required. The antennascope is attached to the matching network at the antenna, or at the end of the half-wavelength coaxial line, and the dip oscillator coupled to the input circuit of the instrument. The resistance dial of the antennascope is set to 50 ohms, or to the impedance of the transmission line. The dip oscillator is tuned back and forth across the operating frequency of the array until a null (zero) reading is observed, indicating that the oscillator is at the resonant frequency of the driven element. If a complete null is not found, the resistance dial of the antennascope is changed slightly and the frequency of the oscillator varied back and forth. When a complete null is obtained, the resistance reading of the antennascope shows the feedpoint resistance of the driven element. This reading should be very close to the impedance value of the transmission line. If it is not, alterations to the driven element matching device are in order. If none is used, the feedpoint resistance of the driven element may be varied slightly by small alterations in the length of the director element. If the indicated feedpoint resistance is low, the director should be shortened a bit. Length changes are made equally to each tip. If the feedpoint resistance is high, the director should be lengthened. Changes of small magnitude will have no observable effect upon antenna operation as long as the self-resonant frequency of the director is not allowed to fall within the operating passband of the array.

When the null of the antennascope occurs at the approximate resistance setting selected (and also at the center of the frequency range of the array) the adjustments are complete. Care taken in the installation of the transmission line to reduce unwanted coupling to the field of the antenna helps to keep the SWR on the transmission line to a minimum value. The line should drop down below the beam for at least a half-wavelength before a horizontal run is started.

ANTENNA EVALUATION WITH SHUNT-FED SYSTEM

This representative evaluation employs the gamma matching system. The same general procedure is employed with a T-match or delta match system except that like adjustments must be made simultaneously to both sides of the match. To start the evaluation, the driven element must be resonant at the test frequency. The dimensions given in this handbook are recommended. The antenna is placed in the clear, as described previously, and an antennascope connected to the matching system directly or through a half-wavelength coaxial line. The antennascope is coupled to a dip oscillator and both instruments are adjusted for the lowest reading on the antennascope. When a near-null is found, the gamma capacitor is adjusted so as to enhance the null reading. If the omega match is used, both capacitors are adjusted. If the null is incomplete, the resistance dial of the antennascope is varied until the null is complete. The feedpoint resistance of the match can now be read on the antennascope. If the resistance is too low, it is necessary to lengthen the

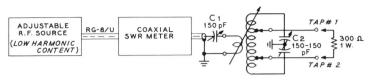

Fig.3 Balanced antenna fed by a two-wire transmission line can be checked by a coaxial SWR meter and an antenna tuner. Tuner is adjusted for lowest SWR when a composition resistor equal to line impedance is placed across the terminals.

gamma rod a slight amount. If the reading is high, the rod should be shortened.

The rod length controls the transformation ratio between the feedpoint resistance of the driven element and the feedline impedance. The variable capacitor tunes out the reactance of the rod. Adjustment of these two variables produces a good match between antenna and transmission line. If the null is found outside the operating frequency range of the beam, it is necessary to alter the length of the driven element to move the null to the center of the range.

A final check of the SWR should prove the accuracy of adjustments with an SWR figure close to unity at the resonant frequency of the driven element. The SWR should gradually and evenly increase on both sides of resonance, remaining less than 2-to-1 within the operational range of the antenna.

SWR CHECK-OUT OF A BALANCED TRANSMISSION LINE SYSTEM

In the vhf range, some amateurs prefer to use a balanced two-wire feed system instead of a coaxial line to reduce transmission line loss. It is possible to make SWR measurements on such a system but unfortunately the accuracy of measurements made on such lines is dependent upon the degree of current balance on the line. Undesirable currents on the line may be caused by coupling between the field of the line and the field of the antenna, or by an imbalance to ground between the two wires of the line. Directional couplers do not distinguish between normal line currents and spurious parallel current flowing in a balanced line and thus show a reading having little relationship to the actual SWR value on the line. The degree of error in the reading of the instrument may be checked by interchanging the transmission line terminals at the SWR meter and repeating the measurement. If the two readings vary by more than a few degrees on the meter scale of the instrument, the current imbalance in the line is high enough so that neither reading may be relied upon. In this case, it is necessary to employ a coaxial SWR meter and couple it to the balanced line through a suitable matching system, such as shown in Figure 3. This system resembles the usual antenna coupler employed to match an unbalanced transmission line to a balanced load. For example, let us assume that we wish to measure the SWR on a 300 ohm two-wire line by the use of an SWR meter designed for a 50 ohm coaxial line.

BALANCED LINE CHECK-OUT TEST

1. A 300 ohm 1 watt carbon (noninductive) resistor is placed across taps 1 and 2 of the coupling circuit. These taps are placed close to, and equidistant on either side of the center turn. The leads from the coil taps to the resistor should be as short as possible.

2. A small amount of power is now applied to the SWR meter. The switch on the meter is set to forward, and rf drive is adjusted for full scale reading on the meter. The instrument is now switched to reverse, and capacitors C1, C2 and the link coupling of the coupler are adjusted for zero (null) meter reading. If a complete null is unobtainable, taps 1 and 2 should be shifted until a null is reached by adjustment of the three variable controls. Once this null is obtained, these adjustments should not be changed, as the matching system now makes a suitable impedance transformation between the 50 ohm coaxial line and the 300 ohm balanced line.

3. The test resistor is removed and the 300 ohm line is attached in its place. It is important that extraneous devices such as antenna relays or rf ammeters be removed from the transmission line during these measurements, since they introduce points of reflection which confuse the results.

4. SWR measurements are now made, as explained in the previous section. It is well to remove the transmission line from the antenna coupler after a frequency change of about 200 kHz and recheck the setting of the unit, since the transformation ratio is dependent upon the frequency of measurement. A single setting will deliver accurate SWR readings over several hundred kilohertz. Beyond this, C1, C2 and the coupling link will probably have to be readjusted.

Chapter 11

Erecting the Beam Antenna

Many amateurs mount their Yagi beam on a tower that is separated from their residence. Towers may be fixed, fixed-rotatable, tilt-over, or telescoping and are commonly made either of plated (galvanized) iron or aluminum. Each type of tower has its virtues and the choice depends upon space available, desired antenna height, and the size of the buyer's pocketbook.

Experience has proven that antenna height is more important than antenna type or power gain. "A poor antenna high up is better than a good antenna low down", as an amateur once said. Most amateurs consider this statement true, based upon their experience.

SELECTION OF A TOWER

The principal advantage of a fixed tower is that it is easy to assemble and less expensive than a crank-up (telescoping), or a tilt-over tower. Since they are often less rugged than a crank-up tower, fixed towers usually must be guyed, often at several different levels. In many cases, crank-up and tilt-over towers also should be guyed for increased safety.

The main disadvantage of a fixed tower is that the sections must be bolted together either on the ground and the tower then erected, or mounted on top of one another after the first section is secured to the base. Erecting a fixed tower by bolting one section atop another up in the air is tricky and dangerous and calls for a strong safety belt, gin pole, block and tackle, and two or three reliable helpers. The assembler on the tower must wear a safety belt fastened so that he has the use of both his arms. As the tower is assembled, it must be guyed. Each guy should be broken electrically with strain insulators spaced about

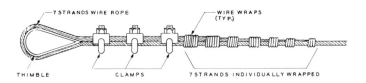

Fig.1 Stranded steel guy wires are used with a turnbuckle, thimble and three cable clamps. Guy is wrapped off, wire by wire, after the last clamp. This shows termination of 7-strand guy wire.

10 feet (3 m) along the guy. A minimum of three guy sets at each level is required, the guys sets spaced 120° apart around the tower. Maximum vertical separation between guy sets should not be more than 35 feet (10 m). Stranded steel guy wires are commonly used with a turnbuckle, thimble and three cable clamps at each termination of the guy (Figure 1). For most towers, except the very largest, 3/16-inch (0.48 mm) diameter type EHS cable is satisfactory.

The guy wires are terminated at ground level by guy anchors. For a light tower and well-compacted soil, an earth-screw anchor, available at large metal distributors in the U.S. and Canada, may be used. For a large tower, a guy anchor sunk in a concrete block is required. In this case, the complete tower installation should be designed and supervised by a licensed Civil Engineer.

THE CRANK-UP TOWER

A good crank-up, crank-down tower is expensive, but permits the antenna to be lowered for installation and maintenance and for protection in bad weather (Figure 2). The crank-up tower is far more expensive than the fixed tower but many amateurs consider the obvious advantages worth the extra price. Most crank-up towers are made of steel, galvanized after welding to retard rusting. The tower is triangular in cross-section, each tower segment nesting within a larger one. The sections are raised and lowered by a wire cable and pulley mechanism which can be driven by an electric motor. In the best designs, after a section is raised to its fullest extent, it then rests on a safety catch which supports its weight rather than depending on the cable for this purpose.

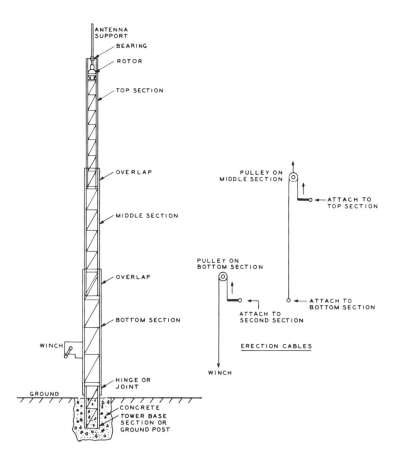

Fig.2 Representative crank-up tower. Tower is triangular in cross-section and is usually made in 20-foot lengths. Sections telescope within each other when the tower is retracted. Typical erection cable sequence is shown at right. A cable and winch combination permits the user to raise all sections from the ground. Crank-up towers may have as many as six separate sections. Larger models are motor driven and have remote indicator for height. All towers should have safety locks to prevent sections from dropping in case of a cable break. Heavy duty crank-up towers often have a single set of heavy, metal guy rods at the top of the bottom section.

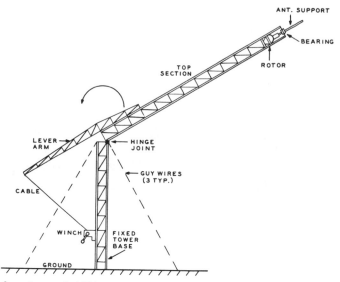

Fig.3   One form of tilt-over tower. The tower itself may be either rigid or telescoping type. The main portion of the tower is supported above ground on a fixed base, hinged at the top. A cantilever arm and winch allow the owner to lower the tower for antenna work. Smaller tilt-over towers are mounted to a ground post which serves as an erection mechanism. Base of tower should be locked to prevent inadvertent upset if safety catch fails.

Once a crank-up tower has been raised it should never be climbed under any conditions. The tower sections are heavy and should a cable or safety catch fail, the telescoping sections collapse to the ground with tremendous force. A well-known west coast amateur was killed when his crank-up tower safety mechanism slipped and the tower crashed unexpectedly. A crank-up tower is perfectly safe if it is erected and operated according to the manufacturer's instructions and properly guyed, if guys are required. But it should never be climbed when extended. If the owner uses care and common sense he should experience no trouble. Remember--any antenna tower can be full of hidden dangers and should be approached with caution.

THE TILT-OVER TOWER

Another popular tower design features a short, fixed tower post atop which is the main tower, hinged so that it can tilt over to allow the antenna to descend to ground level (Figure 3).

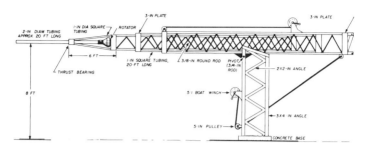

Fig.4 A compact, tilt-over, telescoping tower in the retracted position. Extended height is 57 feet, plus additional height provided by pipe extension mounted above the rotator. Light, vhf antennas may be mounted as high as 20 feet above the top thrust bearing. Heavier, hf antennas are limited in height to only a few feet above the top bearing.

Like the crank-up tower, the tilt-over tower permits the operator to work completely on the ground for antenna and rotator installation and servicing. This eliminates the hazard of tower climbing and the danger of a safety catch slipping and the crank-up sections collapsing to the ground. Crank-up and tilt-over towers should be locked when erect so that vandals cannot lower the tower or do other damage. A heavy chain and a padlock will do the job.

TOWER MAINTENANCE

Despite what you may hear, galvanized steel will rust over the years, and great differences exist between a cheap galvanizing job and a workmanlike job of hot-dip galvanizing. When the "rustproof" tower starts to rust, the spots should be sanded and several coats of rustproofing paint, topped with aluminum paint, should be applied. Cables, pulleys and hinges should be oiled and greased regularly (at least twice a year) with the proper weight of oil or grease and the complete installation given a close visual check for defects or rust every week or so.

Guy wires should be examined every few months. Galvanized steel wire is commonly used with small towers. It will eventually rust and must be replaced. Stainless steel cable is best, but it is expensive and must be used with the proper turnbuckles, thimbles and shackles. In the case of a large tower, a registered Civil Engineer can assist you with the proper maintenance procedure.

FENCES AND WARNING SIGNS

In many communities a radio tower is considered an "attractive nuisance" as far as young children go, and the owner may be liable for damages if a youngster is hurt climbing the tower. The tower should be enclosed by a fence having a locked gate, or it should have the lower portion wrapped with heavy chicken wire or fencing that makes climbing practically impossible. In addition, a warning sign that cautions the observer against climbing the tower or touching the guy wires, locks and cables is recommended. Unable to find the sign he wanted, one amateur erected an impressive sign reading, "DANGER--100,000 ohms!"

INSTALLING THE BEAM ANTENNA ON A FIXED TOWER

It's a long, long way from tower top to ground and installing a beam antenna can be a dangerous, risky undertaking unless the installer and his assistants do the job properly and carefully. Each installation is unique and there are many ways of erecting the antenna. Of these methods, only one is correct for a particular installation. Raising a beam is a job with a certain amount of danger in it and time spent in analyzing the job pays dividends once the work is underway. In addition, a certain amount of work at the top of the fixed tower is required and with forethought this work can be reduced to a minimum, making the job of the "top man" safer--but still dangerous.

BEFORE THE WORK STARTS

Before antenna or tower installation begins, the installer should examine the work area for safety. The antenna tower should not be located so that the antenna or tower can accidentally touch high tension lines. Amateurs and CBers have been hurt, and killed, when their beams slipped or were blown about by the wind and accidentally touched a nearby high tension line. Always remember--keep clear of high voltage! It kills!

The whole procedure must be thought through before the job starts. Each member of the work crew should know what his task is and understand the erection plan. The installer atop the tower must wear a safety belt. This will secure him to the tower and allow him to use both hands.

No one should stand near the tower base when work is being done atop the tower. A falling tool can be a lethal

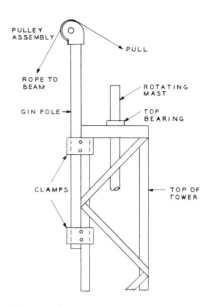

Fig.5 Gin pole is clamped to tower leg to permit antenna to be raised above tower top so it can be positioned and lowered onto mast. Gin pole is heavy steel pipe and should be quite short as there is considerable strain on the pole and tower leg when antenna is raised into position.

weapon. Finally, the beam should be tied to the top of the tower with a safety rope so that if the working rope, or halyard, slips, the beam will not come crashing to the ground.

Before the job starts, the beam is placed on the ground, or on convenient supports, and dimensions double-checked. Joints are examined for tightness and bolted connections inspected. The working area should be cleared of unnecessary clutter and spectators told to stay away. Free advice adds nothing to an antenna-raising party. The work is arranged so that the ground crew does the lifting and the installer atop the tower merely guides the antenna into position and fastens it in place. To accomplish this, a large pulley is placed atop a gin pole so that when the antenna arrives at the top it is roughly in position, ready to be bolted securely to the mast (Figure 5). The gin pole permits the antenna to be raised above the tower top so that it can be positioned and lowered onto the mast. The gin pole is a steel pipe as heavy as a tower leg and should be quite short as there is considerable strain on the pole during the erection process. The gin pole is rigidly attached to a tower leg by means of U-bolts. The rope through the gin pole pulley should be twice as long as the tower is high.

RAISING A SMALL BEAM OR "TRIBANDER"

A beam for the higher frequency bands, or a tribander, can be installed on a fixed tower by two persons. In the major-

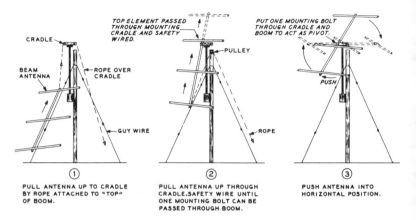

① PULL ANTENNA UP TO CRADLE BY ROPE ATTACHED TO "TOP" OF BOOM.

② PULL ANTENNA UP THROUGH CRADLE. SAFETY WIRE UNTIL ONE MOUNTING BOLT CAN BE PASSED THROUGH BOOM.

③ PUSH ANTENNA INTO HORIZONTAL POSITION.

Fig.6 Erection process for a hf beam when a fixed, guyed tower is used. Antenna is hoisted in a vertical position, sliding up the tower guys as it is pulled into position by a rope. Installer is required atop the tower to position antenna in mounting cradle.

ity of cases, this is accomplished by tying a rope about the supporting boom of the antenna at one parasitic element. The antenna is hoisted to the top of the tower from ground level. If the tower is guyed, the beam should be placed "outside" the guy wires. In fact, the guys may be employed as a "track" for the beam, the antenna sliding up the guys as it is pulled aloft by the rope. If a guy is unsuitably placed for this operation, a temporary rope track can be installed, the rope(s) running from the tower top to stakes pounded in the ground at appropriate points.

The beam is pulled up with the elements riding on the track, as shown in Figure 6. The antenna is hoisted with the boom in a near-vertical position until the top end reaches the pulley. The installer atop the tower can now reach one end of the boom. He loosens the rope a bit and raises the antenna hand over hand a few feet at a time until he reaches the center of the boom. As he does this, he tilts the antenna into a horizontal position. The safety rope is attached to the antenna during this process and is not removed until the antenna is anchored securely to the boom support plate.

The antenna installation is now finished. At all times the beam has been supported either by the guy wires, the halyard, or the safety rope. Even if the installer loses his grip on the antenna, it is held in position. The dangerous moment in any antenna installation is when the installer tires, or shifts his grip

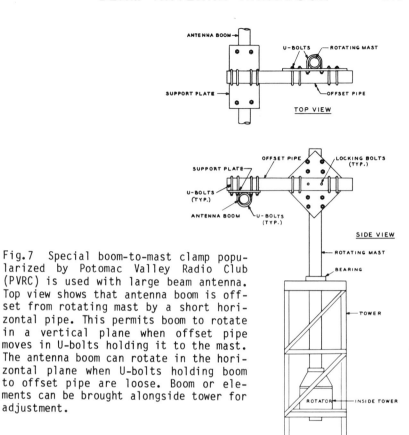

Fig.7 Special boom-to-mast clamp popularized by Potomac Valley Radio Club
(PVRC) is used with large beam antenna.
Top view shows that antenna boom is offset from rotating mast by a short horizontal pipe. This permits boom to rotate
in a vertical plane when offset pipe
moves in U-bolts holding it to the mast.
The antenna boom can rotate in the horizontal plane when U-bolts holding boom
to offset pipe are loose. Boom or elements can be brought alongside tower for
adjustment.

on the antenna. It is during these periods that the antenna can
become unbalanced, and the strength of one man on the tower
may be insufficient to prevent it from falling. This is especially
true if the installer has to use one arm to hold onto the tower!

RAISING THE LARGE BEAM ANTENNA

A large, multi-element high frequency beam antenna may
weigh more than 100 pounds (46 kg) and offer considerable wind
resistance. With these heavy beams, it has been found that the
simplest approach is to assemble the elements to the antenna
boom atop the tower with the boom held in a vertical position
beside the tower. This involves a special boom-to-mast mount
which offsets the boom from the rotating mast, permitting the
boom to rotate and tilt about a center joint (Figure 7) so that

the boom can be brought alongside the tower for element attachment.

The large beam antenna requires a large, husky tower that permits two installers to work at or near the top. In order to facilitate beam assembly, it may be necessary to temporarily remove one guy wire to allow the beam to move freely during the assembly process. If this is done, a safety guy should be temporarily installed to the tower leg just below the antenna work area to equalize the stresses on the tower.

THE SPECIAL ANTENNA MOUNT

The antenna mount consists of a short length of pipe the same size and weight as the rotating mast. It is held to the mast in a horizontal position by a square mounting plate and multiple U-bolts. Holes are drilled through the pipe and the mast to accommodate locking bolts which are inserted after the antenna is assembled. The extended end of the offset pipe is attached to a second mounting plate with multiple U-bolts. This plate, in turn, supports the antenna boom. When all U-bolts are loose the antenna elements can rotate in a vertical plane about the offset pipe, and the pipe can rotate the antenna boom in the vertical plane about the tower. The whole assembly is turned in the horizontal plane by means of the antenna rotator inside the tower.

USING THE ANTENNA MOUNT

After the beam dimensions have been checked, they are removed from the boom and the elements and adjacent boom area are marked with colored plastic tapes so that the installer will know the correct positioning when he works atop the tower. A temporary gin pole is used to raise the boom to the top of the tower. The boom is now attached to the mounting plate and held in a vertical position near the center of gravity (balance point) of the assembled antenna, which has been previously checked on the ground.

The element nearest the balance point of the antenna is bolted into position first. This element is then used as the master element to which all other elements are aligned in a parallel position. Elements are added one at a time on each side of the alignment element so that the center of gravity remains near the balance point, otherwise it may be impossible to tilt the boom back and forth.

When all elements are attached and properly aligned, the boom is tilted into the horizontal position with the elements positioned vertically beside the tower. The last step is to rotate the boom to position the antenna elements horizontally. When everything is properly aligned, the locking bolts are tightened.

ERECTING AN ANTENNA ON YOUR PROPERTY

Serious thought must be given before erecting an antenna on your property. Your local municipality or development may have established standards and restrictions governing the installation and use of towers and antennas. These legal hazards may be written into local building codes, zoning ordinances and deed restrictions (known as "conditions, covenants and restrictions" and abbreviated as CC and Rs). It is best to find out the details of these items before you erect your antenna or tower, or even before you buy or build a new residence.

Zoning Ordinances concern the type of buildings and structures you can erect in your neightborhood. The ordinances may restrict towers and antennas entirely, or restrict their height.

Building Codes concern the safety of buildings and structures permitted by local zoning ordinances. The codes may limit the placement of a tower to certain areas of your property or define the type of base and support (guy wires) required.

Conditions, Covenants and Restrictions are requirements written into a purchase deed and may include restrictions on outside antennas, the height of buildings and structures, or establish local architectural control on the property. They may also limit or control additions or changes to the property.

Complying with these requirements is mandatory. A good knowledge of existing antenna tower limitations, before work is started, will save time, money and anguish in the long run.

The following steps should be undertaken before your tower and antenna are installed.

1.   Check with your local Department of Building and Safety or Zoning Board to see if your residence is zoned for an amateur radio tower. Read the zoning ordinance for details. Note if a distinction is made between towers attached to the residence, either by guy wires or mounting, and towers that are free-standing.

2.   Check to see if a building permit is required. Find out if the proposed tower has to be checked by a licensed Mechanical Engineer in order for the permit to be issued, or if a city Building Inspector must check

tower base, guy wires, etc., to insure that the installation meets local safety requirements. If a permit is required, be sure to get it before work is started. Your homeowner's insurance may not cover the tower, and you might have given your neighbors, who may not like the tower, a reason to require you to take the tower down.

3. In some cases you may need either a <u>zoning variance</u> or a <u>conditional use permit</u> to erect a tower higher than the local zoning regulations permit. Variance provisions are used to provide flexibility from dimensional regulations such as setback from a lot line, or height restrictions. A conditional use permit is used where a tower or antenna is not otherwise allowed. A public hearing is usually required before such permits are issued.

4. Before buying property, read the deed restrictions. If you already own a home, a local title insurance company or an attorney can obtain a copy of the deed restrictions, if any, for you.

In short, look before you leap! Study your local building code and zoning ordinances to determine if there are any restrictions that apply to antennas and towers. Check the CC and Rs of any new property you buy to make sure you are not signing away your right to have a transmitting antenna. In case of doubt, consult an attorney on these matters.

For general information concerning legal problems associated with radio amateur antenna structures, write to the Membership Services Department, American Radio Relay League, 225 Main Street, Newington, CT 06111, and ask for their pamphlets reviewing the legal aspects of amateur antennas and the digest of cases dealing with these problems.

Chapter 12

Antenna Roundup

This chapter features some unusual beam antennas that are of general interest. One of the most popular designs is a compact three element Yagi for the high frequency bands that offers a favorable combination of high gain, good front-to-back ratio and small size. This antenna, plus other useful beams, is included in this chapter.

THE W6SAI COMPACT YAGI BEAM

Early experiments conducted on three-element beams indicated that appreciably higher gain could be obtained from a wide spaced array than from a narrow spaced one. Later experiments, better controlled and using improved measuring techniques, showed the gain difference between the two designs was not as great as previously thought, being on the order of 1.5 dB for a change in boom length from 0.2 to 0.55 wavelength when the elements are properly tuned. The relative narrowness of the 40 through 12 meter bands provided the impetus to design a close spaced, three element Yagi which sacrifices bandwidth for small size and good power gain. The results of this experiment are described in this section.

A compact, light, three element 20 meter Yagi on a 16'6" (5 m), 0.24 wavelength, boom was designed and constructed, and checked against a wide spaced array having a boom length of twenty-four feet (7.32 m). The smaller beam performed well and the difference in signal reports on reception and transmission between the two antennas confirmed that the gain of the small antenna was close to that of the larger one. Tests on an antenna range with scale models indicated that the compact antenna had a power gain of better than 7 dB over a dipole and a front-to-back ratio at the design frequency of about 30 dB. The

FIGURE 1— W6SAI COMPACT 3-ELEMENT BEAM

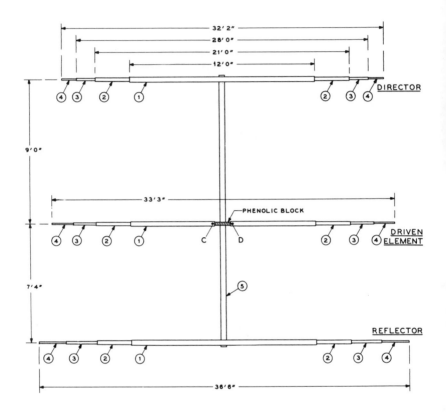

ITEM	DESCRIPTION	NUMBER PCS REQUIRED
①	1 1/8" O.D. X .058" WALL 6061-T6 DRAWN TUBING, 12' LONG	3
②	1" O.D. X .058" WALL 6061-T6 DRAWN TUBING, 12' LONG	3 PCS, CUT IN-TO 5' LENGTHS
③	7/8" O.D. X .049" WALL 6061-T6 DRAWN TUBING, 12' LONG	2 PCS, CUT IN-TO 4' LENGTHS
④	3/4" O.D. X .035" WALL 6061-T6 DRAWN TUBING, 12' LONG	3 PCS, CUT IN-TO 4'9" LENGTHS
⑤	2" O.D. X .058" WALL 6061-T6 DRAWN TUBING, 12' LONG	2 PIECES, SPLICE, AND CUT TO 18' 6"

NOTES:
1. 6063-T832 ALLOY MAY BE USED.
2. JOINTS OVERLAP APPROXIMATELY 6 INCHES.
3. OVERALL LENGTHS ADJUSTED BY TRIMMING TIPS.

TABLE 1 - W6SAI COMPACT YAGI BEAM

BAND (FREQ)	DIRECTOR FEET	DIRECTOR METERS	DRIVEN ELEMENT FEET	DRIVEN ELEMENT METERS	REFLECTOR FEET	REFLECTOR METERS	SPACING (D) FEET	SPACING (D) METERS
40 M (7.15)	63' 7"	19.39	65' 9"	20.03	72' 2"	22.00	17' 9"	5.41
30 M (10.12)	44' 11"	13.70	46' 5"	14.15	51' 0"	15.54	12' 6"	3.83
20 M (14.17)	32' 2"	9.81	33' 3"	10.16	36' 6"	11.13	9' 0"	2.74
17 M (18.11)	25' 1"	7.66	25' 11"	7.91	28' 6"	8.68	7' 0"	2.14
15 M (21.22)	21' 4"	6.54	22' 2"	6.75	24' 4"	7.41	5' 11"	1.82
12 M (24.94)	18' 3"	5.56	18' 10"	5.74	20' 8"	6.31	5' 1"	1.55
10 LO (28.60)	15' 10"	4.85	16' 5"	5.00	18' 0"	5.50	4' 5"	1.35
10 HI (29.20)	15' 6"	4.75	16' 1"	4.90	17' 8"	5.39	4' 4"	1.33
6 M (50.10)	9' 1"	2.77	9' 4"	2.86	10' 4"	3.14	2' 6"	0.77

$$L_D = \frac{455}{f(MHz)} \quad L_{DE} = \frac{470}{f(MHz)} \quad L_R = \frac{516}{f(MHz)} \quad S_D = \frac{127}{f(MHz)}$$

$$S_R = S_D \times 0.82$$

experiment showed that a compact Yagi design has power gain comparable to a larger array at the expense of bandwidth and provides excellent front-to-back ratio.

DIMENSIONS OF THE COMPACT BEAM

The parameters of the W6SAI compact beam are given in Figure 1. Computed dimensions for other bands are listed in Table 1. A boom length of 16'6" (5 m) is used. Director-to-driven element spacing is 9' (2.74 m) as less spacing than this requires critical director adjustment for maximum gain. Reflector-to-driven element spacing is 7'4" (2.23 m). The reflector is slightly longer than normal to provide maximum front-to-back ratio consistent with good gain. Turning radius of the antenna is 20 feet (6.1 m) and the complete beam weighs about 20 pounds (9 kg). Operating bandwidth of the array (Figure 2) is about 300 kHz between the 1.5-to-1 SWR points at the design frequency of 14.15 MHz. Front-to-back ratio remains better than 25 dB

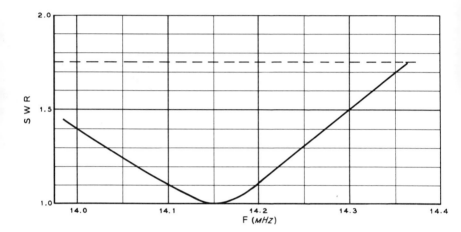

Fig.2   Design data and typical SWR curve for the W6SAI compact Yagi beam antenna. Design frequency is 14.15 MHz. Formulas may be used to apply this basic design to other frequencies.

across the operating range, reaching a maximum of about 30 dB near the hf end of the band.

The inductomatch feed system described in an earlier chapter is used with a coaxial balun. The feedpoint resistance of the compact beam is close to 20 ohms at the design frequency. An inductance of about 0.5 microhenry is required for the 14 MHz design and takes the form of a "hairpin" about 28" (71 cm) long made of No. 8 copper wire or aluminum utility wire (Figure 3). An adjustable shorting bar is placed at the far end of the hairpin as shown in the illustration.

The driven element of the compact Yagi is cut shorter than resonance to provide the capacitive reactance required by the inductomatch. Accordingly, the driven element is resonated at about 14.30 MHz with the aid of a dip oscillator before the antenna is placed atop the tower. The inexpensive coax balun design shown in Chapter 7 is used to couple the driven element

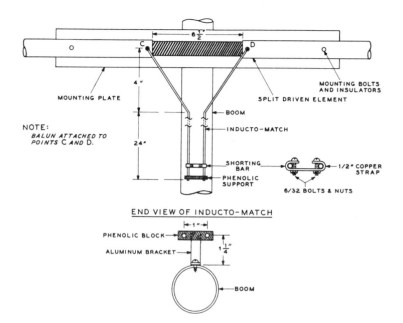

Fig.3 Top view of boom and element showing inductive matching system. Halves of driven element are driven onto insulating rod. Element is insulated from mounting plate and boom. In x 2.54 = cm.

to the transmission line. Slight variances in dimensions and the effect of nearby metallic objects on tuning are compensated by minor adjustments to the shorting bar on the inductomatch.

ANTENNA CONSTRUCTION

The W6SAI compact beam is built on a length of 2" (5 cm) diameter aluminum tubing. Irrigation pipe is used, or spliced tubing having a wall thickness of .058" (1.47 cm) can be substituted for greater rigidity. The parasitic elements are clamped directly to the boom using fixtures such as discussed in Chapter 8. Both parasitic elements are made of telescoping sections of aluminum tubing as detailed in Figure 1.

The driven element is made in the same fashion but is split in the center, and each half is driven onto a phenolic or hard wood rod, turned on a lathe to present a "press fit" to the inside diameter of the tubes. The rod is about a foot long (30 cm), and a six inch (15 cm) gap is left at the center between the tubes. Rod and tubes are drilled to pass 10-32 bolts (part of feedthrough insulators) which are used as electrical connections for the halves of the element and as insulating supports. When completed, the element is mounted to an aluminum plate, which, in turn, is affixed to the aluminum boom by means of U-bolts or sturdy angle plates cut of aluminum stock. Element joints are coated with Penetrox compound to inhibit corrosion and the joints are fixed in position by hose clamps. Needless to say, all mounting hardware used in the antenna should be stainless steel or plated to prevent rust and corrosion.

The inductomatch is bolted to the terminals of the driven element and lies parallel with the boom. The open ends of the wires are supported by a phenolic block which is bolted to the boom by a small aluminum bracket. A shorting strap made of a length of 1/2-inch (1.3 cm) wide aluminum strip is bolted to the inductomatch and designed to slide along the wires. When the proper position for it has been determined, it is held in place by bolts, nuts and lockwashers. The coaxial balun is fabricated and placed atop the boom in close proximity to the driven element. The two center connections of the balun attach to the driven element terminals in parallel with the wires of the inductomatch. With proper balun placement on the boom, the center leads to the antenna element are very short. The balun form is held permanently to the boom with aluminum angle plates.

ANTENNA ADJUSTMENT

The only electrical adjustment to the array is placement of the shorting strap on the inductomatch. Correct placement is found to be very close to 17-1/2" (45 cm) from the antenna terminals. Lengthening the stub lowers the resonant frequency of the antenna system, while shortening the stub raises the frequency. A stub length of 13" (33 cm), for example, shifts the resonant frequency up to about 14,250 KHz, while a stub length of 21" (53 cm) lowers the resonant frequency to approximately 14,075 KHz. At either extremity of shift, the SWR at the resonant frequency rises to about 1.2-to-1 and the entire SWR curve sharpens and increases accordingly.

Once the antenna is in the final operating position, an SWR curve is run and results checked by changing the length of the transmission line between the SWR indicator and the array. If the proper measuring technique is used, results should vary less than ten percent when a change in line length is made.

USING THE COMPACT BEAM DESIGN ON OTHER BANDS

This compact and effective beam antenna can be scaled up or down for operation on other amateur bands, or on other frequencies. Bandwidth (defined by the 1.75-to-1 SWR points on the transmission line) is better than two percent of the

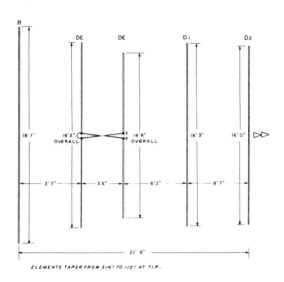

ELEMENTS TAPER FROM 3/4" TO 1/2" AT TIP.

Fig.4 LPY bandpass antenna for 10 meter band. Operating range is 28.0 to 29.0 MHz. Elements are 3/4-inch (1.9 cm) diam. with 5/8-inch (1.6 cm) diam. tips. Elements are supported above a 2-inch (5 cm) diam. boom. An overhead support to each end of the boom from a center post is recommended.

design frequency, so a 40 meter version of this beam operates over a span of about 170 KHz. A 15 meter version covers about 500 KHz (the complete 21 MHz band). While the beam may be used for reception at frequencies considerably removed from the nominal operating bandwidth, the SWR on the transmission line rises abruptly, and loading problems with the transmitter may result. In addition, the front-to-back ratio deteriorates rapidly with off-frequency operation.

AN LPY BANDPASS ANTENNA FOR 10 METERS

Shown in Figure 4 is a bandpass beam antenna for the ten meter band. It is built on a 21 foot (6.4 m) boom and is made up of two log periodic elements, two parasitic directors and a reflector. Power gain is 8 dB or better, and the front-to-back ratio is about 20 dB. This compares favorably with a four element Yagi beam on a comparable boom. Feedpoint resistance of the antenna is close to 200 ohms. It can be fed directly with either 50 or 75 ohm coax and a 4-to-1 balun.

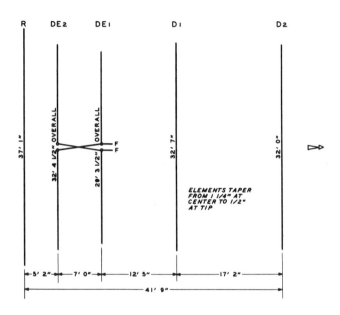

Fig.5   The 20 meter LPY bandpass antenna covers 13.9 to 14.4 MHz. Array provides 9 dB gain with over 30 dB front-to-back ratio at center of range. Feedpoint resistance is about 200 ohms so 4-to-1 balun can be used to match a 50 ohm coax line.

     The antenna is built on an aluminum boom, 2" (5 cm) in diameter. The driven elements are supported at the boom on insulating blocks, while the parasitic elements are mounted directly to the top of the boom. The driven elements are cross-connected with No. 10 aluminum or copper wire and the rear driven element (DE2) is shunted with a 12" (30 cm) long loop of wire at the end of the transposed feedline to improve the match to the transmission line.

AN LPY BANDPASS ANTENNA FOR 20 METERS

     This LPY design is very practical for 20 meter operation, providing over 9 dB gain with a front-to-back ratio of at least 30 dB over the phone band, and better than 20 dB from 13.9 MHz to 14.4 MHz. The SWR is 1.2-to-1 or better, over the same 500 kHz range. The antenna dimensions are shown in Figure 5. The beam is built on a 42 foot (12.8 m) boom made of 3" (7.6 cm) diameter aluminum tubing (Figure 6). Element lengths are given for a tapered design, using 1-1/4 inch (3.2 cm) diameter

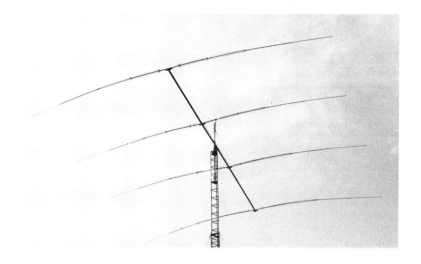

Fig.6 The LPY beam at K6HCP. This antenna is manufactured by KLM Electronics, Morgan Hill, CA 95037. Boom is 42 feet (12.8 m) long. KLM also manufactures bandpass beam of this type for 40 meters.

center sections, tapering down to one-half inch (1.3 cm) diameter at the tips. Reflector spacing is reduced to conserve boom length, and the front-to-back ratio varies only slightly when reflector spacing is increased. Spacing of the driven element pair is adjusted to provide a 200 ohm feedpoint resistance. The lengths of the driven elements are adjusted to provide proper bandwidth for the log periodic section.

Inner director element length is adjusted for the best front-to-back ratio and its spacing to the log periodic section can be varied to help achieve the proper feedpoint match. The outer director, which is the shortest, is adjusted to control the high frequency response of the beam. The element spacing also has a significant effect upon the front-to-back ratio of the array. The spacings of the two directors are fixed for maximum forward gain and good front-to-back ratio. Adjustments are then made to the driven element lengths to correct the impedance for the 200 ohm termination. A 4-to-1 balun (Figure 7) is used to match the array to a 50 ohm coaxial transmission line.

A LOG PERIODIC ANTENNA FOR 40 OR 80 METERS

Beam antennas for the lower frequency amateur bands are big and bulky, especially if they are designed to be rotated.

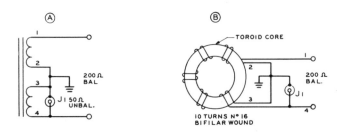

Fig.7   Balun suitable for LPY antenna. (A) Schematic of 4-to-1 balun made up of bifilar windings on ferrite core. (B) Windings are wound in parallel and equally spaced around the core. The core is Q-2 material having an outside diameter of 2.4 In (6.1 cm) and an inside diameter of 1.4 In (3.6 cm). Balun kit is available from Amidon, 12033 Otsego Street, North Hollywood, CA 91607.

Some amateurs have reached a compromise solution matter through the use of fixed, vertically polarized log periodic beams, aimed in the most important direction for DX work. Good power gain and a low angle of radiation can be achieved with modest antenna height through the use of quarter-wavelength vertical elements in a log periodic design, working against a resonant ground radial system. This is similar to larger installations used by some commercial stations for medium frequency, point-to-point work.

A design for a log periodic antenna suitable for either 40 or 80 meter operation is shown in Figure 8. Five vertical radiators are used, fed with a two-wire transmission line. Four radiators have two quarter-wavelength radials, but the longest radiator employs four radials for optimum operation at the low frequency end of the useful range. The vertical radiators and radial sets are transposed for proper phase relationship and the feedline is terminated with a 4-to-1 balun to match a 50 ohm coaxial trans-mission line.

The array can be suspended between two masts, or trees, leaving about 10 feet (3 m) clearance under the antenna. For 40 meter operation, the taller mast is 48 feet (14.6 m) high and the shorter mast 35 feet (10.6 m) high. The vertical elements are suspended from a catenary cable, made of 1/4-inch nylon line stretched between the two supports. The horizontal radials are anchored to convenient tie-points 10 feet (3 m) above the ground. For 80 meter operation, the taller mast is 75 feet (22.8 m) high for 3.8-4 Mc coverage. The shorter mast is 55 feet (16.8 m) high.

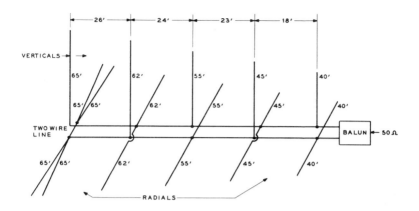

Fig.8 The W4AEO LP beam for 40 and 80 meters is made of aluminum wire. Beam is supported from two poles and is directional to the right in a line through the elements. Elements and radials are transposed along an open wire line. A 4-to-1 balun is used to match 50 ohm coax line.

The radiators, radials and transmission line are constructed of No. 15 aluminum utility wire, which can be purchased in the United States and Canada in quarter-mile rolls. Center insulators at each tie-point for radials and verticals are made of 1/4-inch (6 mm) thick plastic material. Feeder spacing is 1-1/2 inches (3.8 cm). A 4-to-1 balun, such as described earlier in this chapter, is placed at the apex of the array to provide a good match to the transmission line. Over the operating range of the antenna, the SWR is less than 1.5-to-1. Power gain is estimated to be about 8 dB. (Note: This antenna is based upon a design of George Smith, W4AEO.)

WIRE BEAM ANTENNAS

The majority of beam antennas used by radio amateurs are built of aluminum tubing, supported at the center of gravity and rotatable in the azimuth plane. Commercial point-to-point stations, on the other hand, often use large curtain arrays made of heavy wire slung between towers and "aimed" in a fixed direction. Fixed arrays are employed because the commercial station maintains schedules with stations in known directions, and random antenna orientation is not required. Commercial antenna arrays are so large and costly, however, that they are out of the question for the average radio amateur. Nevertheless, many hams have taken a page from the commercial station's notebook and have erected small wire beam antennas aimed at areas of the world having a high density of radio amateur population.

Slung between masts or nearby trees, these inexpensive and lightweight beam antennas have much to offer for general amateur use. In areas of the world where aluminum tubing is difficult or expensive to obtain, or in cases where the station operator is interested in communications in one or two general directions, the fixed wire beam is a simple and effective solution to the antenna problem.

WIRE BEAM DIMENSIONS

Over a period of years, the physical dimensions of parasitic elements constructed of small diameter aluminum tubing have been derived from experimental data and computer programs to provide efficient rotary beam designs exhibiting high gain and low SWR values on the transmission line. These antennas are capable of being assembled and erected without complicated tuning adjustments. The length-to-diameter ratio of aluminum tubing elements used for such arrays in the 7 to 30 MHz range is about 300-to-1 and most available data and formulas are based on elements having this physical ratio. Antenna arrays made of wire, on the other hand, have length-to-diameter ratios of approximately 10,000-to-1. In addition, the wire elements are supported at the ends by insulators that contribute a small capacitive shortening effect. These variations must be taken into account when wire is substituted for larger diameter tubing in beam antenna designs, and appropriate modifications are made to the element dimensions.

Generally speaking, a resonant dipole decreases in length as the diameter of the element is increased (Chapter 2). The length of a uniform diameter tubing dipole is approximately 95 percent of a free-space half wavelength. An equivalent dipole made of thin wire measures close to 97 percent of a free-space half wavelength provided it is suspended in the clear with no end supports. When good grade glass or ceramic insulators and dry rope are used to support the ends of the wire element, the end effect of the supports partially compensates for the "thin-ness" of the wire, and the net result is a dipole measuring close to 96 percent of a free-space half wavelength. This indicates that the element of a wire beam antenna supported at the element ends should be cut about one percent longer than the elements of an equivalent beam built of uniform diameter tubing. The overall operating efficiency of both types of elements is high and one form of element will work as well as the other.

TYPES OF WIRE BEAMS

Various forms of fixed, wire beam antennas have been developed during the past decades and some of them are of particular interest to the radio amateur. Among the most popular of these simple wire antennas are the W8JK beam, the Quad, the ZL-Special, the Curtain arrays (Lazy-H and Bi-Square), and the parasitic beam. The Quad antenna is completely described in detail in All About Cubical Quad Antennas (see book list at the back of this handbook). Other forms of wire beam antennas are discussed in this chapter. For additional data on other wire arrays, the reader is referred to the Radio Handbook, published by Howard W. Sams Co., 4300 West 62nd Street, Indianapolis, IN. 46268.

THE W8JK BEAM

The Flat-top beam conceived by John Kraus, W8JK, consists of two close-spaced dipoles, or arrays of dipoles. For simplicity, the phase relationship between the dipoles is 180 degrees and obtained by crossing the elements at points of high current or voltage (Figure 9).

For maximum low-angle radiation, the W8JK beam is mounted in the clear with the plane of the elements parallel with the earth. The great circle path to the target area should be determined and the antenna "aimed" in the proper direction. As the pattern of the W8JK beam is quite broad, a single beam can cover a complete continental area, and two beams erected at right angles will provide almost complete worldwide coverage.

CONSTRUCTING THE W8JK BEAM

The W8JK beam is assembled between bamboo or wood spreaders as shown in the illustration. The elements are made of Formvar coated, No. 12 hard-drawn copper wire fixed between spreaders which in turn are suspended by rope bridles. Before the elements are attached to the spreaders, each bamboo pole should be wrapped between the joints with vinyl tape to retard splitting, and the wrapped pole given two coats of varnish or shellac. If bamboo is not at hand, the spreaders may be made of wood strips. All joints in the antenna wires must be securely soldered, as rf currents in this array are quite high. A short, two wire balanced transmission line is attached to the center of the antenna at the crossover point.

The world coverage of a two-section W8JK beam is indicated in Figure 10. The beam pattern, as shown by the shaded area, is fairly broad.

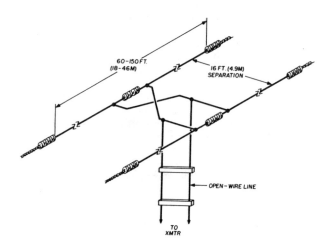

Fig.9 General purpose W8JK beam employs Transmatch and open wire line. Larger dimensions permit operation on 80 meters, as well as higher bands. Smaller dimensions restrict operation to 40 meters and above. Dimensions are not critical as beam is tuned to operating frequency by Transmatch. Dimensions may be halved for operation at 21 MHz and above. The beam pattern is bidirectional as shown below and one W8JK beam mounted between two support points gives good world coverage.

Fig.10 From central USA W8JK beam pattern covers Europe on both long and short paths.

TWO AND THREE ELEMENT WIRE PARASITIC BEAMS

Two and three element parasitic beams can be built of wire and bamboo for a fraction of the cost of an array constructed of aluminum tubing. Delivering power gain equal to the more expensive and complex "rotaries", these simple fixed beams may be built in a matter of hours at an amazingly low cost. Figure 11 and Table 2 summarize compact two and three element wire beams suitable for use in the 40 through 10 meter amateur bands.

ANTENNA CONSTRUCTION

The elements of the wire beam are made of No. 12 hard-drawn copper wire fixed between bamboo spreaders which are suspended by rope bridles. Overall antenna dimensions are compact enough so that a three element beam is easily built for 10, 12 or 15 meters if spreader arms of sufficient length can be found. The bamboo spreaders are prepared in a fashion similar to that described for the W8JK beam and the wire sections of the dipole are threaded through the end insulators and the dipole placed under tension while the end joints are made. Each insulator is fastened to the spreaders by a short length of rope looped about the spreader, as shown in the illustration. Even though the parasitic and driven elements are different lengths, the poles can be held at right angles to the wires by adjusting the rope lengths between the insulators and the spreaders. The last step is to place a rope bridle across the end of each spreader. The sides of the bridle and the spreader should form an equilateral triangle for best support. The coax transmission line is now connected across points D-E on the dipole and the connections are wrapped with vinyl tape.

INSTALLING THE BEAM

The beam pattern is unidirectional, with the main lobe radiated through the director at right angles to the wires. The antenna is erected in a horizontal plane, and because of the unique bridle support it is possible to flip the antenna over like a hammock in order to reverse the directional pattern. The beam may be supported between two masts, or the house and a single tree or pole, and should be as high above the ground as possible, with a height of 30 feet (9 m) a minimum for any band. Ropes attached to the end of the spreaders permit reversal of the antenna direction from the ground and will also help in steadying the array in a heavy wind. The folded dipole side of the beam is heavier than the director side, and the two element array tends to tilt up unless held in a horizontal position by the guy ropes. Make sure the feedline drops vertically beneath the array for twenty feet or so before it is led off at an angle.

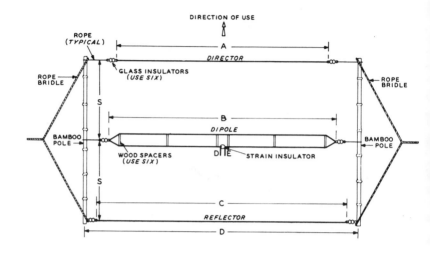

TOP VIEW, 2 ELEMENT BEAM

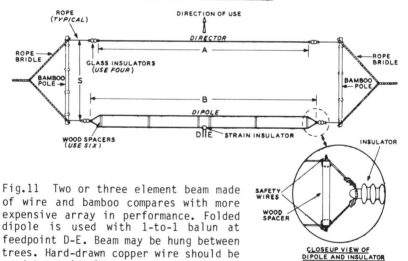

Fig.11 Two or three element beam made of wire and bamboo compares with more expensive array in performance. Folded dipole is used with 1-to-1 balun at feedpoint D-E. Beam may be hung between trees. Hard-drawn copper wire should be used to avoid element stretching. Table 2 gives dimensions for hf bands.

TABLE 2 - WIRE YAGI BEAM DIMENSIONS

BAND	DIRECTOR - A		DIPOLE - B		REFLECTOR - C		SPACING - S	
(FREQ)	FEET	METERS	FEET	METERS	FEET	METERS	FEET	METERS
40 M (7.15)	65' 2"	19.86	65' 9"	20.03	69' 8"	21.23	19' 9"	6.04
30 M (10.12)	46' 0"	14.02	46' 5"	14.15	49' 2"	15.00	14' 0"	4.27
20 M (14.17)	32' 10"	10.02	33' 2"	10.11	35' 2"	10.71	10' 0"	3.05
17 M (18.11)	25' 9"	7.84	25' 11"	7.91	27' 6"	8.38	7' 9"	2.38
15 M (21.22)	21' 11"	6.69	22' 1"	6.75	23' 6"	7.15	6' 8"	2.04
12 M (24.94)	18' 8"	5.69	18' 10"	5.75	20' 0"	6.09	5' 7"	1.73
10 LO (28.6)	16' 3"	4.97	16' 5"	5.01	17' 5"	5.31	4' 11"	1.51
10 HI (29.2)	15' 11"	4.86	16' 1"	4.91	17' 1"	5.20	4' 10"	1.48

THE LAZY-H BEAM

The Lazy-H array is a simple and effective beam that provides approximately 5 dB power gain at the design frequency. It is erected in the vertical plane and consists of four dipole elements, stacked two over two. Sufficient support height is required to place the lower set of elements at least one-half wavelength above the ground and free of nearby metallic objects. The radiation pattern of the Lazy-H is a "figure-8" and resembles that of the two-section W8JK beam. The Lazy-H has considerably greater operating bandwidth for a maximum value of SWR on the transmission line than does the W8JK beam.

Upper and lower segments of the Lazy-H are interconnected by an open wire line section that is transposed to provide the proper phase relationship between the elements. For power of 150 watts or so, the line section is made of open wire TV line (Saxton 2501, 450 ohm line, or equivalent). For higher power, the line should be made of No. 12 wire spaced with four inch ceramic spreaders. The quarter-wave stub placed at the bottom of the array are made of the same material as the center transformer section (Figure 12).

The Lazy-H beam is adjusted in the same manner as the W8JK beam. The beam is tuned to the design frequency by

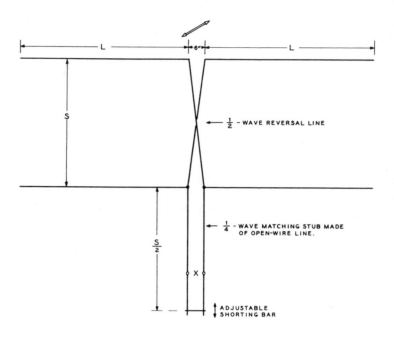

LAZY-H DIMENSIONS

BAND	LENGTH – L		SPACING – S	
	FEET	METERS	FEET	METERS
40	65' 7"	20.00	68' 9"	20.97
30	46' 4"	14.12	48' 7"	14.82
20	33' 0"	10.10	34' 8"	10.58
17	25' 10"	7.89	27' 2"	8.28
15	22' 1"	6.74	23' 1"	7.07
12	18' 9"	5.73	19' 8"	6.01
10	16' 4"	4.98	17' 1"	5.22
6	9' 4"	2.85	9' 9"	3.00

Fig.12   Lazy-H beam is inexpensive and provides good gain. Coax line and 4-to-1 balun provide balanced feed at point X on stub. If shorting bar is removed and open wire stub run to a Transmatch, the beam may be used on harmonic frequencies.

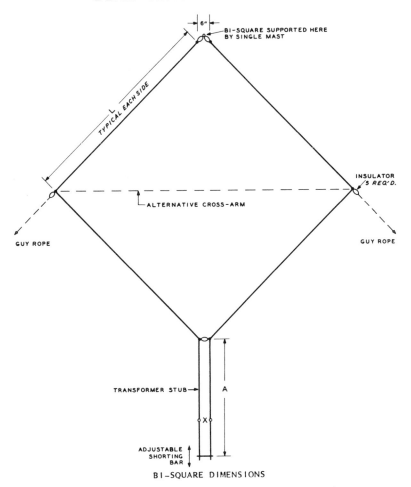

BI-SQUARE DIMENSIONS

| | LENGTH – L | | LENGTH – A | |
BAND	FEET	METERS	FEET	METERS
40	65' 7"	20.00	34' 4"	10.47
30	46' 4"	14.12	24' 3"	7.39
20	33' 0"	10.10	17' 4"	5.27
17	25' 10"	7.89	13' 7"	4.15
15	22' 1"	6.74	11' 6"	3.51
12	18' 9"	5.73	9' 10"	3.00
10	16' 4"	4.98	8' 6"	2.59
6	9' 4"	2.85	4' 10"	1.48

Fig.13   Bi-square beam can be suspended from a single pole. The feed system is the same as for the lazy-H antenna.

adjusting the shorting bar placed across the bottom end of the lower stub. A dip oscillator is used for this adjustment, in conjunction with a calibrated receiver. Once the correct position of the bar is established, the balun feed system is attached to the stub at some point (X) above the bar as previously discussed. When adjustments are completed, the shorting bar and feedpoints are securely soldered. In a manner similar to the W8JK, the Lazy-H beam may also be operated on a harmonic frequency with the use of a tuning device such as a transmatch.

THE BI-SQUARE BEAM

The Bi-Square array is a simple and effective beam antenna that may be suspended from a single pole (Figure 13). This antenna is a cousin of the Lazy-H and, in spite of the oblique elements, is horizontally polarized. The power gain of the Bi-Square is slightly less than that of the Lazy-H, being approximately 4 dB. The pattern is a bidirectional "figure-8". An important advantage of the Bi-Square is that two beams may be suspended from a single central pole without interaction if the arrays are placed at right angles to each other. This offers a solution to the problem of placing two beam antennas in a very small space. When two Bi-Square antennas are suspended from a single pole, the transformer stubs should be well separated or symmetrically arranged in the form of a square (the diagonal conductors forming one stub) in order to minimize coupling between them.

Each side of the Bi-Square beam is approximately one-half wavelength long, and only a single crossarm is required to support the center points. An alternative design is to omit the crossarm and tie the center points of the diamond to nearby ground stakes by means of guy ropes. The array should be erected in the clear so that the bottom of the beam is at least one-quarter wavelength above ground.

Acknowledgements

The authors wish to express their appreciation to the following amateurs for their suggestions and help in the preparation of this handbook. In addition, the work of Peter Viezbickie of the National Bureau of Standards has been a valuable aid in the design of some of the antennas shown in this handbook. To all concerned, many thanks.

Chester Buchanan, W3DZZ
Victor Clark, W4KFC
Doug DeMaw, W1FB
W.B. Foote, K6BCM
Jack Gutzeit, W2LZX
Gunter Hoch, DL6WU
Ken Holladay, K6HCP
George Jacobs, W3ASK
John Kraus, W8JK
Simo Lehto, OH8OS
Rod Maney, KL7SA

Fred Mason, KH6OR
Wilse Morgan, KL7CQ
Gary O'Neil, N3GO
Pedro Piza, Jr., NP4A
"Buzz" Reeves, K2GL
Joe Reisert, Jr., W1JR
Willy Sayer, WA6BAN
Mike Socha, W8UA
"Skip" Tenney, W1NLB
Harold Tolles, W7ITB
Hans Zimmer, W9ON

OTHER BOOKS FOR RADIO AMATEURS, CB OPERATORS, SHORTWAVE LISTENERS, STUDENTS, & EXPERIMENTERS

ALL ABOUT CUBICAL QUAD ANTENNAS, by William I. Orr W6SAI and Stuart D. Cowan W2LX; 112 pages, 75 illustrations.

This well-known classic has been updated to include: new Quad designs; new dimension charts for every type of Quad from 6 to 80 meters; additional gain figures; an analysis of Quad vs. Yagi; Mini and Monster Quad designs; Delta, Swiss, and Birdcage Quads; and an improved Tri-Gamma match to feed a triband Quad efficiently with one transmission line. Also covered are feed systems and tuning procedures for maximum gain and minimum SWR. Much of this data has never before been published.

BEAM ANTENNA HANDBOOK, by William I. Orr W6SAI and Stuart D. Cowan W2LX; 271 pages, 205 illustrations.

This popular new edition gives you: correct dimensions for 6, 10, 15, 20, and 40 meter beams; data on triband and compact beams; the truth about beam height; SWR curves for popular beams from 6 to 40 meters; and comparisons of T-match, Gamma match, and direct feed. Describes tests to confirm if your beam is working properly, tells how to save money by building your own beam and balun, and discusses test instruments and how to use them. A "must" for the serious DX'er!

THE RADIO AMATEUR ANTENNA HANDBOOK, by William I. Orr W6SAI and Stuart D. Cowan W2LX; 191 pages, 147 illustrations.

This clearly written, easy to understand handbook contains a wealth of information about amateur antennas, from beams to baluns, tuners, and towers. The exclusive "Truth Table" gives you the actual dB gain of 10 popular antenna types. Describes how to build multiband vertical and horizontal antennas, Quads, Delta Quads, Mini-Quads, a Monster Quad, DX "slopers", triband beams, and VHF Quagi and log periodic Yagi beams. Dimensions are given for all antennas in English and Metric units. Tells how antenna height and location affect results and describes efficient antennas for areas with poor ground conductivity. Covers radials, coaxial cable loss, "bargain" coax, baluns, SWR meters, wind loading, tower hazards, and the advantages and disadvantages of crank-up tilt-over towers.

SIMPLE, LOW-COST WIRE ANTENNAS FOR RADIO AMATEURS, by William I. Orr W6SAI and Stuart D. Cowan, W2LX; 192 pages, 100 illustrations.

Now-another great handbook joins the famous Cubical Quad and Beam Antenna Handbooks. Provides complete instructions for building tested wire antennas from 2 through 160 meters-horizontal, vertical, multiband traps, and beam antennas. Describes a 3-band Novice dipole with only one feedline; the "folded Marconi" antenna for 40, 80, or 160 meters; "invisible" antennas for difficult locations-hidden, disguised, and disappearing antennas (the Dick Tracy Special, the CIA Special). Covers antenna tuners and baluns, and gives clear explanations of radiation resistance, impedance, radials, ground systems, and lightning protection. This is a truly practical handbook.

THE TRUTH ABOUT CB ANTENNAS, by William I. Orr W6SAI and Stuart D. Cowan W2LX; 240 pages, 145 illustrations.

Contains everything the CB'er needs to know to buy or build, install, and adjust efficient CB antennas for strong, reliable signals. A unique "Truth Table" shows the dB gain from 10 of the most popular CB antennas. The antenna is the key to clear, reliable communication but most CB antennas do not work near peak efficiency. Now, for the first time, this handbook gives clear informative instructions on antenna adjustment, exposes false claims about inferior antennas, and helps you make your antenna work. With exclusive and complete coverage of the "Monster Quad" beam, the "King" of CB antennas.

INTERFERENCE HANDBOOK, by William R. Nelson WA6FQG; Editor: William I. Orr W6SAI; 253 pages, 152 illustrations.

This timely book covers every radio frequency interference (RFI) problem, with solutions based on years of practical experience. Covers amateur radio, CB radio, and power line problems with proven solutions. Contains case histories and lists valuable tips for stereo and TV owners to cure interference. Covers mobile, telephone, CATV, and computer problems as well.

ALL ABOUT VERTICAL ANTENNAS, by William I. Orr W6SAI and Stuart D. Cowan W2LX; 192 pages, 95 illustrations.

Properly designed, built, and installed vertical antennas do a fine job in small places. This clear, well illustrated book covers the design, construction, installation, and operation of 52 vertical antennas: efficient Marconi antennas for 80 and 160 meters, multiband verticals, vertical loops, phased arrays, and shunt-fed towers. Also described are "radio" and electrical grounds, matching systems, tuners, loading coils, and TVI, plus the precautions necessary to protect yourself, your home, and your equipment from lightning damage . . . and much more! It's the most practical, authoritative vertical handbook published.

These popular handbooks save you time, trouble, and money in getting the most out of your equipment and your hobby. They condense years of study and successful experience into clear and interesting texts to help you obtain maximum results.

Radio Amateur Callbook handbooks are available at better electronics dealers and bookstores everywhere. See your nearest dealer or write for a free catalog:

RADIO AMATEUR CALLBOOK
P.O. Box 2013, Lakewood, New Jersey 08701